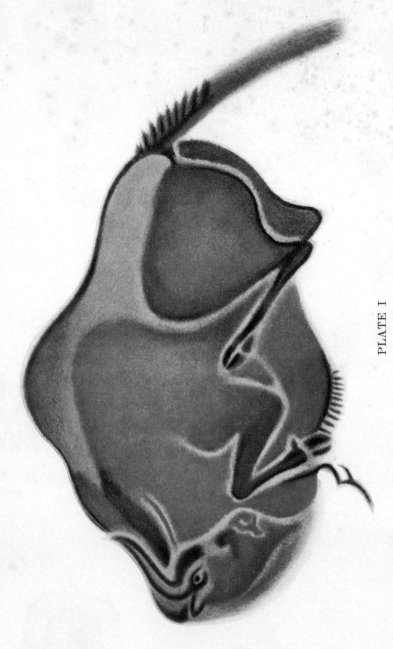

PLATE I

Bison lying down—a polychrome painting on the ceiling of the cave of Altamira, near Santillana del Mar, Santander. After E. Cartailhac and H. Breuil.

Reduced in size.

FOSSIL MAN IN SPAIN

BY

HUGO OBERMAIER

PROFESSOR OF PREHISTORIC ARCHÆOLOGY
AT THE UNIVERSITY OF MADRID

WITH AN INTRODUCTION BY

HENRY FAIRFIELD OSBORN

VICE-PRESIDENT OF THE
HISPANIC SOCIETY OF AMERICA

NEW HAVEN: PUBLISHED FOR
THE HISPANIC SOCIETY OF AMERICA BY THE
YALE UNIVERSITY PRESS
LONDON · HUMPHREY MILFORD · OXFORD UNIVERSITY PRESS
MCMXXV

11-12-47

FOSSIL MAN IN SPAIN

Translated into English from the original text of *El Hombre Fósil,* Madrid, 1916, as authorized by the Junta para Ampliación de Estudios e Investigaciones científicas of the Spanish Ministry of Education, with extensive additions and alterations by the author, up to June, 1922, incorporated in the text by the translator, CHRISTINE D. MATTHEW.

Revised and approved for The Hispanic Society of America by HENRY FAIRFIELD OSBORN.

DEDICATED
IN FRIENDSHIP AND ADMIRATION
TO THE
DUKE OF BERWICK AND ALBA

after the rise of Carthage. Then the *Carthaginians* entered
Spain as colonists, and were dominant there during the second
half of the third century B.C., making many settlements and
founding the fortress of Novo Carthago, the modern Cartagena,
with the best harbor of southeastern Spain. The ancient Greeks
cannot be considered as having any appreciable influence in
Spain, for they occupied few sites south of the Pyrenees,
although dominant in southern France in their colony of
Massalia (Marseilles).

7. *Seventh invasion—from Italy.* Firm historic ground is reached
with the advent of the *Romans,* of blended *Alpine* and *Mediterranean* stock, who drove the Carthaginians out of the
Iberian Peninsula in 201 B.C. and completed its conquest by
taking Numantia in 133 B.C.

8. *Eighth invasion—from northern Europe.* The dominance of
Roman civilization endured from 201 B.C. to 406 A.D., when the
Vandals, Suebi, and *Alans* invaded Spain from the north.
These tribes are regarded by anthropologists as branches of
the *Nordic Race,* and this invasion constitutes the first recorded
entry of these peoples into the racial stock and social development of the Iberian Peninsula.

9. *Ninth invasion—from northern Europe.* In 415-419 A.D. the
Visigoths, led by Wallia, destroyed the Alans and drove the
Vandals and Suebi into the northwest. In 428 Gaiseric, king of
the Vandals, left Spain to found the Vandal kingdom of Carthage in Africa, but before their departure he and his followers overran and plundered southern Spain. With the
defeat and departure of these, the influence of the Visigoths
became increasingly stronger, their period of dominance extending from 531 to 711 A.D., during which kings of the Visigoths were established in Spain. The same racial stock, or one
very closely related, continued in power in the line of the
"Kings of the Goths" ruling in the Christian northwest of
Spain from 718 to 914 A.D.

These two Nordic invasions (8 and 9) are of deep interest,
both to the anthropologist and to the man of letters, inasmuch as they introduced into Spain the northern blood—the
typical fair hair, blue eyes, and lofty stature of the Nordic
Race. It has been claimed that Cervantes was of this stock,
and there can be no doubt in regard to Camoëns, the soldier-
poet of Portugal.

10. *Tenth invasion—from Africa.* In 711 the Saracen invaders, consisting of *Syrians, Arabs,* and *Berbers*—and therefore chiefly of *Semitic Race*—entered Spain with their Mahometan religion and Arabian culture, inspired by a fierce fighting spirit which overcame the resistance of the native inhabitants and established the Moorish power in southern Spain, where it remained firmly seated for many centuries, being finally broken and driven out in 1492.

Thus—aside from many lesser invasions, cultural and linguistic—the prehistory and history of Spain include ten great invasions, each with its distinctive culture, art, industry, and religion. These cultures were the expression of at least six racial stocks, namely, the Neanderthal, the Crô-Magnon, the Mediterranean, the Celtic-Alpine, the Semitic, and the Nordic. Prehistoric Man is coming into his own with the daily increasing proofs that his spiritual and mental powers were equal to ours, if not superior, and also with the realization that many of these fossil and prehistoric men are our direct ancestors, whether we be of Mediterranean, of Alpine, or of Nordic stock.

The author of the present volume, Dr. Hugo Obermaier, wrote his great work on *Der Mensch der Vorzeit* in 1912. For a long period he worked under the superb opportunities afforded by the Institut de Paléontologie humaine founded by the Prince of Monaco in 1910. Under the tutelage of the dean of French archæologists, Emile Cartailhac, and with the comradeship of the present leader of modern French archæology, Henri Breuil, his life was especially devoted to work in northern Spain. It was here that he conducted the writer of this Introduction through that classic center of Crô-Magnon art, the cavern of Altamira, and also to the most remarkable Old Stone Age deposit ever discovered, namely, the cultural layers in the cave of Castillo, which cover the long period from the Acheulean industry in stone to the beginning of the Age of Copper. On entering the circle of Spanish archæologists, Dr. Obermaier produced his scholarly and exhaustive account of *El Hombre Fósil* in 1916. Before allowing the present volume to appear, he has devoted months to the tireless and careful revision of his Spanish text, and to extensive alterations and additions, all

I close with grateful acknowledgment to The Hispanic Society of America and in particular to its president, Mr. Archer M. Huntington, for their generous interest in bringing out this English edition of *Fossil Man in Spain,* which I trust may bring to the notice of a larger public the abundance and importance of the scientific treasures of Spain.

I am also deeply indebted to Professor Henry Fairfield Osborn, President of the American Museum of Natural History, New York, for the cordial and active interest that he has taken in the preparation and publication of this work, and to Miss Christine D. Matthew, who has accomplished the difficult and responsible work of translation, and wish to express to both my appreciation of their disinterested effort to further the progress of science in regard to fossil man.

HUGO OBERMAIER.

Madrid,
  February, 1922.

CONTENTS

ILLUSTRATIONS

CHAPTER I

TERTIARY MAN AND THE PROBLEM OF THE EOLITHS

The Tertiary Period in Europe—Human remains of Tertiary age—Supposed traces of Tertiary man—Eoliths—Thenay—Otta—Cantal—Boncelles and the Fagnian industry—Kent and Saint-Prest—Classification of Pleistocene eoliths—Table of Eolithic industries—Geographic distribution of eoliths—Eolithic art—"Figure-stones"—Criticism of the eolithic theory—Action of running water—Eolithic deposits at Steinheim—Earth pressure—Eocene eoliths of Belle-Assise—Moraine débris—Wave action of the sea—Atmospheric influences—Frost—Heat—"Podolitos"—Eoliths used by existing savages—Objections presented by palæontology—Conclusions.

THE Tertiary Period is divided into four epochs. Two of these, Eocene and Oligocene, are considered as Early Tertiary or Palæogene; the other two, Miocene and Pliocene, as Late Tertiary or Neogene. During the Palæogene Europe enjoyed a most excellent climate; in fact, the south of this continent during the Eocene was bathed by a tropic sea. The Baltic district, with its mild temperate climate, gave rise to magnificent forests of conifers, which extended there with unsurpassed vigor and fertility, and from which, to-day, we derive that fossil resin known as amber. The higher mammals, attaining a maximum of fecundity, spread rapidly over the entire continent, dominating all other animal life. Meanwhile huge mountain ranges arose in Europe and at the same time great continental areas were submerged in the ocean.

Thus passed the Palæogene; but with the dawn of the following Neogene the paradisal climate that marked the earlier period already showed signs of change. It ceased to be uniform, and there ensued the varying seasons of the year that were destined to have such a preponderating influence in the biology of our planet. Nevertheless, the vegetation remained subtropical and flourished under the protection of a tranquil sky and a climate similar to that enjoyed by

certain parts of the Mediterranean region, as, for instance, Andalusia and southern Sicily. Broad-topped trees
predominated, and the palms, like queens of this earthly
paradise, proudly spread their fan-shaped leaves. This
picturesque domain was overrun by great herds of enormous
mastodons and rhinoceroses, which, together with the precursors of the horse, terrible carnivores, crocodiles, and
monkeys, gave life to that sylvan scene.

The Tertiary Period ended with the Pliocene: the climate
became more rigorous until effects of the first frosts were
observable and, in consequence of this climatic change, the
flora lost in splendor and became much like the present
Mediterranean flora. But this change of climate, so notice-
able in the valleys, unquestionably attained its full consequences in the condensation on the mountain crests, resulting in the formation of glaciers. Little by little these glaciers
took possession of the mountain slopes and gradually but
steadily reached their culmination in the First Glacial Stage,
thus marking the commencement of the Quaternary Period.

So far the question whether or no man was witness of the
course of events above recounted remains unanswered. A
fact of such transcendent importance would be demonstrated beyond question by the discovery of human skeletons
of Tertiary age, but up to the present time none of the supposed discoveries of this nature is sufficiently well proved
to withstand any serious scientific investigation. Neither
the "Eocene" skeleton of Delémont in Switzerland, nor the
"Pliocene" remains of Colle del Vento near Savona, Li-
guria, nor those of Castenodolo near Brescia, nor those of
Matera, all in Italy, have supplied any data for the solving
of this interesting problem—being therefore relegated to
oblivion, even as the Indian skull of Calaveras, California.
Neither has it been possible to prove that the discoveries
made by F. Ameghino in South America during the last
fifteen years—*Diprothomo platensis, Tetraprothomo argentinus,* etc.—are of Tertiary age as claimed. (In regard to
supposed human remains of Tertiary age in South America
see Chapter IX.)

In view of these facts, then, it may be affirmed that up to
the present time we have only indirect evidence of the

existence of Tertiary man—traces of human activity, believed to have been found in a number of different places, and consisting of the marks of cutting, hammering, or scratching. Such traces (chiefly fluted, engraved, or grooved) have been observed on the bones of animals and shells of molluscs in Tertiary deposits at Saint-Prest, Sansan, Pouancé, and Billy, France; in the Tertiary basin of Antwerp, Holland; at Monte Aperto near Siena, Italy; in North and South America; and in several other places. These remains would naturally consist of the refuse of kitchen middens and perhaps of primitive implements as well. But invariably such evidence as would confirm these theories is wholly lacking—such, for instance, as the discovery of unmistakable hearths or traces of fire—while, on the other hand, it is easy to explain the supposed traces of human activity as the result of natural causes—such, for example, as the gnawing or biting of animals, earth pressure, or the friction of coarse sand.

What has induced a great number of scientists, especially during the last fifteen years, to believe in the existence of Tertiary man is the discovery of certain stones of unusual shape—their peculiar form being attributed to the work of man at that time. These stones were named "eoliths," that is to say, "stones belonging to the dawn of humanity." As the acceptance of eoliths as authentic would establish many deductions and involve far-reaching consequences, the question has an irresistible and legitimate attraction.

The problem of the eoliths was first presented and developed in 1863 by the Abbé Louis Bourgeois,[1] rector of the seminary of Pontlevoy, Loire-et-Cher, France, who defended the theory with indefatigable vigor. In the above-mentioned department he discovered in fresh-water deposits of the Upper Oligocene near Thenay a great quantity of "flints shaped by human agency." These flints might have been used to cut, bore, scrape, or file, and a number of them might have been exposed to fire, seeing that their surfaces generally are marked by fine cracks. On these grounds the Abbé Bourgeois supported the idea of human beings already living during the Palæogene, pursuing an industry in stone implements that had attained a considerable development, and already acquainted with the use of fire. These discoveries attracted great attention in the scientific world and were accepted unconditionally by a number of scholars.

The controversy concerning Thenay did not subside until the year 1901, when L. Capitan and G. d'Ault du Mesnil showed how purely natural agencies might produce effects very similar to human handiwork, one of the most important being earth pressure above the brittle flint.

It was also at this time that the chemist, A. Carnot, asserted that atmospheric influences alone would be sufficient to account for the crackled surface of the flints which Bourgeois had taken for the effects of fire. Nevertheless, we feel obliged to add that in our opinion the crackling and reddish coloring of the Thenay flints really seem to support the hypothesis that these stones have actually been affected by fire. Only, we do not attribute this to human intervention, but believe it a result of some great conflagration of accidental origin, whereby a large area was fire-swept.

In 1871 Carlos Ribeiro announced the discovery of "worked" flints and quartzites at Otta, a Portuguese site of Upper Miocene age, in the valley of the Tagus.

With the beginning of the year 1877 came still further cause for discussion in the discovery of eoliths at Puy-Courny and other neighboring sites of Cantal, France, in which locality, resting upon corresponding strata of the Carboniferous, there are both fresh- and salt-water deposits of Oligocene age. Intervening in these sediments were found flint-bearing strata that doubtless afforded excellent material for the manufacture of the eoliths occurring in the superposed strata which consisted of calcareous deposits, fluvial sands, and gravel. In these strata were found the remains of flora and fauna—the latter including mastodons, rhinoceroses, primitive horses, and gazelles (*Dinotherium giganteum, Mastodon longirostris, Rhinoceros schleiermacheri, Hipparion gracile, Tragocerus amaltheus, Gazella deperdita*) which characterize an Upper Miocene of mild climate.

Huge masses of basalt and trachyte conjoined with abundant deposits of ashes and volcanic mud bear witness to the colossal eruptions of the craters of Cantal. A part of these

I. TERTIARY

5. Phase of Saint-Prest   (Saint-Prestian)   Upper Pliocene
4. Phase of Kent   (Kentian)   Middle Pliocene
3. Phase of Cantal   (Cantalian)   Upper Miocene
2. Phase of Thenay   (Thenayan)   Upper Oligocene
1. Phase of Boncelles   (Fagnian)   Middle Oligocene

Eoliths have been found not only in the Iberian Peninsula, in England, France, Belgium, Holland, Germany, Austria, and Italy; but also in northern and southern Africa; in India, especially in the Upper Miocene of Burma; in South America; and in Australia. The greater part of these discoveries occurred in accumulations of gravel.

The "Eolithophiles" or partisans of the eolithic theory —among whom are Abbott, F. Ameghino, M. Antón, Blanckenhorn, Bonnett, Bourgeois, Bracht, Capitan, W. Freudenberg, Hahne, Harrison, Johnson, Klaatsch, Krause, Lankester, MacCurdy, Menzel, G. and A. de Mortillet, de Munck, Nötling, Ribeiro, Rutot, Schweinfurth, Sergi, Verworn, and others—were content, for the most part, to accept them simply as primitive industries of the Tertiary and Early Quaternary.

But some—among them Boucher de Perthes, Dharvent, Newton, and Thieullen—went further, and proclaimed the existence of Eolithic ornament and art. According to them, the stony alluvial deposits afforded not only "geometric" stones of the most varied forms, but even perforated pebbles for use as pendants and actual works of "glyptic art." Thieullen called these stones "figure-stones" ("pierres-figures"; German, Figuren-Steine), including in this classification nodules of flint showing accidental resemblance to figures, either human or animal. Thieullen supposes that primitive man may have completed the work of chance, modifying it to suit himself by means of flaking and retouching until he succeeded in producing a figurine relatively true in outline. He further supposes that these figure-stones were used as fetiches or idols. From these proceedings there resulted flints resembling human heads and masks, sometimes also skulls and other separate members of the human body, as well as other forms, such as heads of monkeys, carnivores, and horses, figures of birds and their embryos, oxen, toads, fishes, seals, and hippopotamuses.

Rutot himself was greatly astonished to learn of forms of dogs, horses, and birds from the Miocene gravels of Cantal, for these animals belong to a fauna that does not correspond with the Tertiary fauna of these sites. The bewilderment of the Belgian scientist is natural; nevertheless, these extravagances were no more than the ultimate consequence of his own principle of "continuous selection."

From the time when the eolithic theory first aroused the interest of the scientific world, objections began to be raised against its acceptance. Thereupon, A. Rutot and his followers—geologists, archæologists, and palæontologists—weighed the *pro* and *contra* of the question with much greater interest than before. There can be no doubt that one of the most fortunate results of the controversy which centered on the problem of the eoliths was greatly to augment the thoroughness of critical investigation. A great number of "Eolithophobe" investigators—such as d'Acy, Arcelin, Boule, Breuil, van den Broek, Cartailhac, P. Choffat, Commont, Cumont, W. Boyd Dawkins, Déchelette, Evans, Hamy, Harvard, M. and R. Hörnes, Howorth, Lapparent, Laville, Mayet, Meunier, Obermaier, Ranke, Sarasin, R. R. Schmidt, Sollas, Vilanova, Virchow, S. H. Warren, Wernert, Wiegers —espoused the negative side and expressed views unfavorable to the eolithic theory, based on scientific considerations of weighty import.

Since it had been observed that, on the one hand, the great majority of eoliths occurred in places where large deposits of their essential material, flint, were found; and, on the other hand, that their presence almost always coincided with fluvial formations due to the action of running water; it was, therefore, most reasonable to suppose that there might be a causal relation between these shattered petrous formations and the action of swift-running water. Thence it came that, together with A. Laville, M. Boule, and E. Cartailhac, the present writer eagerly desired an opportunity to observe the action of swift-running water upon masses of flint.

The chance to make this interesting investigation came in 1905, at the chalk mills of Guerville, in the neighborhood of

Mantes and close to the Seine. These mills consist of tanks filled with water, in which the lumps of chalk with flint nodules embedded in them are rapidly rotated. In order to separate these nodules from the chalk and to pulverize the latter, chalk-lumps and water are subjected by means of turbines to a centrifugal motion with a velocity of about four meters per second. At the risk of being tedious we may add that before commencing the experiment every factor that could lead to error in the conclusions was eliminated, and especial care was taken that the lumps of chalk placed in the tanks should be intact and not subjected to the slightest artificial modification.

On carefully examining the flint fragments resulting from the operation of pulverizing the chalk, we found ourselves confronted with typical eoliths, strikingly similar to those found in alluvial river deposits. The eoliths produced by the chalk mills, equally with those found in river deposits, showed forms with either partial or entire retouch around the edges, notched edges more or less deeply incurved, specimens that might be classed as scrapers, burins, and even planing tools. The resemblance between the natural and the artificial eoliths is so close that it even includes the exceptional and irregular forms.

Finally, we noted at Mantes certain sharp-edged types, and others in which the edge had been completely worn away. The sharp-edged types resulted after remaining in the mill for from eight to ten hours, the others after a longer time in the water. L. Capitan, who at that time was a vigorous advocate of the eolithic theory and who, himself, had more than sufficient cause to give especial attention to this subject, did not hesitate to recognize "the striking similarity" of the specimens produced at Mantes to the eoliths found in alluvial deposits. No great effort, therefore, was required to refute the objections that were raised, the more so that at this time a deposit of eoliths was discovered at Steinheim in the valley of Stuben, Würtemberg, by P. Wernert and R. R. Schmidt. In this case the accumulation of eoliths belonged apparently to the Middle Quaternary.

"We are able to show at the site itself how the fragments of flint were borne along by the stream in the principal valley and suddenly drawn into whirlpools caused by the inflow of a tributary stream. By this means the flints were subjected to a strong rotary movement which, however, was limited and intermittent in action, and therefore did not result in such continuous wearing away as would transform the flints into rounded pebbles.'' Rutot himself, who visited the site in 1911, wrote regarding it: ''Here there can be no possible doubt: these are 'pseudo-eoliths.' ''

The flooding of small streams, quite as often due to violent storms as to a long-continued thaw, is a matter of common observation. Great floods due to tempests may have caused the formation of the Tertiary eoliths; and the inundations resulting from thaws during the Glacial Epoch may have been responsible for the formation of many Quaternary eoliths—always bearing in mind that, as at present, so also in times past, the same causes under the same conditions must always produce the same effects.

Another cause contributing to the formation of eoliths, aside from the effects of swift-flowing water on the flints as described above, is earth pressure. A. Arcelin had already made mention of this phenomenon in 1885, and the present author has repeatedly had occasion to note the effect of vertical and oblique earth pressure on the flints of several distinct strata. These opinions have lately been amply verified through the investigations of H. Breuil in Clermont, Oise.

Near here, at the gravel pit of Belle-Assise, is found the chalk which serves as a stratigraphic base. Above the chalk is a clayey deposit in which are found abundant nodules of flint interspersed with strata of sand and coarse gravel. This deposit was the one under investigation. Above it there lay a heavy deposit of Bracheux sand, belonging to the Thanetian or basal Eocene. A stratigraphic examination proved that flints from the lowest strata must date at least from the Lower Eocene. Above the Thanetian sands at Belle-Assise were deposits of coarse gravel, either Pliocene or Quaternary. A careful study of the flints from the deposit next above the chalk showed that many of them appeared to bear marks of ''artificial workmanship.'' (Figure 2.)

Among them may be noted flints with pronounced patina,

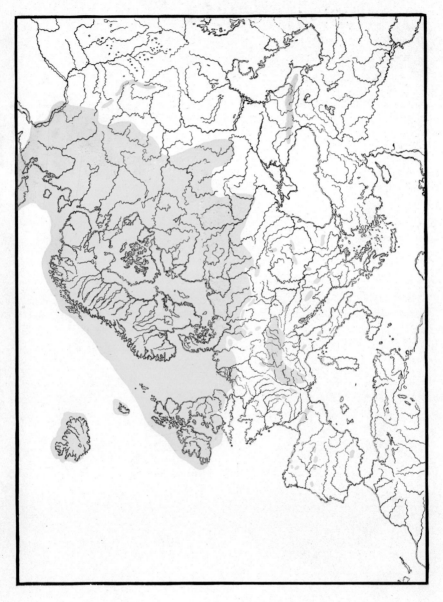

PLATE II

Europe during the maximum glaciation of the Pleistocene. Blue tint indicates the regions covered with ice.

CHAPTER II

THE GLACIAL EPOCH

Introduction—The maximum glaciation of Europe—In the Alps—In northern Europe—Local centers of glaciation—Asia—North America —South America—Africa—Australia—Polyglaciation—Four glacial stages in the Alps—Four glacial stages in the Pyrenees—Glacial stages in northern Europe—Glacial stages in England—Glaciation in central Europe—Glacial stages in North and South America—Erosion and deposition due to glaciation—Lakes—Volcanoes of the Glacial Epoch—The "loess"—European coastlines during the Glacial Epoch—Conclusions.

THE geologic time division extending from the close of the Tertiary Period to the beginning of the present Holocene or Recent Epoch is commonly known as the Glacial, Diluvial, or Pleistocene Epoch. Together with the Holocene, it forms the Quaternary Period. To this epoch belong numerous superficial deposits—beds of former glaciers, characteristic forms of the sub-glacial till (kames, eskers), huge mounds of lateral and terminal moraines, and extensive terraces of fluvio-glacial gravels (Plates IV, V, and VI). A careful study of these formations has led to the conclusion that large areas of our earth were formerly covered by enormous glaciers and ice-fields. On these grounds this time division has been aptly entitled the "Glacial Epoch."

Since Europe was the principal theater of these glacial phenomena, and since they have been more exhaustively studied there than elsewhere, we will commence with that continent in considering the effects of the maximum glaciation.

The great ice-cap of the Alps has been studied with especial attention during the last thirty years, as will be realized by those familiar with the work of Penck and Brückner, *Die Alpen im Eiszeitalter*. At the beginning of the maximum glaciation the Rhone, the Aar, the Reuss, and the Linth were great rivers of ice, continually thrusting their frozen masses toward the Swiss "Midland" and little by little augmenting its ice-fields. But the course of these glacial masses was obstructed by the barrier of the Swiss Jura, and they piled up before it. In this way an immense sea of ice was formed, many hundred meters in thickness. Moreover, on encountering the Jura barrier the ice mass divided, one branch flowing southward through the depression of Lake Geneva, and the other northward toward the gap of Basle.

Nevertheless, a part of the ice mass overflowed some of the lower peaks of the Swiss and French Jura in the form of glacial streams which west of the Jura were again united, their course extending from a distance some fifteen kilometers beyond Basle as far as Lyons. The principal branch of the Rhone glacier, diverted toward the southwest and reënforced by the Arve glacier, advanced as far as the present site of Lyons, extending its immense amphitheater From Mâcon in the north to Vienne in the south. Farther southward it united with the glacial complex of the Isère and the Durance which ended at Sisteron. The farthest traces of the glaciers of the Maritime Alps are found to the north of Saint-Martin Vesubie, some thirty kilometers from the Riviera, where palms now grow and flourish.

The Rhine glacier, enlarging and deploying toward the north, remained independent. Lake Constance must be considered as a depression of its terminal amphitheater. To one side the Iller glacier flowed to the northward of the Alps, its terminal moraines extending beyond Kaufbeuren.

East of the Iller glacier were the glaciers of the Lech and the Isar, which left erratic deposits within ten kilometers of Munich. The Inn glacier gave rise to an immense moraine girdle of which the central point is the present site of Rosenheim, while the present city of Salzburg is in the midst of the terminal moraines of the Salza glacier. The ice from all these glaciers, flowing northward, united in one mighty ice-field which covered a considerable part of the high plateau of Bavaria. East of these, at Traun, was another center of glaciation which reached its limit north of Gmunden. The glaciers of Steier and Enns extended as far as the present watering place of Hall. Farther eastward there were a large number of local centers of glaciation, such as

The Rosseg and Tschierva glaciers in the Bernina Alps. Modern
"valley glaciers" of Alpine type.

Glacier on the northern slope of the Maladetta group in the Spanish
Pyrenees. A modern "hanging glacier" of Pyrenean type.

PLATE III

the Schafberg, the Höllengebirge, the Traunstein, and the Sensengebirge.

On the southern slope of the Alps the glacial flow was greater than to the eastward. Nevertheless, there was no such complete glaciation over the plain south of the Alps as that which obtained to the north. The glacier of Ticino extended far, its terminal moraines forming the margin of Lake Maggiore. The Adda and Oglio glaciers reached, respectively, to the regions south of Lake Como and Lake Iseo. These glaciers were partly fed by snow from the passes of St. Gotthard and St. Bernard. The moraine amphitheaters found to the north of the Gulf of Venice are all of little importance, except one in the neighborhood of Udine. The glaciers to the eastward did not reach to the plain. This was true of the glaciers of the Save, which extended to Radmannsdorf above Krainburg; of the Drave, which extended as far as St. Paul, thirty-five kilometers from Klagenfurt; and of the Mur, which extended to Judenburg. A small center of glaciation may be recognized in the Steiner Alps.

Thus it is seen that during the maximum glaciation the Alps were covered by a great ice-cap. Nevertheless, their lofty peaks emerged above the ice and acted as barriers, diverting its flow in various directions and thus forming a number of glacial streams (Plate II).

In the north of Europe the ice-sheet was enormous. During its maximum extension wide regions lay buried beneath it. This was true of all Scandinavia, the greater part of England and Holland, almost all of northern Germany, and two-thirds of Russia. The divide of this great ice-sheet was the mountain range of northern Scandinavia, from which the ice extended on the one side toward the glacial sea, and on the other westward toward the Atlantic. This last caused the formation of immense ice-fields between Iceland, at that time entirely covered by the ice mass, and the British Isles together with the Faroe and Shetland Islands —ice-fields which constituted a serious obstruction to the natural discharge of the glacial flow from northern Europe. In this way a great ice barrier was formed in the North Sea.

In Great Britain, especially in the north, there was another center of glaciation which arose from the accumulation of ice on the mountains of Scotland and northern England. This glaciation entirely covered the British Isles, excepting only the district south of the Thames. The ice-fields of Scandinavia and Scotland were united in a solid mass which extended to the continent and covered Holland and the region of the lower Rhine up to where the Ruhr flows into it. From there the margin of the ice has been traced eastward to the mountain ranges of central Germany north of the Harz Mountains, and thence it inclined southward to the region of the Saale. Turning northward, its traces are found at the foot of the Thüringer Wald, of the Erzgebirge, of the Riesengebirge, and of the Sudetes. Farther eastward, it follows the northern slope of the Carpathians, describing a huge S as it enters the Russian border. It then runs almost parallel to the Volga and to the Ural Mountains toward the Timan Mountains, until finally its traces are lost in the Arctic Ocean.

All of northern Europe was covered by a mass of ice, estimated at seventy million cubic kilometers, which in Scandinavia seems to have been two thousand meters thick. Neither the depression of the Baltic nor of the North Sea availed to halt its advance. It has been estimated that in Denmark it attained a thickness of one thousand meters, and even along the edges a thickness of several hundred meters, in spite of melting.

The two centers of glaciation above described were the largest, but by no means the only ones in Europe, where, in fact, a number of local glaciations of varying intensity and extent may be distinguished. Thus, in western Europe, we may mention the glaciations of the Serra da Estrella in Portugal, and of the Cantabrian Mountains, Central Cordilleras, Iberian Mountains, and Sierra Nevada, in Spain (Plates III-VII). In the Pyrenees the glaciation on the northern French side of the divide was much more severe than that on the Spanish side. (Chapter VI, geologic section.) Centers of glaciation in France were the Auvergne Mountains and the Cévennes.

In central Europe there were also important centers of glaciation—the Vosges Mountains, the Black Forest, and the Swiss Jura. The last-named had a number of local gla-

Moraine amphitheater of the Pleistocene glacier of Mulhacén, in the Sierra Nevada, Spain.

Bed of the Pleistocene glacier of Pinar, in the Sierra de
Gredos, Spain. In the old channel of the ice there are now
five lakes—"Las cinco Lagunas."

PLATE IV

ciations on its western slopes. In the Harz Mountains, the Fichtelgebirge, and the Bohemian Mountains the glaciation was less extensive, as also in the Erzgebirge, the Sudetes and the Carpathians of the Transylvanian Alps. It has been shown that there was also a partial glaciation in the Balkans, chiefly in the ranges of Zelen Gora, Maglic, and Visocica in Bosnia Herzegovina, the Golija and Kopaonik Mountains in Servia, the Kunora Mountains in central Albania, the Pirin Mountains in Macedonia, and the Rila Mountains in eastern Rumelia.

In southern Europe, besides those already mentioned in Spain, there were some small glaciers in the Apennines of Italy, and in Corsica. During the Glacial Epoch the glaciers of the Caucasus were far larger than at present, and the Ural Mountains, which now have no glaciers, were then a center of glaciation which extended over the territory of Petschora.

In Asia the mountains of Olympus in Mysia, the mountains of Lebanon, Mount Ararat, Mount Demavend, and the mountains near Trebizond and Erzerum, all show traces of glaciation. Much greater in extent were the Pleistocene glaciers of the huge mountain ranges of central Asia, chief among them being the Himalayan and the Karakoram. The northern part of Siberia was entirely covered by a thick unbroken sheet of ice. In contrast to the "living" inland ice, this huge frozen mass remained stationary except only along the seacoasts and on the mountain slopes, and covered the vast Siberian tundras with "dead" ice which, in certain of their far northern regions, remains to the present day (Figure 3). This phenomenon is due to the peculiar climatic conditions caused by the continental situation of northern and eastern Asia, where the humidity is much less than in the oceanic continents of Europe and America. Quite recently unquestionable evidences of glaciation have been discovered in Japan.

In North America an area of twenty million square kilometers was covered by the ice-fields of the maximum glaciation. The center of this glaciation lay within the territory to the west and east of Hudson Bay. The terminal moraines of this mass of continental ice begin in the east near

Fig. 3. "Fossil" glacier on Liachov Island in the Arctic Ocean. After E. von Toll.

New York, and attain their southern limit where the Ohio
flows into the Mississippi. From there the moraines follow
the course of the Missouri until in the west, north of the
Columbia River, they mark where the ice-fields joined with
the glacier which descended from the Rocky Mountains. In
Alaska the huge ice-cap united with the stationary ice which,
in the Arctic latitudes, was the equivalent of the true glaciers. Following the Rocky Mountains southward beyond the
limits of the great ice-sheet, evidences are found of a number
of former local glaciations, diminishing in importance
toward the south.

In South America north of the equator centers of glaciation are found in the mountain ranges of Santa Marta in
Colombia, and the Sierra Nevada of Santa Maria in Vene-
zuela. South of the equator the traces left by the Pleistocene
glaciation are of great importance, especially in the mountain range of the Andes, throughout Chile and Argentina,
and in Patagonia, including Tierra del Fuego. In the last-
named country the terrestrial deposits and the character of
the seacoast indicate an ancient glaciation of great extent.

As might be expected, traces of glaciation in Africa are
rare, but nevertheless they can be found in the Atlas Mountains and the ranges of Abyssinia, the peaks of Kenia, Ruwenzori, and Kilimanjaro, and the high mountain ranges
of the Transvaal.

The greatest heights in New South Wales and the Ade-
laide Mountains in Australia were formerly capped with
ice, as also the heights of Tasmania and New Zealand.

If it is true that at the present time there are still a few
investigators who believe in the theory of monoglaciation—
that is to say, in a single uninterrupted glacial period during
the Pleistocene Epoch—it is, nevertheless, clear that almost
the entire scientific world has accepted polyglaciation. Ad-
herents of the latter theory claim that during the Glacial
or Pleistocene Epoch there was a series of successive glaciations, alternating with interglacial stages marked by a
warm climate. Indeed, the combined evidence of geologic
researches and of reports on the floras and faunas of

Europe and America compels the admission of polyglaciation as an irrefutable fact.

This is proved by the fact that in the high plains at the
foot of the Alps there are found four distinct terraces of
fluvio-glacial gravels, deposited in such a manner as to show
that each one corresponds to a period of glacial deposit,
while the erosion of each terrace corresponds to an interglacial period (Figure 4). The most recent deposits are quite

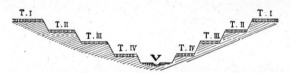

Fig. 4. Diagram showing the four fluvio-glacial terraces of river
valleys on the northern borders of the Alps. (Compare Fig. 5.)

T. I—terrace of the first glaciation.
T. II—terrace of the second glaciation.
T. III—terrace of the third glaciation.
T. IV—terrace of the fourth glaciation.
V—present river bed.

porous and are well preserved, while those belonging to
the earlier Pleistocene are much weathered and metamor-
phosed. Only in the neighborhood of Munich are the deposits
found in direct superposition, and that they are not in
lateral gradations is owing to the accident of local geologic
conditions. Near Deissenhofen may be seen the deposits of
the latest glacial· stage. These rest upon the gravels and
moraines of the third glaciation, which are much weathered.
Finally, beneath these are found the deposits of the second
glaciation, the surface of which shows pockets of weathered
material from six to eight meters deep, a phenomenon
showing that the surface of these gravels was also formerly
in direct contact with atmospheric influences, and for a long
period.

Each of these four terraces still has its corresponding
morainal amphitheaters (Figure 5). The moraines of the
Upper Pleistocene are well preserved, while those of the
Lower Pleistocene are partly obliterated and in places
very much indurated. It is an important fact that, even
before the formation of the more recent deposits, these

ancient gravels and moraines had already been transformed into breccia. Further, there can be no doubt that a considerable part of the more recent deposits was formed at the expense of the older gravels and moraines, as is proved by the presence of many blocks of morainal breccia in the Upper Pleistocene deposits.

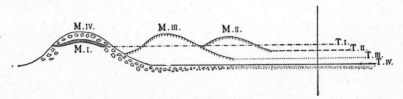

Fig. 5. Longitudinal section through the four moraine zones on the
northern borders of the Alps. (Compare Fig. 4.)

> M. I—moraines of the first glaciation.
> M. II—moraines of the second glaciation.
> M. III—moraines of the third glaciation.
> M. IV—moraines of the fourth glaciation.
> T. I – T. IV : the fluvio-glacial terraces corre-
> sponding to these moraine zones.

On the ground of the existence of these four glacial complexes of different ages, and separated by long interglacial stages, Penck and Brückner accept four glacial stages which bear the names of four Alpine rivers and occur in the following order:

Glacial Stages	Glacial deposits in the vicinity of the glaciated area	Difference in level from the present limits of perpetual snow
Recent Epoch		
IV. Würm	Gravels of the fourth or lowest river terrace (Niederterrassenschotter)	About −1200 m.
3. Interglacial Stage		
III. Riss	Gravels of the third river terrace (Hochterrassenschotter)	About −1300 m.
2. Interglacial Stage		
II. Mindel	Second layer of shotter—second river terrace (Jüngerer Deckenschotter)	About −1300 m.
1. Interglacial Stage		
I. Günz	Upper layer of shotter—first or highest river terrace (Älterer Deckenschotter)	About −1200 m.

During the long post-glacial time the glaciers receded to their present limits. This recession was not absolutely uniform, but was characterized by a succession of oscillations, as may be seen in the following table:

Stages	Phases	Difference in the level of perpetual snow from the present time
Recent		About −00 m.
Post-glacial	Daun Retreat	About −300 m.
	Gschnitz Retreat	About −600 m.
	Bühl Advance	About −900 m.
	[Achen Retreat (?)	About −700 m.]
IV. Würm	Maximum.	About −1200 m.

The writer has found it possible to apply this Alpine classification to the French Pyrenees, where he has been able to demonstrate the existence of the same four fluvio-glacial terraces. At the present time the moraines of the third and fourth glaciations may still be observed south of Foix-sur-Ariège and near Lourdes.

It has not been possible, however, to classify definitely the glacial areas of north Germany, where the deposits are by no means so extensive as in the Alps, and are, moreover, rendered very difficult of interpretation on account of their interpenetration. Nevertheless, it may be affirmed that there were repeated glaciations in northern Germany, and it may safely be asserted that the maximum glaciation there coincided with the Mindel Glacial Stage in the Alpine region. Recent investigations have shown that the famous "Baltic" terminal moraine is due entirely to the first great advance of post-glacial times, corresponding to the Bühl advance in the Alpine region. Of late years C. Gagel, O. von Linstow, and many other geologists have declared themselves in favor of admitting the existence of three glacial stages, basing their theory on weighty arguments, inasmuch as an equivalent of the Günz Glacial Stage would seem to be lacking in northern Germany.

The chronology of geologic evolution in northern Europe during the Post-glacial Stage is given in Chapter X. There the retreat of the ice also took place by degrees, as shown in the following table:

Stages	*Phases*
Recent	
Post-glacial	4th Retreat: Scandiglaciar (or Finiglaciar)
	Central Swedish Halt
	3d Retreat: Gotiglaciar
	South Swedish Halt
	2d Retreat: Daniglaciar
	Baltic Advance
	1st Retreat: Germaniglaciar
IV. Würm	

James Geikie, who has devoted much study to a synthesis of the English glaciation, for a number of years past has accepted the theory of six successive glacial stages, as follows:

VI. Glacial Stage	Upper Turbarian
5th Interglacial Stage	Upper Forestian
V. Glacial Stage	Lower Turbarian
4th Interglacial Stage	Lower Forestian
IV. Glacial Stage	Mecklenburgian
3d Interglacial Stage	Dürtenian (formerly known as Neudeckian)
III. Glacial Stage	Polonian
2d Interglacial Stage	Tyrolean (formerly known as Helvetian)
II. Glacial Stage	Saxonian
1st Interglacial Stage	Norfolkian
I. Glacial Stage	Scanian

Finally, in 1914, Geikie concluded that only the Scanian, Saxonian, Polonian, and Mecklenburgian represented true glacial stages, and that stages V and VI were no more than post-glacial oscillations.

But science encounters difficulties of the first magnitude when an attempt is made to determine the exact number of glaciations in mountains of moderate height in Europe. This is due to the fact that the evidences of glaciation there are less pronounced than in ranges of great altitude, and also to the fact that the latest glaciation destroyed in large measure the traces of preceding glaciations. Nevertheless, it has been possible to demonstrate the occurrence of several glaciations in the Carpathians (three stages) and also in the

Black Forest, the Balkans, the mountains of Corsica, and in the Caucasus.

Very divergent are the opinions obtaining in regard to the number of glacial stages in North America, for, while Chamberlin recognizes three, others raise the number to six or seven. Leverett believes that there also there were four principal glacial stages, basing his belief on the fact that the accumulation and, above all, the decomposition of the gravels and moraines in the New World took place under conditions and in proportions strikingly similar to those found in the Alps.

Leverett's four stages are as follows:

IV. Glacial Stage	.	. .	Wisconsin
III. Glacial Stage	.	. .	Illinoian
II. Glacial Stage	.	. .	Kansan
I. Glacial Stage	.	. .	Nebraskan

Up to the present time the existence of two glaciations has been demonstrated in Ecuador, Argentina, and Patagonia.

It is easy to understand that the geologic events of the Glacial Epoch should have had far-reaching effects upon the earth's surface. The areas covered by ice and snow were greatly denuded by erosion. In the territory belonging to the great northern ice-fields of Europe and constituting their area of deposit there lie from six to seven hundred thousand cubic kilometers of gravels from the Scandinavian rocks; which presupposes a loss of some 2000 feet in the height of the Scandinavian range during the Glacial Epoch.

The great volumes of water which streamed from the border of the ice-fields during each glacial stage gave rise to a multitude of lakes in central and eastern Europe. The Sea of Azov was united with the Caspian, extending northward to Kazan and uniting with the Sea of Aral.

The number of active volcanoes in Europe during the Pleistocene was considerable, although not so great as during the Tertiary. Mention may be made of those in the Ægean Sea (Santorino and others), together with the Latial volcano in the Alban Mountains of Italy. Of the same age are

the Eifel Mountains in the middle Rhine districts, and also
several in northern Bohemia and in Moravia. It has been
shown that the volcanoes of the central plateau of France
were also active during the Post-glacial Stage. (For Spain
see Chapter VI, geologic section.)

The "loess" is a characteristic Pleistocene formation consisting of a deposit of fine wind-borne dust solidified by
natural compression into a yellowish friable stone. According to Richthofen, E. Schumacher, W. A. Obrutchev, G.
Merzbacher, W. Soergel, and others, it is formed chiefly of
particles of quartz, combined, however, with other mineral
constituents, among which limestone occurs in proportions
which have been known to exceed 30 per cent. Near the
surface of loess deposits the lime content is often eliminated
by weathering, which results in the so-called "loess loam"
formation.

In Europe the loess extends like an immense mantle over
enormous areas which formerly were on the margin of the
glaciated regions. Thus it is found in southern England, in
France, in central and eastern Europe, along the line that
marks the ancient limits of the northern ice-cap, and it also
occurs as a broad isolated belt along the northern borders of
the Pyrenees, while it completely encircles the ancient
boundaries of the great Alpine glaciation (Figure 6).

This remarkable formation consists chiefly of fine material from the moraines and the products of infiltration
from the same. We must therefore consider that the glaciated regions were the centers in which the material of the
loess was prepared by mechanical and chemical disintegra-
tion. Above these ice-fields the aerial conditions formed at
times an anticyclone from which violent winds blew down
over the adjoining unglaciated regions with their sparse
vegetation, carrying the loess dust over all the surrounding
area, where, as a "foreign" formation, it was finally deposited.

The loess must therefore be considered as a formation
of æolian origin and, for the most part, of glacial age. The
period of deposition would begin toward the close of an
interglacial stage when the glaciers were slowly augmenting and advancing; it would continue in increased measure

Fig. 6. Loess formation at Gedersdorf, Lower Austria. From a photograph by A. E. Forster. (The loess is artificially terraced.)

CHAPTER III

PLANTS AND ANIMALS OF THE GLACIAL EPOCH[1]

Geographic relations of the Iberian Peninsula—Connections with Africa and Europe—Chronologic table—Animal life in western Europe when man first appeared—Early Pleistocene fauna—Evidences of Tertiary man—Division between the Pliocene and Pleistocene—Warm and cold faunas—Heidelberg man—Second Glacial Stage—Second Interglacial Stage—Middle Pleistocene fauna—Primitive flint implements—Warm fauna of interglacial times—Third Glacial Stage—Late Pleistocene fauna—Flora of the interglacial stages—Climate of the Late Pleistocene —Climatic transitions of the Third Interglacial Stage—Fourth Glacial Stage—Period of the first cave men—Arctic-Alpine fauna—Distribution of the reindeer—Arctic molluscs—Post-glacial time—Disappearance of the Neanderthal race—Appearance of the Crô-Magnon race—Climate and fauna of the steppes—Fauna of the Third Glacial Stage—Arctic-Alpine flora of the glacial stages—Animals common both to warm and cold climates—Influence of Post-glacial environment on the development of the Crô-Magnon race—Extinction of Pleistocene species.

WE depend very largely on our knowledge of the contiguous areas in Africa to the south and France to the north for our picture of life conditions in the Iberian Peninsula during the Glacial Epoch. The glaciers of the Pyrenees, of which we have recently spoken, descended far into the valleys to the north and to the south. But we have little direct evidence of the general refrigeration and period of bitterly cold weather with which the Glacial Epoch closed. We know that while the Alpine and the Scandinavian glaciers were threatening southern France and the whole of northern Europe in their successive periods of advance which are known as the First, Second, and Third Glacial Stages, life conditions were still so tolerable that men, both in France and in Spain, were dwelling in river valleys and resorting for protection to shelters on the sunny sides of cliffs and mountain slopes. It was only during the Fourth Glacial Stage that life in the open became impossible —at least during the winter months—and that the prehistoric period of the cave man began.

The first cave men were the low-browed Neanderthals—a race widespread over all of western Europe for a very long antecedent period. The second cave men were high-browed, large-brained Crô-Magnons, who came in at the beginning of the very long cold period known as Post-glacial Time.

Since it is most important to keep these climatic and time divisions clearly in mind, we may introduce this chapter by a simplified statement, as follows:

Post-glacial Time.

Closing phases of the Ice Age (otherwise known as the Glacial Epoch, Pleistocene, or Quaternary).

Final appearance of the *mammoth,* of the reindeer, and other mammals of cold northern type in France and in extreme northern Spain.

Final cave period. Western Europe inhabited by the Crô-Magnon race of men.

FOURTH GLACIAL STAGE.

Period of maximum refrigeration.

Mammoth and reindeer driven to the extreme south of France—the reindeer even penetrating into northern Spain.

First cave period. Men of the low-browed Neanderthal race.

Third Interglacial Stage.

Closing with cold dry phase of steppe climate and life.

Opening with warmer conditions, favorable to the last survivors of the African and Asiatic types of large game mammals.

Europe probably inhabited by ancestors of the Neanderthal race—first living in the open, and gradually retreating to the caverns.

THIRD GLACIAL STAGE.

Great glaciers in the Alps—also in Scandinavia, reaching Great Britain and covering all of northern Germany. Climate nevertheless tolerable in the river valleys of Spain, France, and Great Britain.

No evidence of cave life during this period.

Second Interglacial Stage.

A very long warm period, favorable to the large African-Asiatic mammals.

Ancestors of the Neanderthals probably living in the river
valleys.

No evidence whatever of cave life.

SECOND GLACIAL STAGE.

Scandinavian ice-fields closing the North Sea and reaching
Great Britain. Extremely cold conditions in the North and
Baltic seas, indicated by the presence of mammoth and reindeer on the northeastern coast of England. Great glaciers
covering northern Germany and descending from the Alps.

First Interglacial Stage.

A period of temperate climate. African and Asiatic elephants
and hippopotami roaming all over northern France, Germany, and southern England.

In Germany the Heidelberg man—a very remote ancestor
of the Neanderthal man, attributed to this period[2]—is
found on the stream Elsenz near Heidelberg, associated
with remains of the Etruscan rhinoceros.

FIRST GLACIAL STAGE.

The least extensive—not reaching Great Britain, but extending
into northern Germany across the Baltic Sea from Scandinavia, and also covering the Alps.

No evidence of widespread refrigeration or of profound
change in the flora or fauna of Spain, France, or southern
Britain.

Pre-glacial Time.

This period marks the transition from the close of the Age of
Mammals to the beginning of the Age of Man. It is the close
of the Tertiary and the beginning of the Quaternary, known
to geologists as the Pliocene. The significant climatic feature
is the very gradual approach of cooler conditions of climate
all over northern Europe, which succeeded the long prevail-
ing warm conditions of the Age of Mammals.

It is in this transition epoch that the first evidences of the
flint industry of man are found on the eastern coast of
Britain. This flint industry is known as the Foxhallian
—a name derived from Foxhall, England—and constitutes the sole evidence we have at present of the existence
of man during Pliocene time in western Europe, the
most astonishing discovery of recent times.

Animal Life in Western Europe when Man First Appeared in Pre-glacial Time.

The Early Pleistocene fauna of some authors, or "post-Pliocene" group of others, corresponds in part to the preglacial phase, but is chiefly a fauna with Pliocene survivals.

Pliocene survivals in northern Italy, southern France, and southern England:

Borson's mastodon	*Mastodon borsoni*
Short-jawed mastodon	*Mastodon arvernensis*
Tapir of Auvergne	*Tapirus arvernensis*
Hipparion (?), three-toed horse	*Hipparion* (?) (last appearance)

Culminating phase of

Macaque	*Macacus*
Lion of Auvergne	*Felis arvernensis*
Hyena of Perrier	*Hyæna perrieri*
Etruscan rhinoceros	*Rhinoceros etruscus*
Etruscan bear	*Ursus etruscus*

Appearance of

Straight-tusked elephant	*Loxodonta antiqua*
Southern elephant	*Elephas meridionalis* (type)
Steno's horse	*Equus stenonis*
Wild ox	*Bos* (also *Leptobos*)

This phase of life corresponds with E. Haug's phases of Villefranche and Saint-Prest, France; with the marine Calabrian of southern Italy, described by M. Gignoux; and with the two first phases of the Early Pleistocene according to E. Koken. Faunas typical of this group have been found at Val d'Arno, Italy; Crozas, near Vals, Haute-Loire, France; Perrier, near Issoire, Puy-de-Dôme, France; the Sands of Chagny, Saône-et-Loire, France; Saint-Prest, near Chartres, Eure-et-Loir, France; Norwich Crag, eastern England; and the Doveholes, near Buxton, Derbyshire, England.

Very recently a large bed of flints with evidences of fire has been found on the eastern coast of England near Norwich and beneath the Late Pliocene deposits known as the "Red Crag" and the "Norwich Crag." The authenticity of the flints as of human origin is disputed by some archæologists, but is accepted by others, including Louis Capitan, the veteran archæologist of France, and Henri Breuil, who is frequently quoted in these pages. This discovery of Fox-hall is the first evidence we have of the existence of Tertiary man.

This was followed by the advent of the Glacial Epoch in Scandinavia and northern Germany and what is known as the First Glacial Stage in which both the Scandinavian and Alpine glaciers were formed, and there was a general lowering of temperature, especially in the north of Europe. This introduced the Quaternary or Pleistocene Epoch.

The Pleistocene Epoch was characterized chiefly by the appearance of a series of glacial stages. There is not the slightest ground for assigning the First Glacial Stage to the Pliocene, as advocated by M. Boule, M. Schlosser, W. Soergel, Boyd Dawkins, and others. On the contrary, the writer is entirely in agreement with E. Haug, E. Koken, A. Penck, and others, who contend that the beginning of the First Glacial Stage coincides with the beginning of the Pleistocene. This view is supported by weighty palæontologic evidence. A careful study of the faunas found in deposits belonging to the disputed boundary between Pliocene and Pleistocene shows that the Pliocene genera were gradually disappearing, while new types of Asiatic origin came to constitute the larger portion of the fauna. Among these new genera were the elephants and the primitive ancestral types of horse, ox, and bison. These new types appeared very suddenly, and their triumphant entry justifies a division between two geologic stages and serves to characterize a new epoch.

This glacial period was followed by a warmer interval known as the First Interglacial Stage. It would seem that part of the fauna of the Forest Bed of Cromer, England, belongs to the First Interglacial Stage. According to E. T. Newton the African hippopotamus, trogontherian mammoth, a species of saber-tooth tiger, Steno's horse (*Hippopotamus major, Elephas trogontherii*—not *E. meridionalis, Machairodus* sp., *Equus stenonis*), and others are found there, apparently with an intermixture of other faunal elements such as the wolverine (*Gulo luscus*), musk ox (*Ovibos*

moschatus), and others. The warm fauna agrees well with
that of the Second Interglacial Stage, and consequently the
cold elements would correspond to the following Third
Glacial Stage. Of the same age, or perhaps still older, is
the reindeer (*Rangifer tarandus*) of Steinheim on the Murr,
and the ancestral musk ox (*Præovibos priscus*) of Frankenhausen in Thuringia. In the lower gravels of Süssenborn,
near Weimar, from eight to ten meters below the surface,
W. Soergel came upon remains of a species of reindeer related to the Scandinavian (*Rangifer* cfr. *tarandus*), which
may probably be attributed to the Second Glacial Stage.
These gravels were doubtless deposited previous to the
maximum glaciation of Scandinavia, which covered that
region with ice.

The reader should keep clearly in mind the marked distinction between animal life in the north of Europe at this
time—especially in the latitude of the Forest Bed of
Cromer, which is nearly fifty-three degrees north—where
the reindeer, musk ox, woolly mammoth, and other cold
northern types appear; and the south of Europe—namely,
in Italy, southern France, and Spain, where the warm fauna
flourished even throughout the First Glacial Stage of the
north. It was only in the final period of the Ice Age that
these northern animals reached the latitude of the Pyrenees,
namely, forty-three degrees north.

*Heidelberg Man Appears during the First Interglacial
    Stage.*

The Piltdown or Dawn Man of England is of a somewhat
uncertain geologic age. It may be very old—of Tertiary or
early Pleistocene time—and it furnishes additional proof
that human beings had reached western Europe by the latter
part of the Tertiary or the beginning of Quaternary time.

With the Heidelberg man the case is different. In the
author's opinion[2] the Heidelberg man—known only from the
well-preserved lower jaw, which closely resembles that of
the well-known Neanderthal race of a later period—was
contemporaneous with the First Interglacial Stage. The jaw
was found associated with remains of a number of quadru-

peds in a stage of evolution corresponding with First or Second Interglacial time.

The Second Glacial Stage was far more extensive than the first, since the Scandinavian glacier crossed the North Sea and also covered a large part of northern Germany. The Alpine glaciers descended to greater distances—in fact, this is the first really great glaciation of Europe. It was, however, followed by a recession of the ice and another long period of temperate climate which is known as the Second Interglacial Stage.

The animals belong to the "Cromer" phase of E. Haug. Faunas typical of this group have been found at Mosbach, near Wiesbaden, Germany; the Sands of Mauer, near Heidelberg, Baden, Germany; Süssenborn, near Weimar, Germany; Steinheim on the Murr, Würtemberg, Germany; Abbeville, Somme, France; Solilhac, near Blanzac, Haute-Loire, France; and at Montmaurin, Es-Taliens, and Mont-saunés in southern France. The middle Pleistocene fauna of the Second Interglacial Stage—with the trogontherian mammoth (*Elephas trogontherii*)—is characterized as follows:

Final phase and extinction of

Etruscan rhinoceros	*Rhinoceros etruscus*
Steno's horse	*Equus stenonis*
Hyena of Auvergne	*Hyæna arvernensis*
Bear of Auvergne	*Ursus arvernensis*
Saber-tooth tiger	*Machairodus*
Macaque	*Macacus*

Culminating phase of

Trogontherian mammoth	*Elephas trogontherii*

Earliest stage of

Straight-tusked elephant	*Elephas antiquus*
Merck's rhinoceros	*Rhinoceros merckii*

First appearance of

Deninger's bear	*Ursus deningeri*
Cave lion	*Felis spelæa*
Striped hyena	*Hyæna striata*
Giant deer	*Cervus megaceros*

According to some authors Heidelberg man lived at this time; according to others western Europe was inhabited by descendants of Heidelberg man which were ancestral to the coming Neanderthal race. Whatever tribes were living in western Europe at this time lived in the open and have left none of their fossilized remains by which we may recognize their relationships. The climate was still temperate, and there is no evidence whatever of the beginning of cave life. Man, however, becomes well known through his increasing and widespread flint industry, for—according to the leading archæologists—it was during Second Interglacial time that man was living on the river terraces and fashioning the Pre-Chellean and Chellean flints. These flints are of very massive character and indicate that man was a courageous hunter of the wild game of every variety which abounded in every part of Spain, France, and southern England.

Convincing evidence of a warm temperate climate during the interglacial stages is afforded by the occurrence of certain warmth-loving molluscs, such as *Zonites acieformis, Paludina diluviana, Corbicula fluminalis,* and also by typical forms in the "Eem" fauna of northern Germany, which includes *Tapes aureus* var. *eemensis* Nordm., *Gastrana fragilis, Lucina divaricata,* and *Haminea navicula.*

The presence of mammals characteristic of a warm environment—monkeys, hippopotamuses, rhinoceroses, and hairless elephants—is further confirmation of the existence of a warm climate.

The First Interglacial Stage was apparently equally mild. The deposits at Tegelen in Limburg, Holland, the lignites found at Leffe in the Bergamasque Alps, Italy, and the gray clay of Durfort near the Sauve, Gard, France, probably all belong to the First Interglacial Stage. The fossilized remains of plants and animals found embedded in the white clay of the Borlezza ravine near Pianico, Italy, apparently belong to the Second Interglacial Stage.

The Third Glacial Stage witnessed great glaciers in the Alps and also in Scandinavia, reaching Great Britain and covering all of northern Germany. The climate, nevertheless, remained tolerable in the river valleys of Spain, France, and Great Britain, and there is still no evidence that the primitive tribes inhabiting these countries were forced to retreat to caves. The period of the cave man had not yet begun.

The animal life on which man subsisted underwent a considerable transformation. The Etruscan rhinoceros, southern mammoth, and other large quadrupeds of First and Second Interglacial times disappeared and were replaced by the straight-tusked elephant (*Elephas antiquus*) and by Merck's rhinoceros, which we find pass gradually into a new fauna which still retained some of its southern elements when it gained some northern elements such as the giant deer.

The late Pleistocene fauna of the Third Interglacial Stage —late phase of the straight-tusked elephant—is characterized as follows:

Last appearance of

Straight-tusked elephant	*Elephas antiquus*
Merck's rhinoceros	*Rhinoceros merckii*
African hippopotamus	*Hippopotamus major*

Frequent occurrence of

Cave bear	*Ursus spelæus*
Cave lion	*Felis spelæa*
Cave hyena	*Hyæna spelæa*
Giant deer	*Cervus megaceros*

This phase corresponds to the "Chellean" of E. Haug— according to him, the Third Interglacial Stage. From their stratigraphy there can be no doubt that the following deposits in Switzerland belong to the Third Interglacial Stage: Flurlingen, near Schaffhausen, with remains of Merck's rhinoceros; and the lignites of Dürnten in the canton of Zurich, with remains of the straight-tusked elephant and Merck's rhinoceros, which were covered by moraines of the Fourth Glacial Stage. Faunas typical of this group are also found in the "Grotte du Prince," in Italy near Mentone; the tuffs of Burgtonna and Graefentonna, near Gotha, Germany; the "Chellean" gravels of the Seine, Paris; and the "Chellean" gravels of the Thames Valley, England.

Climatic changes are indicated by interglacial deposits

characteristic of warm forest phases, such as are typically represented by the flora of Celle-sous-Moret and Hötting (p. 380). At these times the climate was much warmer than at present, but, nevertheless, there is no very strong reason to assume that all of Europe was then covered by an impene-

Fig. 8. Fossil plants from the breccia of Hötting, near Innsbrück, Tyrol. After R. von Wettstein. 1 Pontic rhododendron (*R. ponticum*). 2 Box (*Buxus sempervirens*). 3 Scotch fir (*Pinus sylvestris*) and yew (*Taxus baccata*).

trable forest. The forests alternated with regions of bush and meadow, and it is probable that warm steppes extended over large areas.

Of great importance are the discoveries in the breccia of Hötting, near Innsbrück in the Tyrol. This site is 1200 meters above sea level, on the left bank of the Inn. The breccia lies above basal moraines belonging to the second, or, more probably, to the third glaciation. Above it lies a moraine of the Fourth Glacial Stage. R. von Wettstein has enumerated forty-one species of plants occurring in this deposit—among them *Rhamnus hoettingensis,* a new species of buckthorn related most closely to *Rhamnus latifolia* of the Azores and Canary Islands; *Rhododendrum ponticum,* the Pontic Alpine rose which now grows wild in south-western Spain, Pontus, and the Caucasus, where the limit of perpetual snow is over 3000 meters above sea level; and other plants now found in southern and southeastern Europe as well as in the forest zone of Colcida, where their highest limit is 1800 meters below the snow line. None of these species is now found in the neighborhood of Hötting. There are also other species in the breccia which still exist not far from Hötting but are no longer found at an altitude of 1200 meters. Such a combination of plants indicates that the mean annual temperature at that time must have been from 2° to 3° Centigrade warmer than at present, from which it may be inferred that the snow line was some 400 meters higher. The small glaciers then existing were found only on the loftiest summits of the central district, the Alps being then a forested region, and while the flora of their northern slopes was Baltic in character, that of the southern slopes showed Illyrian features. In the Late Pleistocene of central Europe an interesting climatic cycle is clearly recognizable, as follows:

IV. Glacial Stage	Tundra, in part with stunted Arctic forests.
3d Interglacial Stage	
Late	Loess steppes, with scanty growth of trees.
Middle	Forests of deciduous trees with climate milder than the present.
Early	Loess steppes, with scanty growth of trees.
III. Glacial Stage	Tundra, in part with stunted Arctic forests.

The outstanding feature of Third Interglacial time—both to the climatologist and to the anthropologist—is the clear demarcation of a succession of climatic phases which indicate that Europe was gradually deforested, that the forests became more scanty and were interspersed with steppes and open plains, and that this period was followed by increasing cold with cold winds and the gradual appearance of a cold steppe climate with violent dust storms and open conditions of life. These climatic transitions certainly exerted a very great influence on the evolution of man, as especially observed in a succession of deposits such as those of Celle-sous-Moret, which closes with indications of a cold steppe climate and tuff deposits in which a new type of flint industry occurs, known as the Acheulean.

The interglacial vegetation was characterized by a deciduous forest flora, as evidenced by a number of deposits. This flora indicates a climate milder than the present. At Celle-sous-Moret, Seine-et-Marne, lying above Pleistocene gravels containing remains of the straight-tusked elephant (*Elephas antiquus*), there is a tuff deposit with fossilized remains of fig, box, Canary laurel, and Judas tree (*Ficus carica, Buxus sempervirens, Laurus canariensis,* and *Cercis siliquastrum*). The presence of these indicates a climate both warm and humid, and a flora Dalmatian in character. The mean annual temperature of the Seine Basin was then from 15° to 16° C., whereas now it is not over 11° (Munier-Chalmas). The upper levels of this "warm" deposit at Celle-sous-Moret are composed of tuffs with flora indicating a cooler climate associated with an Acheulean industry.

The fossil flora of the steppes shows a near relationship to that of the tundras, the transition from one to the other being hardly perceptible. As may be seen at the present time in Asia, the winter of the steppes is very severe, with many windstorms, conducing largely to the denudation of their surface. The summer is short, but comparatively warm, and in consequence there is an abundant growth of grass and shrubs. Similar conditions doubtless prevailed in Europe during the formation of the Pleistocene loess, and sparse growths of stunted trees bore witness to their inclemency. In the deposits of the "Mammoth Hunters" at

Gobelsburg, Austria, pieces of carbonized wood, identified as *Pinus,* were found embedded in the loess. From a study of these pieces it was concluded that the annual growth of the Pleistocene *Pinus* was but a tenth of that of pines in the same region at the present time.

It must be borne in mind that what has been said of tundra and steppe conditions applies only to central Europe and the northern part of western Europe. Conditions in southern Europe, including the southern slope of the Alps, were quite different. On the northern Alpine slopes there was a scanty growth of conifers which extended more than 500 meters above sea level. On the southern slopes of the Alps the present limit of perpetual snow is 3000 meters, while during the Glacial Epoch it stood at 1800 meters. Such conditions would bring the tree line to a height of 900 meters above sea level, so that in these parts long glacial streams might have advanced through a veritable forest region. Still milder conditions prevailed in the Mediterranean zone, strictly speaking.

Close of Third Interglacial Stage and Duration of Fourth Glacial Stage. Period of the First Cave Men of Neanderthal Race.

Cold conditions of climate are now settling down on all of northern Europe, and for the first time the warm temperate forms entirely disappear and are replaced by the new wave of northern animal life known as the Arctic tundra fauna—animals which doubtless bordered the tundras and ice-fields of all the preceding glaciations. The ice-fields of the fourth glaciation were more limited than those of the third and second—they did not reach Great Britain— yet the fall in temperature was far more severe and widespread. This cold wave lasted several thousand years, reaching as far south as the Pyrenees and beyond, which explains the first period of cave life. Everywhere men of Neanderthal race resorted to the caverns for shelter.

The most distinctive mammals of the period were the woolly mammoth (*Elephas primigenius*) and the reindeer (*Rangifer tarandus*).

We have seen that the tundra was uniformly carpeted with grass and shrubs and occasional sparse and stunted forests which, during each glacial stage, covered those areas of central and western Europe that remained free of ice. In view of the scanty resources of the tundra, the number of animals living there was large; and, since a fauna must depend very closely upon the flora and the climate, it is not

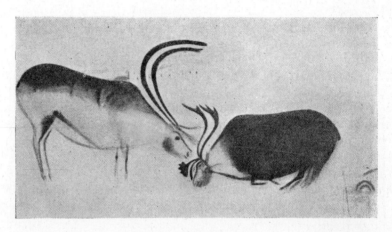

Fig. 9. Reindeer—a polychrome painting on the rock wall of the cavern of Font-de-Gaume, Dordogne, France. After H. Breuil. *Greatly reduced in size.*

surprising to find a typically Arctic circumpolar fauna in an environment with an equally Arctic flora. The fauna of central Europe during the Glacial Epoch was characterized by two "cold" groups, closely related to each other and at present separated by a vast extent of territory. One of these groups comprises animals of the Arctic regions which were driven southward by the great northern ice-sheet; the other consists of Alpine animals which were driven down to the plains by the huge glaciers covering the mountains. This Arctic-Alpine fauna of the tundras is evidenced by many fossil remains and includes the following forms:

In view of the geologic conditions in Europe during the different glacial stages (Plate I), it might be expected that the flora then existing in the territory between the great northern ice-sheet and the Alpine glaciation would be Arctic-

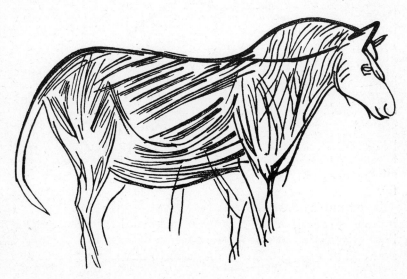

Fig. 16. Wild horse engraved on the rock of the cave of Buxu, Asturias, Spain. After H. Obermaier and Count de la Vega del Sella.

Greatly reduced in size.

Alpine in character. In fact, fossil remains of *Salix polaris* (Arctic willow), *Betula nana* (dwarf birch), *Dryas octopetala* (mountain avens), *Arctostaphylos uvaursi,* and *Polygonum viviparum* were discovered by A. Nathorst at Schwarzenbach in the Canton of Zurich, Switzerland, directly above the clays of the basal moraine. And he also discovered near Deuben, Saxony, evidence that in former times there was a true northern tundra flora along the border of the great northern ice-field. In the post-glacial tuffs of the Swabian plain near Schussenried there have been found fossil remains of plants (of species such as *Hypnum sarmentosum, H. aduncum* var. *grœnlandicum,* and *H. fluitans* var. *tenuissimum*) which at the present time are re-

stricted to regions near seventy degrees north latitude and
to the loftiest summits of the Alps. It would be easy to
enumerate a list of such typically northern deposits in
Germany, the Baltic region, Denmark, and southern Scandinavia,—some belonging to the glacial stages, and some to
the first post-glacial retreat,—their Arctic character being
indicated by the presence of mosses, Arctic willows (*Salix
retusa, S. herbacea, S. polaris*), dwarf birch, and mountain
avens. But we will mention only that this same boreal flora
also occurs repeatedly in England, as, for example, north of
London, where Clement Reid has found a typical Arctic
flora (*Salix lapponum, Armeria arctica,* and others) in
glacial deposits of the Lea Valley. Nevertheless, in those
parts where glaciation was less severe, as in Bohemia and
the region of the middle Rhine, there were probably some
sparse stunted groves of birch, quaking poplar, and Scotch
fir.

The tundra flora of those areas strongly affected by the ice
indicates the rigorous climate of a glacial stage, with very
long winters and very short, cold summers. The beginning
and end of each glaciation appears to have been marked by
a typical steppe phase, its geologic equivalent being the
loess previously described.

Glancing at the faunal lists of sites named in this chapter
(see Appendix), it will be found that a number of species
are common both to the warm and the cold climates. These
species consist either of those that are easily adaptable, or
those that flourish indifferently in a cold or warm environment. Among the most frequently occurring forms are the
carnivores—the cave bear (Figure 14), cave lion (Figure
15), cave hyena, leopard, lynx, wildcat, wolf, fox, and dhole
(*Ursus spelæus, Felis spelæa, Hyæna spelæa, Felis pardus,
F. lynx, F. catus ferus, Canis lupus, C. vulpes, Cuon europæus*). Of common occurrence also are a number of Cervidæ, including the giant deer (*Cervus megaceros,* also
known as *C. euryceros* or *C. hibernicus*), stag (*C. elaphus*),
and moose (*Alces palmatus* or *C. alces*). The Equidæ are
represented by the wild horse (*Equus caballus*), both forest
and Celtic types; and the Bovidæ by the primeval ox (*Bos
primigenius*) and primeval bison (*Bison priscus,* Figure

17). In addition there are the otter (*Lutra vulgaris*), beaver
(*Castor fiber*), and others. In the early Pleistocene many of
these species are represented by their more primitive ancestral forms. The frequent occurrence of roe deer, wild
boar, brown bear, rabbit, wild ox, and bison (*Cervus capreolus, Sus scrofa ferus, Ursus arctos, Lepus cuniculus, Bos
primigenius, Bison priscus*) indicates a mild climate, intermediate between the extremes of glacial and interglacial
time.

Fig. 17. Wild ox and bison. *a* Primitive ox (*Bos primigenius*) painted
in red on rock at Albarracín, Teruel, Spain. After J. Cabré. *b*
Bison (*B. priscus*) engraved on rock and partly painted, in the
cave of Pindal, Asturias. After H. Breuil.
Both designs greatly reduced in size.

Influence of the Post-glacial Environment on the Social and Artistic Development of the Crô-Magnon Race.

In the lists of plants and animals given above, and in the
above-described succession of tundra conditions by steppe
conditions, we are picturing the environment of a great race
of people—chiefly the Crô-Magnon—whose fine qualities
were doubtless developed by the very difficulties with which
they had to contend. They continued to be *cave men*, for the
climate was still extremely severe, but cave men of a very
different order from the Neanderthals whom they dis-
possessed.

In the lists of animals the reader may find those which the
Crô-Magnons especially selected for their industry and for

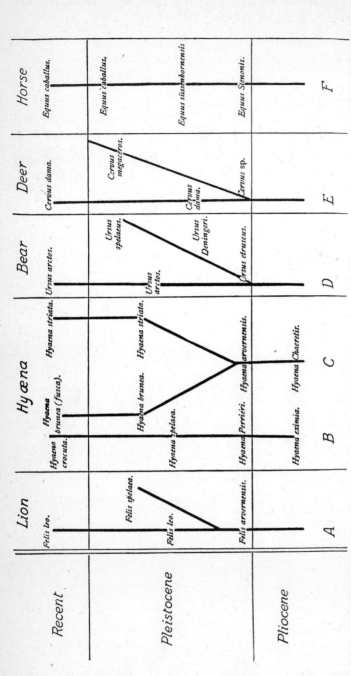

Fig. 18. Diagram showing the ancestry of the most important species of Pleistocene mammals, extending from Middle Pliocene to recent times.

A The "Lion of Auvergne," a typical Pliocene ancestral form, giving rise to the lion of present times, with the cave lion of the Glacial Age (*Felis spelæa*) as an extinct side branch.

B *Hyæna eximia* of Pliocene times, a form ancestral to the hyena of Perrier of Early Pleistocene age, to the cave hyena of the Glacial Age, and to the spotted hyena of present times.

C *Hyæna Chæretis*, a Pliocene form, ancestral to the "Hyena of Auvergne," from which *Hyæna brunea* and *Hyæna striata* (the striped hyena) of Glacial and present times are descended.

D *Ursus etruscus*, the Etruscan bear, a Pliocene form extending into the Pleistocene and giving rise to the brown bear (*Ursus arctos*) of present times, as well as to the extinct side line represented by Deninger's bear (*Ursus deningeri*) and by the cave bear (*Ursus spelæus*).

E The deer of Pliocene and Early Pleistocene time, ancestral to the existing *Cervus dama*, as well as to the extinct giant deer or Irish elk (*Cervus megaceros*) of Pleistocene times.

F Steno's horse, a Pliocene form ancestral to the horse of Süssenborn, and through that line to the modern horse (*Equus caballus*).

their art, which—somewhat in the order of frequency—we may enumerate as follows:

Fig. 19. Elephants of the Glacial Epoch. After H. Breuil. *a, b* Hairless elephants painted in red on rock in the caves of Castillo, Santander, and of Pindal, Asturias, both in Spain. *c* Mammoth engraved on rock in the cave of Font-de-Gaume, Dordogne, France. *Greatly reduced in size.*

Reindeer (*Rangifer tarandus*)	used in all the arts
Woolly mammoth (*Elephas primigenius*)	supply of ivory
Primeval bison (*Bison priscus*)	very frequent
Primeval ox (*Bos primigenius*)	less frequent
Wild horse (*Equus caballus*)	three species—very frequent
Stag (*Cervus elaphus*)	fairly frequent — frequent in Spain
Woolly rhinoceros (*R. tichorhinus*)	rather rare
Cave lion (*Felis spelæa*)	rather rare
Cave bear (*Ursus spelæus*)	rather rare

The causes responsible for the extinction of a great number of Pleistocene species are many and various. In many cases the cause, aside from climatic conditions, was unquestionably a hyperspecialization and at the same time the beginning of degeneration. Of the European fauna the cave bear, cave hyena, cave lion, giant deer, mammoth, and woolly rhinoceros did not disappear until the Post-glacial Stage, and disappeared earlier in the south than in the north. In no case was Pleistocene man the "destroyer" of this interesting fauna.

CHAPTER IV

EARLY PALÆOLITHIC INDUSTRIES

*The Age of Stone—Palæolithic and Neolithic—Divisions of the Palæo-
lithic—Succession of industries in the Somme Valley—Life in the Old
Stone Age—Dwellings—Tools and weapons—Game and the chase—
Early Palæolithic industries in France—Pre-Chellean industry—Saint-
Acheul—Abbeville—Fauna—Primitive stone implements—Chellean cli-
mate, fauna, and industry—Hand ax or coup de poing—Small imple-
ments—Other Chellean deposits—Acheulean climate, fauna, and industry
—Types of hand ax—Miniature forms of La Micoque—Levallois blades
—Possible uses of the Acheulean hand ax—Mousterian climate, fauna,
and industry—Cave dwellings—Growing isolation of tribal groups—
Combe-Capelle—Le Moustier and the climax of the Mousterian industry
—The Mousterian "hand point"—Earliest known use of bone—Abri
Audi—Aberrant types—Western Europe—Southern Europe—Central
Europe—Eastern Europe—Migration routes of the Old Stone Age—
Africa—Asia—America—Australia—Uniformity of Early Palæolithic
industries—Primitive peoples of the present time—Early Palæolithic
sepultures—Belief in a future life—Cannibalism—Magic—Conclusions.*

HAVING discussed in the preceding chapters, albeit
very briefly, the nature of the earth's surface
during the Pleistocene Epoch and also the nature
of the fauna which peopled our planet during the repeated
climatic changes of that time, we may now commence the
study of Pleistocene Man. The name given to this entire
period of civilization is the "Old Stone Age" or "Palæolithic," in contradistinction to the "New Stone Age" or
"Neolithic"—the latter representing a more advanced
stage of civilization which developed in the present geologic
epoch.

The Palæolithic includes a number of subdivisions,
namely, the Pre-Chellean, Chellean, Acheulean, and Mousterian (Early Palæolithic); and the Aurignacian, Solutrean,
and Magdalenian (Late Palæolithic).[1] Our eighth chapter is
devoted to seeing the way in which this classification corresponds to the geologic divisions of Pleistocene time—a
problem which has a variety of offered solutions.

This classification is conclusively verified by a whole

series of deposits which also go to show that each subdivision occupied a considerable lapse of time.

As a representative station and one of the most complete as regards stratigraphy we shall later describe the Spanish cave of Castillo in the province of Santander (Chapter VI).

In the valley of the Somme, near Amiens in northern France, V. Commont was also able to demonstrate a stratigraphic succession that is very enlightening in regard to the principal stages of Pleistocene industries, which there occur in levels very distinctly separated one from another, as follows:

i	Magdalenian	Only a few scanty deposits are found
h	Solutrean	Surface of the loess and upper loess-loam
g	Aurignacian	Upper part of the upper loess
f	Late Mousterian	Middle of the upper loess
e	Early Mousterian	Base of the upper loess
d	Late Acheulean	Lower loess loam
c	Early Acheulean	Lower sandy loess
b	Chellean	Fine sands of the upper levels of the second fluvial terrace
a	Pre-Chellean	Coarse gravels of the second and third terraces of the Somme

Throughout Palæolithic times man led a life more or less nomadic, ignorant of the use of metals and the art of polishing stone, possessing neither domestic animals nor pottery. The warm climate of the Pre-Chellean and Chellean and the mild temperature of the Acheulean caused man, in Early Palæolithic times, to prefer stations in the open, and so he encamped on the lower slopes of hills, at the foot of steep rocky cliffs, or on the sandy shores of rivers. In such places he cleared the chosen site of brush, and lighted fires to serve as protection from beasts of prey during the night. These primitive men sought in preference the neighborhood of rivers. There the gravels afforded abundant nodules of flint, pebbles of quartzite and of other kinds of rock, well adapted for making tools and weapons of stone, simply and rudely fashioned. It may be supposed that there were also tools and weapons of various kinds made of wood, such as maces, spikes, clubs, stakes pointed and hardened in the fire, etc.

It will easily be understood why no such implements are ever found, if one considers the perishable nature of wood.

The chief occupation of these men was the chase. W. Soergel has recently drawn attention to the fact that in the Early Palæolithic stations the remains of giant fauna are far more numerous than those of smaller animals. The only means of hunting hippopotamus, elephant, and rhinoceros—against which crude weapons of wood or stone would be impotent—would be by means of a trap or sort of stocks made ready on the river shores where these pachyderms would naturally resort, or in places where they had worn a trail to their accustomed watering place. In connection with this is the fact that the fossil bones found in Palæolithic deposits belong for the most part to young animals. It is known that the little ones precede their mothers on the march, and therefore, thanks to their inexperience, are the first to fall into a trap and the easiest to hunt.

The bear, a very wary animal, was difficult to hunt. Possibly this was effected by closing the entrance to his den, suffocating with smoke and thus killing him. Less important to primitive man was the chase of such lesser animals as the various species of wild cattle, horses, and Cervidæ. This would perhaps be effected by means of a drive, or by barring passage to the animals in narrow valleys or rocky districts. It would follow that almost all the victims would be either young animals, pregnant females, or sickly individuals. Hunting by means of surprise in the case of sleeping or exhausted animals would also be practiced—a means in common use with the Bushmen, who have brought it to the height of perfection. Neither is it impossible that the use of lasso, throwing-stick, and snare was known. The remains of carnivores are of rare occurrence in stations of human industry for the reason that these animals were not killed for food but in self-defense.

The game was dressed where it was killed, and only the utilizable parts carried back to the camp of the tribe, the remainder being left to the beasts of prey. When, with continued hunting, game became scarce, the tribe would journey to other hunting grounds not yet depleted. The abandoned camps were often covered by the deposits of rivers in flood, thus concealing all traces of man's former presence, and so it is that bones and artefacts may now sometimes be found in river sands and gravels.

The earliest known Palæolithic industry has been provisionally named the "Pre-Chellean," and up to the present time it has been found only in western Europe. Thanks to the fortunate discoveries of V. Commont, the first evidences of its existence were found in the second terrace of the Somme near Saint-Acheul—in the neighborhood of Amiens, Somme, France—embedded in coarse gravels which contained no animal remains. The lack of accompanying fauna at this site was compensated by abundant discoveries at Abbeville, at the mouth of the Somme, at a site corresponding to the same levels of the same terrace as that at Saint-Acheul explored by Commont. This fauna, studied in masterly fashion by G. d'Ault du Mesnil, bears the unmistakable character of the Middle Pleistocene, with elements such as *Elephas (meridionalis) trogontherii, E. antiquus, Hippopotamus major, Rhinoceros merckii, R. etruscus, R. leptorhinus, Machairodus,* numerous Cervidæ (among them *Cervus solilhacus* and *C. somonensis), Equus stenonis,* etc. (various species of deer, elephants, and rhinoceroses, Steno's horse, hippopotamus, saber-tooth tiger, and others).

It would appear that the same cultural stage is represented in the Seine Basin, where this Middle Pleistocene fauna, which bears witness to a warm interglacial climate, is found together with an exceedingly primitive stone industry that, considered either *in toto* or separately, is unquestionably of human origin. Poor and rude as this industry appears in most cases, none the less it cannot be doubted that it presents genuine "implements," that is to say, artefacts that have been formed not by blind chance but by deliberate intention (Figure 20). These implements are primitive precursors of the "coup de poing" or "hand ax," and there are also flakes, more or less atypical, which—as a result of the fracture of lumps or nodules of stone—are found in a variety of forms, some pointed, some long and leaf-shaped, and others, again, irregularly polyhedral. The makers of these implements were evidently dependent on the accidental and crude forms of flake obtained by fracture,

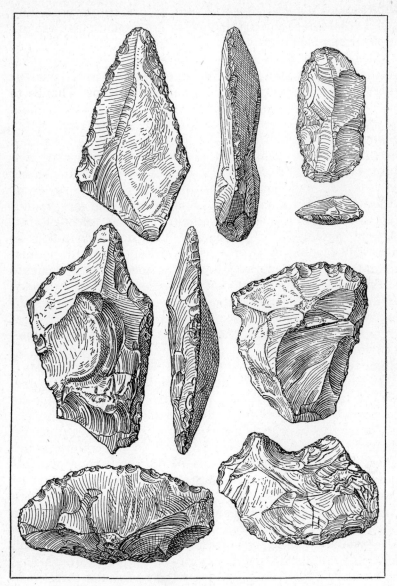

Fig. 20. Pre-Chellean flint implements from Saint-Acheul.
One-half actual size.

showing no capacity to shape them in any adequate fashion. On this account almost all the forms consist of fragments, with sometimes long and sometimes broad pieces predominating, and they are generally exceedingly irregular and clumsy in outline. Thus there resulted implements in the form of points, knives, scrapers with outcurved and incurved edges, planing tools, and others. The way in which these stone implements accommodate themselves to the

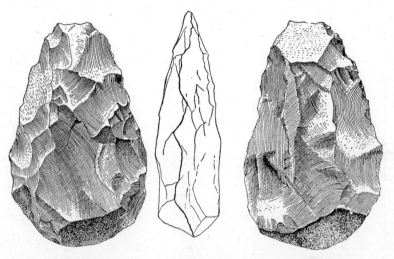

Fig. 21. Chellean hand ax or *coup de poing* of quartzite from Torralba, Soria, Spain, of the typical almond shape.
Two-fifths actual size.

grasp of the hand indicates, almost certainly, that they were not hafted.

More recent and further evolved than the industry just described is that known as the Chellean, a name derived from the well-known type station of Chelles, Seine-et-Marne, a small village east of Paris near where the Marne flows into the Seine. This industry also belongs to an interglacial stage with a warm climate, as is shown by the flora of La Celle-sous-Moret, Seine-et-Marne (p. 380), and by the presence of *Corbicula fluminalis*. This conclusion is confirmed by the list of mammals found in Chellean deposits—

Hippopotamus major, Elephas antiquus (straight-tusked elephant), *Rhinoceros merckii, Equus stenonis* (Steno's horse)?, and *Trogontherium* being found at Chelles; and *Hippopotamus, Rhinoceros merckii, Elephas antiquus, E. (trogontherii) primigenius* (mammoth), wild oxen, and horses of large size at Saint-Acheul. (As regards the existence of an ancient "cold" Chellean, as yet purely hypothetical, see Chapter VIII.) It must be noted, however, that several of the ancient pachyderms, such as *Rhinoceros*

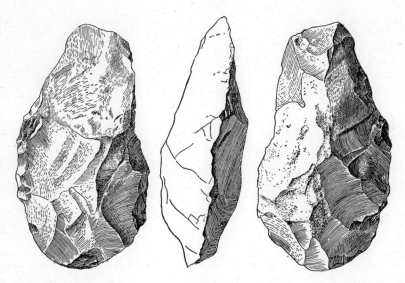

Fig. 22. Chellean hand ax or *coup de poing* of flint from San Isidro, Madrid.
One-third actual size.

etruscus and the typical form of *Elephas trogontherii,* are absent from this list, which tends to give the Chellean fauna an aspect less ancient.

The type of implement characteristic[2] of the Chellean industry is known as the "coup de poing" or hand ax—defined by the school of Mortillet as applying to forms made from a nodule of stone, elongate, generally of flint, to which an amygdaloid shape is given; that is to say, a shape rounded at the base and pointed at the top.

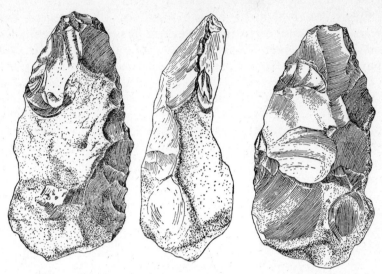

Fig. 23. Chellean hand ax or *coup de poing* of flint from San Isidro, Madrid.

Two-fifths actual size.

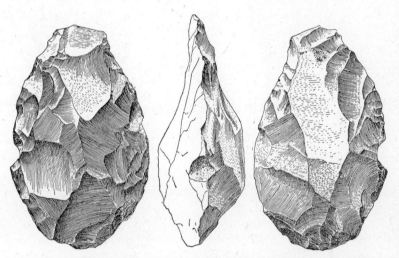

Fig. 24. Chellean hand ax or *coup de poing* of chalcedony from Torralba, Soria, of the typical almond shape.

One-third actual size.

Thus the two sides of the hand ax are conchoid and rounded, or convex in form, while it has cutting edges. The method of retouch varies greatly. In some cases it is only partial and effected in such manner as to leave intact parts of the edge and especially the base of the implement, so that the natural bulk of the nodule affords a convenient grasp (Figure 23). The hand axes belonging to this stage include only coarse and massive types; the two sides show a very simple retouch, the outlines are clumsy, and the edges irregular and crooked. The form of these Chellean hand axes varies greatly. The commonest type is rather long, almond-shaped, and pointed at the top (Figures 21, 24). There are also types like discs, rounded and heavy, as well as lance-shaped and ovoid types with little suggestion of the "almond

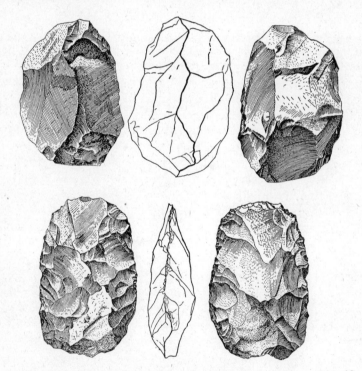

Fig. 25. Chellean hand axes from Torralba, Soria. *Above:* Discoid type, of limestone. *Below:* Ovoid type, of flint.
One-third actual size.

shape," which are included in this class on account of the character of their bilateral retouch (Figure 25). Judging from their primitive form these implements would seem to have served many various purposes, and in most cases to have been grasped in the hand, although it is very possible that some of them may have been fastened to a haft of wood or bark.

Here we may mention that early investigators failed to remark that along with the hand axes there were a number of small implements like irregular flakes, some with in-curved edges, other forms pointed, with long or short point, and carefully retouched. There were also leaf-shapes, broad and thick, implements with straight edge and rounded back, coarse gravers, planing tools, scrapers with incurved edges, and broad scrapers. It may be definitely affirmed that all the small forms of implements belonging to the Early Palæo-lithic were already created in Chellean times, even though they continued to be derived from the accidental form of a clumsy flake. Their evolution and specialization was re-served for later times (Figure 26).

In the basins of the Somme and of the Seine there are found on all sides authentic Chellean deposits, which also are by no means rare in central and southern France. But, in general, these discoveries are situated either in the "loam," where no remains of fauna can be preserved, or else near the surface with an admixture of later industries, so that their value as scientific evidence is purely relative.

The natural evolution from the Chellean constitutes the Acheulean industry, the name being derived from that now famous suburb of Amiens, in the valley of the Somme, known as Saint-Acheul. Generally speaking, this stage was marked by a continuation of the warm climate of the Chel-lean, not only in southern, but also in western and central Europe. This is indicated by the presence of the straight-tusked elephant (*Elephas antiquus*) in the Early Acheulean of Saint-Acheul (lower sandy loess) ; of Merck's rhinoceros (*Rhinoceros merckii*) together with an Acheulean industry in the lower loess at Achenheim near Strasbourg, Alsace; and of both these pachyderms in the lower tuffs at Weimar, Germany.

But already in the Late Acheulean there is evidence of a marked change in climate. The lower loess-loam of Amiens shows, associated with this industry, remains of mammoth and woolly rhinoceros (*Elephas primigenius* and *Rhino-*

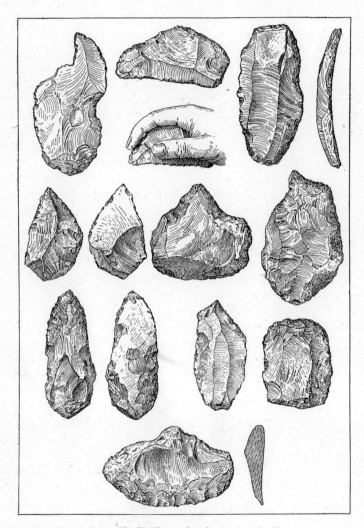

Fig. 26. Typical small Chellean implements of flint from Saint-Acheul, France.
One-half actual size.

ceros tichorhinus), and a complete absence of the "warm fauna," although the reindeer has not yet appeared. A mild steppe climate is indicated—characterized by great herds of wild horses (*Equus caballus*)—and at the same time we

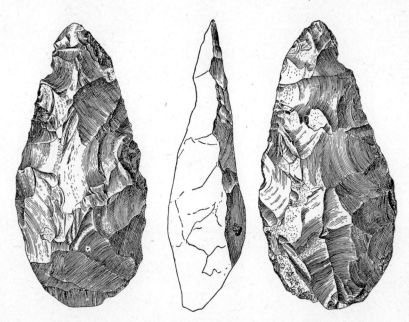

Fig. 27. Early Acheulean hand ax of flint from San Isidro, Madrid.
One-third actual size.

find that primitive man began occasionally to seek refuge in the caves.

During the Acheulean the hand ax attained the height of perfection. The characteristic form of this implement in Early Acheulean times was a flattened oval, thin, and with a straight axis when seen in side view. In general these hand axes were carefully worked on both sides as well as along the edges (Figures 27, 28, 29). Besides these, there were other forms, more pointed, which indicate transition to the lance-point form which, together with the fine triangular hand ax, is typical of the Late Acheulean. These implements are made with extreme care, the sides being very finely

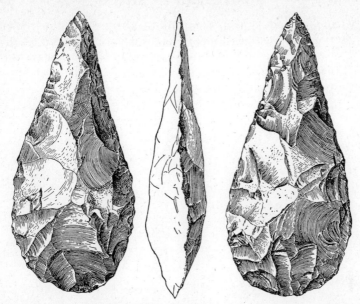

Fig. 28. Early Acheulean hand ax of flint from San Isidro, Madrid,
of fine point form.
One-third actual size.

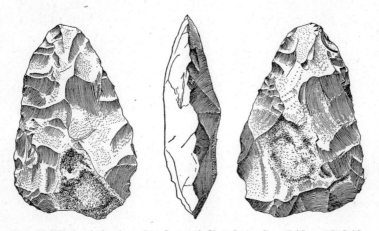

Fig. 29. Early Acheulean hand ax of flint from San Isidro, Madrid,
of coarse triangular type.
One-third actual size.

worked, and the apex either pointed or ending in a very narrow cutting edge (Figure 31).

A peculiar specialization is shown in the industry of La Micoque, Dordogne. Superposed upon a more ancient deposit of primitive industry with remains of *Rhinoceros merckii, Cervus euryceros,* etc., lies the principal deposit,

Fig. 30. Early Acheulean flint "ax" of "Levallois" type from San Isidro, Madrid.
One-third actual size.

consisting of distinct strata with remains of wild horses. It contains a variety of small implements, such as points, scrapers, borers, gravers, and others, representing the small forms of Acheulean industry. The unique feature of this deposit is the presence of miniature hand axes from 2⅓ to 3½ inches long, of the lance-point type, with thick base and very sharp point, which are found in great numbers along with others of oval or triangular shape.

Another specialized industry of the Acheulean is that of Levallois, near Paris, remarkable for the great number of blades and of flat and very broad discs. They are of large size, and retouched only on one side (Figures 30 and 33).

The Acheulean hand axes which are distributed throughout France—the later forms occurring most frequently—differ so markedly from those of the Chellean as to justify the question whether they were generally used as "hand" axes. The painstaking retouch of the edges leads one to

tural stage derived its name. Of secondary importance is the hand ax, which is of medium size and rather careless workmanship. Taken as a whole, this industry is chiefly distinguished by the great development and fine execution of *small forms,* retouched only on one side (Figure 34).

Of prime importance among these small forms—which had already attained a considerable development in Acheulean times—was the Mousterian hand point, and there were also fine double points. Scrapers with distinctive retouch and borers attained a marked degree of development, while planing tools became rarer. Although all of these types are well represented in preceding stages, there can be no question that it is in the Middle Mousterian that they are united into an industrial complex showing a considerable attainment. Typical deposits are found in the chief strata at the station of La Quina in Charente.

It is probable that some of the "hand points" of this stage were hafted; that is to say, tied or gummed to a lance shaft. This seems to be indicated by the fact that the base of these points is broad, and sometimes retouched as if to afford a close fit.

In the same deposits are often found ends of the humerus of bison or wild horse—phalanges, or large fragments of the long bones, which show at certain points deep marks of rasping, cutting, and pounding. These seem to have served as anvils on which wooden lances or similar implements were shaped, and, considered as the earliest evidence of the use of bone, they are of some interest (Figure 35). Instances of the actual use of bone for the manufacture of tools or weapons, however, are extremely rare in the Early Palæolithic, being known in the deposits of La Quina, France, and those of the cave of Castillo, northern Spain, both of which contained slender bone points.

Authorities are much divided in opinion concerning the distribution and the stratigraphic boundaries of the typical Late Mousterian industry. Some have wished to include the phase shown at Abri Audi, near Les Eyzies, Dordogne, which comprises an advanced Mousterian culture with an admixture of early forms of the following Aurignacian stage (Figure 36).

Although in western Europe the Early Palæolithic
evolved, as regards its general features, with extraordinary
regularity, it need occasion no extreme surprise to find instances of the premature appearance of forms belonging to
later cultures, and also of atavistic cultural survivals. Men-

Fig. 35. Bones from Mousterian deposits bearing marks of usage.
After H. Martin.
Somewhat reduced.

tion may be made of the industrial deposits at Montières
near Amiens, where—associated with remains of hippopotamus, Merck's rhinoceros, and the straight-tusked elephant—there were found strata with large blades of worked
stone, interposed between the Chellean and the Early Mousterian,[3] which Commont unfortunately described as "Mousterian." Another deposit with an industry consisting of
blades very similar to the Mousterian forms was discovered
by Lucas near Le Moustier, also at a very deep level. Both
these sites appear to have been special workshops where,
accidentally in the course of cutting the stone, there resulted
implements of a more advanced technique, which, however,
did not survive (Chapter VI).

The Early Palæolithic is found not only in France, but also in the rest of Europe. In Belgium, which, so to say, forms part of northern France, systematic explorations have been made by E. Dupont, J. Fraipont, Marcel de Puydt, A. de Löe, A. Rutot, and others. The stations in the open and

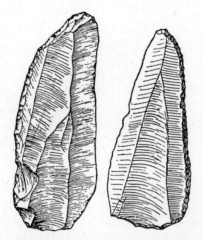

Fig. 36. Typical forms from the "Abri Audi" characteristic of the final Mousterian. After H. Breuil.
Two-thirds actual size.

the caves of Belgium have afforded important discoveries, exactly corresponding with those found in France. It is true that, up to the present, no Chellean industry with warm fauna has been found in Belgium;[4] but excellent series of the Acheulean and Mousterian are found (Mousterian deposits of Spy, etc.). The Mousterian grottos of Saint Brelade and Saint Ouen in the island of Jersey serve to indicate the connection with England, which remained united to the continent until the Late Palæolithic. The gravels of the Thames, Ouse, Avon, and other streams contain the entire succession of Early Palæolithic industries from the "warm" Chellean (as at Gray's Thurrock, with remains of hippopotamus, straight-tusked elephant, Merck's rhinoceros, and the warmth-loving mollusc, *Corbicula fluminalis*) through the Acheulean to the Mousterian. Unfortunately, up to the present time no studies have been made to determine their stratigraphy after modern scientific methods. Chief among the caves yielding hand axes are Kent's Hole near Torquay, Devonshire, Windmill Hill Cave at Brixham, and Wookey Hole on the south side of the Mendips, Somersetshire.

Corsica and Sardinia, having been islands from very ancient times, were never inhabited by Pleistocene man. Of great promise are the discoveries made in Italy, especially in the north, the region which has been most studied. Beside the Grotto delle Fate (Mousterian), there are others of the greatest importance, such as the "Grottes de Grimaldi" or "Baoussé Roussé" near Mentone. Here the lowest levels of the "Grotte des Enfants" contain Mousterian with remains of Merck's rhinoceros, and in the neighboring "Grotte du Prince" L. de Villeneuve, M. Boule, and E. Cartailhac made a section of 52½ feet through strata containing a warm fauna with remains of hippopotamus, straight-tusked elephant, and Merck's rhinoceros (p. 399) associated with a very characteristic Mousterian industry.[5] The upper strata of the grotto do not belong to the same period, as they contain remains of the reindeer with slight indications of an Aurignacian industry.

Many Early Palæolithic discoveries in Italy are found in the gravels of the Pleistocene, sometimes with an admixture of warm fauna. Of great interest are the deposits of the Agro Venosino, especially those at Terranera, Lombardy, where fine Chellean and Acheulean industries are found associated with remains of hippopotamus and straight-tusked elephant. No less interesting are the typical hand axes found by G. Bellucci *in situ* in the valleys of the Tevere and the Chiascio, Umbria, and by Baron G. Blanc in the environs of Rome itself. Finally, attention may be called to the magnificent worked hand axes of quartzite discovered in the Isle of Capri, about ten feet below volcanic deposits, and associated with remains of hippopotamus, straight-tusked elephant, cave bear, deer, wolf, and, it is said, cave lion and woolly rhinoceros (?).

Greece, with its archipelagoes, is yet to be explored.

The corresponding period in Spain is treated in Chapter VI.

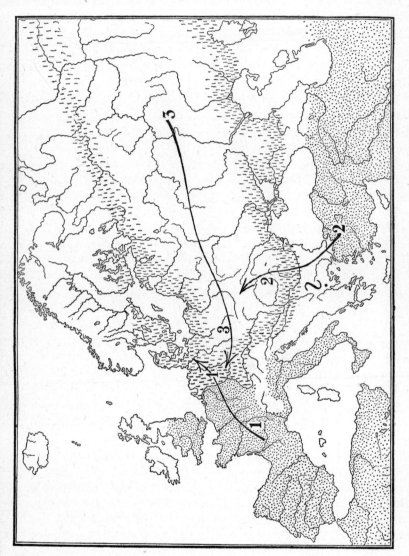

Fig. 37. Distribution and migration routes of Early Palæolithic industries in Europe. Dots indicate the zone of Chellean industry with hand axes (*coups de poing*). Dashes indicate the zone of Pre-Mousterian industry with no hand axes. Arrow 1—western Acheulean. Arrow 2—southern Acheulean. Arrow 3—eastern Acheulean.

In Asia a fine series of ancient hand axes and Mousterian implements has been discovered in Syria, in the region of the Jordan, near Jerusalem, Bethlehem, and Nazareth, and the age of these superficial deposits can be exactly determined from the Acheulean hand axes found in northern Syria in some of the caves of Lebanon. Thus in the cave of Adlûn, together with Acheulean hand axes, there are remains of bison, Mesopotamian deer, primitive goat, and wild boar (*Bos priscus, Cervus mesopotamicus, Capra primigenia, Sus scrofa*), animals not now existing in Lebanon. Together with the above species, remains of cave bear, woolly rhinoceros, and horse have been found associated with a typical Late Acheulean industry in the breccias of Ras-el-Kelb; and the caves of Nahr Ibrahim contain an exceedingly fine Mousterian associated with remains of the bison. Similar industries occur in Asia Minor, Mesopotamia (Chellean-Acheulean of Djerabis on the Euphrates, and others), and in Transcaucasia, where J. de Morgan discovered some Mousterian deposits near Ali Ghez in the region of Eriwan. The material there employed by man was obsidian, which acquires such a pronounced patina as to make it easy to distinguish the ancient implements from later products found at the same place.

Still richer in discoveries is India (region of the Ganges and Indus, and southern India, Figure 38). Of the hand axes from here Edward B. Tylor wrote in 1869 that "they are in no way distinguishable from those of England." They are found actually in the great terraces of the Glacial Epoch, and the massive Chellean hand axes from Madras are much worn, while the fine Acheulean types are quite intact and sharp-edged, a fact which agrees surprisingly with the condition of Palæolithic deposits in northwestern France.

From northern Asia Savenkov was able to show a fine series of hand axes from the loam terraces of Afontova on the left bank of the Yenisei, west of Krasnoyarsk. These were associated with remains of the mammoth, woolly rhinoceros, reindeer, and bison. And finally, our list is completed by discoveries made in Indo-China, Ceylon, and Japan.

Traces of the Early Palæolithic in America are as yet

much disputed by a great number of sceptical investigators.
Most of the early descriptions presented a medley of really
ancient material and much more recent stone implements,
without any critical distinction. We would call attention to
the limited investigation made in 1891 by M. Boule and A.

Fig. 38. Chellean hand axes of quartzite from Madras, India, in the
British Museum, London.
Reduced in size.

Gaudry at Trenton, New Jersey. The "Trenton gravel"
found here is certainly of Pleistocene age and contains hand
axes and also Mousterian types of indisputable antiquity,
associated with remains of the Ohio mastodon, woolly
mammoth, musk ox, and reindeer. The same may be supposed in regard to various similar discoveries in the United
States, made independently, which present an industry
absolutely identical with that of the French stations, as, for
instance, the discoveries made at Claymont, Delaware, and
at Medora, Jackson County, Indiana.

Central America has afforded typical discoveries in superficial deposits, and also in some cases hand axes embedded
in gravels and associated with remains of elephants, which
have been found in the provinces of Chihuahua and Durango,
northern Mexico. Amygdaloid hand axes from ancient de-

posits—but without fauna—have also been found in South America in Brazil, Argentina, and Patagonia.

Australia remains the only continent where, as yet, stone implements of certain Pleistocene age are entirely lacking.

Thus we arrive at the interesting conclusion that in Pleistocene times there already existed a primitive stage of the Early Palæolithic which with remarkable uniformity extended over the whole earth. From this uniformity of industry which can be demonstrated in all quarters of the earth, it follows that there must have been a corresponding uniformity of mentality in that remote humanity, which may well have been able to create those elemental types in separate places at one and the same time, independently of interchanges or of any foreign intrusion. It has been proved —and on this we must insist—that this aggregate of culture is Pleistocene, which does not necessarily involve its being universally contemporaneous, strictly speaking.

Various peoples of Asia, Africa, America, and Australia are even yet in this primitive ''stage of worked stone''; and there are even tribes which either have not yet completely attained the inventory of implements known to the ancient Chelleo-Mousterian culture, or else have proved incapable of preserving it. The latter condition would naturally be especially likely in regions where the struggle for existence was comparatively easy.

Although the study of primitive man in Europe itself— of all continents the most thoroughly explored—has been able to throw but little light upon the first steps of humanity, there can be no doubt that at least it has afforded a number of valuable data.

The European of Pre-Chellean times lived with no settled habitation, as a wandering hunter. Various stone implements—rude but numerous—helped him in a struggle for existence which demanded his extremest efforts against the menace of a huge and dangerous fauna. We know nothing of what progress he may have made in such matters as making weapons of wood, plaiting and weaving, or the dressing of pelts.

But there can be no doubt that in the utilization of implements of stone Pre-Chellean man had already attained a cultural stage in advance of certain tribes of the present time who live in extreme isolation, as, for instance, the pygmies of central Africa, the Andaman islanders, the Semangs of Malacca, the Negritos of the Philippines, and such Asiatic pygmy tribes as the Veddahs of Ceylon, the Senoi of Malacca, the Kubus of Sumatra, and the Toala of Celebes. They know little or nothing of the use and fashioning of stone, and therefore their implements are made of wood, bone, or shell, thus constituting a "Pre-Palæolithic" stage of culture. According to W. Schmidt, the Andamans do not even know how to produce fire. In view, therefore, of the conclusions afforded by modern ethnography, it is safe to assume the probable existence of cultural stages still more ancient and primitive than the Palæolithic (p. 16).

From Chellean man, we find, are derived all the principal forms of stone implements, both large and small; and the use of fire was also certainly known to him (Torralba, Spain). The Acheulean hand axes are in truth masterly implements, such as are sought in vain among primitive tribes of present times. The most ancient Mousterian seems to mark the birth of an inclination for ornament (shells and minerals) and for coloring matter to paint the body—a cultural stage similar to that of the Tasmanians and various existing Australian tribes such as the Kurnai and Chepara.

The sepultures of Early Palæolithic man throw much light upon the evolution of his psychology. The age of the most ancient sepulture at Le Moustier should be Early Mousterian if we trust to the description of the discoverer, because at this site, above deposits of great antiquity, there were others more recent of the type of Abri Audi. The individual buried here was a youth who—according to O. Hauser and others who took part in the excavation—was found in the attitude of sleep with the right side of the face resting on the elbow of the right arm, and the hand clasping the head, beneath which was a pillow-like mound of small fragments of flint. Near the left hand were a hand ax and a scraper, both of Mousterian type, which should probably be considered as funeral offerings. This arm was extended alongside the body.

In 1908 a discovery of the greatest importance was made

by the Abbés A. and J. Bouyssonie and L. Bardon in the small grotto of La Bouffia-Bonneval, near La Chapelle-aux-Saints, Corrèze. This consisted of the sepulture of a man, also in the attitude of sleep and with the right arm upraised. The associated fauna included the woolly rhinoceros, reindeer (frequent), ibex, and others, while the industry indicated a Middle Mousterian.

To this same Mousterian stage belongs the family sepulture of La Ferrassie, Dordogne, which was discovered by D. Peyrony in the years 1909-1911. One of the adult skeletons lay on its back with the trunk slightly inclined to the left and the legs strongly flexed. The body had been first laid upon the ground, without any trench being made to hold it, but the head and shoulders had been surrounded and protected by slabs of stone. The fact that certain parts of the body are missing—probably carried off by wild beasts —leads to the supposition that the rest of the body may have been covered with skins, or a frame of branches. The second skeleton was that of a woman, strongly flexed—that is to say, with arms folded and laid upon the breast, and legs pressed against the trunk—a position indicating that the body must have been fastened or bound. Two children lay buried in small trenches.

The two skeletons of Spy in Belgium may be attributed to the final Mousterian, and were also, apparently, true sepultures. They were discovered by M. de Puydt and M. Lohest in 1886, with associated fauna consisting of the mammoth, woolly rhinoceros, reindeer, cave bear, cave hyena, and others.

These sepultures are trustworthy evidence, precious documents which witness to the existence of a very ancient cult of the dead, united with a belief in another life after death. Intermixed with this belief were sentiments of fear and terror, as is evidenced by the forcibly flexed position of the body at La Ferrassie (Chapter V, palæo-ethnological résumé). J. Bouyssonie insists on the presence of a trench near the children's sepultures filled with ashes and large bones, chiefly those of the wild ox. Similarly at La Chapelle-aux-Saints there was a trench which contained the horn of a bison, and another in which were found large bones of the same animal.

Are these cases of immolated offerings or of funeral feasts? Or do they perhaps signify that the grave was placed under the protection of an animal "totem" of great strength?

The skeleton of La Quina, Charente, associated with a typical Mousterian industry, lay embedded in a muddy deposit, which probably led to the supposition that it was a case of drowning. May one venture the suggestion that this might be a funeral rite, consisting of the exposure of the dead in water?

The skeletal remains of Krapina in Croatia, fragmentary and partly calcined, which are at least of Mousterian age, indicate cannibalism, which might have originated rather from psychic than economic motives.

As to the comparatively frequent discoveries of isolated human bones, they may be interpreted in various ways, but it seems not impossible that in certain cases they indicate "manism" (a cult of ancestors), or else talismans of magic or protection.

None of the industrial stages of the Early Palæolithic seems to have been indigenous to Europe, in the true sense of the word.

As yet we know nothing of the degree of importance attained by the various secondary and regional industrial developments, nor in what proportion the later ex-European influences contributed to their successive evolution. Be that as it may, there is so great a difference between the types and fine workmanship of the Late Acheulean and those of the primitive Mousterian, that it is impossible to suppose the latter derived from the former. The Mousterians of western and central Europe belong to a new people, Neanderthaloids, who were not directly related to the Acheulean tribes.

CHAPTER V

LATE PALÆOLITHIC INDUSTRIES

IF we except southern Europe, where Merck's rhinoceros is found coexistent with the Early Aurignacian, the entire Late Palæolithic civilization developed in a cold climate. This is shown by the fauna of the sites in France and in adjacent countries to the east, which includes the woolly mammoth, woolly rhinoceros, cave bear, cave lion, cave hyena, horse, wild ox, bison, stag, and giant deer. The reindeer and other members of the Arctic-Alpine fauna are not so frequent during the Aurignacian and Solutrean stages, which indicates that these stages enjoyed a more moderate climate intervening between the maximum cold of the Mousterian and of the Magdalenian.

Primitive man during this period still frequented camps in the open, especially on the mounds of loess, where his deserted encampments were soon buried beneath a covering of dust. But if occasion presented men did not despise the caves: on the contrary, they preferred them as dwellings, since from there they could sally out to the foray or the hunt. Their favorite game was the reindeer, of which there were great herds. The flesh and suet provided them with food, the tallow with light and heat, the hide with clothing and covers, the horns and bones served various industrial purposes, and the guts and tendons were used for cord and thread. There is nothing to confirm the supposition that this animal, or the wild horse, either, was domesticated or partly domesticated. The domestication of these two large animals would have been possible only with the help of the domesticated dog, which was absolutely unknown during the Pleistocene. Other animals besides the reindeer were hunted, among them the deer, wild horse, and wild ox, while the chase of the pachyderms was somewhat decreased.

This fact is due not so much to the mammoth and rhinoceros becoming gradually scarcer as to a change in the methods of hunting. The coarse stone implements of the Lower Palæolithic no longer exist, being replaced by an industry of very fine flints. Still more abundant was the manufacture of weapons effective at a distance against sly and furtive game—lance points made of bone, horn, or ivory adapted to a very generalized use. The use of bow and arrow is proved by many representations in mural pictures, as, for instance, the archers of Alpera, etc., eastern Spain, and the Aurignacian archer of Laussel, France (Figures 55, 107; Plate IX). But this does not imply that hunting by means of traps and pitfalls fell into disuse, since the methods of hunting would certainly continue to be adapted to the nature of the game and to the topography of the hunting grounds.

Whenever the cave dwellers deserted a grotto the remains from their food and industry lay around in disorder until buried beneath detritus from the cave, loam, or stalagmitic deposit, where they remained like archives sealed by the hand of Nature, who thus preserved these marvels for future generations.

As typical examples of industrial stratigraphy we will cite here two sections from stations in Dordogne.

I. The cave of Le Ruth, explored by D. Peyrony.

g	Superficial detritus	1.50 m.
f	Early Magdalenian	.10 m.
	Sterile layer	.70 m.
e	Late Solutrean	.70 m.
d	Early Solutrean	.60 m.
c	Proto-Solutrean	.10 m.
	Yellow sterile layer	.20 m.
b	Late Aurignacian	.60 m.
	Sterile detritus	.60 m.
a	Middle Aurignacian	.75 m.
Base	Detritus and sand	

II. The shelter of Laussel, excavated by G. Lalanne.

Detritus and superficial humus
i Late Solutrean
   Sterile layer
h Early Solutrean
   Sterile layer
g Late Aurignacian
   Sterile layer
f Middle Aurignacian
   Sterile layer
e Early Aurignacian
   Sterile layer
d Late Mousterian
   Sterile layer
c Middle Mousterian
   Sterile layer
b Early Mousterian
a Late Acheulean
Base Rock and detritus

Average total thickness, 4.50 meters. We have here cited only those strata which lie in direct superposition, leaving out of consideration a few which extend laterally.

Although the Late and Early Palæolithic stand in close relation to each other as regards their dividing line, yet we cannot believe that the Aurignacian of western and central Europe was directly evolved from the Mousterian and in the same district. It seems rather to be the commencement of a complete and fundamental transformation or modification of the elements of industry, corresponding with the entrance of new and superior racial elements.

As remarked, the beginning of the Late Palæolithic marks the disappearance of the earlier technique of working stone. In place of the large hand axes and flakes, generally broad and clumsy, there appear the typical "blade" industries characterized by long, narrow blade-like implements, more

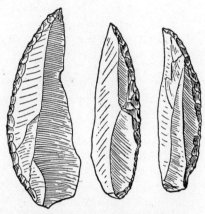

Fig. 39. Early Aurignacian points of Châtelperron type. After H. Breuil.
Two-thirds actual size.

or less prismatic, and by variants of these. Some of these, such as the simple blade shapes, blade-shaped planing tools, etc., are *common to all the stages of the Late Palæolithic.* Others belong exclusively to certain stages, and in consequence these special types are of the greatest value in the identification of these stages. Mousterian forms, such as the "hand points" and scrapers, are found quite frequently in the Early Aurignacian, and it is noteworthy that they do not disappear until analogous forms appear in the later stages. They are almost always simple and clumsy in form, and consist of pseudo hand points, pseudo hand axes, etc., of little importance in the general scheme of the Late Palæolithic.

There can be no doubt that the greater part of these implements of flint, as well as those of horn and bone, which now appear, were hafted. It is sufficient to study ethnological

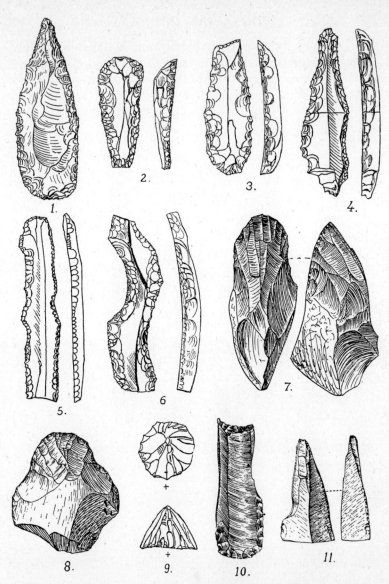

Fig. 40. Characteristic types of Middle Aurignacian flint implements. After H. Obermaier and H. Breuil. 1-4 Blades with heavy marginal retouch. 5, 6 Notched blades. 7, 8 Keeled scrapers. 9 Cone-shaped scraper. 10 Borer with transverse retouch. 11 Borer with central point.

Two-thirds actual size.

collections, chiefly from the Australians, Melanesians, Poly-
nesians, Bushmen, and Eskimos of the present time, to get
an idea of the manufacture, application, and probable use of
the tools and weapons of our ancestors of the Glacial Epoch.

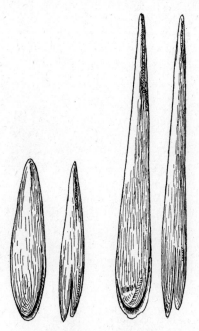

Fig. 41. Bone points with cleft base belonging to the Middle Aurignacian. After H. Breuil.
Two-thirds actual size.

As the accepted standard for all classification of the Late
Palæolithic we will first consider the discoveries made in
France.

The Aurignacian industry derives its name from the cave
of Aurignac in Haute-Garonne, and the commencement of
this stage is the phase of Châtelperron, equivalent to Early
Aurignacian. It is characterized by an industry which still
betrays Mousterian tendencies, and in part by certain new
types, among them the point with curved back of the Châtelperron type (Figure 39).

Of more importance is the Middle Aurignacian, during

which the making of flint blades reached its climax. This industry includes the following characteristic types: large blades with strong marginal or entire retouch, blades with one or more incurved notches, and many gravers—especially the type with rounded point produced by light taps which leave the reverse impression of the removed flakes with their characteristic grooves or channelings. Other notable types are the keeled, conical, and humpbacked planing tools, and the constricted blades (Figure 40). Among the implements of horn and bone (awls, polishers, etc.) especial mention may be made of the "Aurignacian cleft point," a type with a narrow cleft at the base (Figure 41).

The Late Aurignacian is marked by a notable degeneration of the Aurignacian retouch. In addition to the gravers with curved point there are also polyhedral and prism-shaped gravers. Among the forms most characteristic of this phase are the pedunculate point of La Font-Robert and the typical point of La Gravette, which consists of a blade of which the margin—generally the right edge—is grooved vertically the whole length of the implement. The incurved notch on this edge, which extends from the base about a third of the entire length, leads finally to the type known as the "Aurignacian shouldered point" (Figure 42).

The Solutrean industry is so named from the chalky rock of Solutré near Mâcon, Saône-et-Loire. In this stage a great change is observable in the technique of retouch. Instead of the marginal retouch so much in vogue throughout Aurignacian times, there appears the typical retouch of the whole surface, effected through the removal of fine scales of flint by means of pressure.

In the Proto-Solutrean, the forms of which are not yet perfected, this retouch makes its modest appearance and is employed only partially on the implements, a prominent type being the "Solutrean leaf-point" with one side flat and unworked.

The climax of this industrial stage is found in the Early Solutrean, distinguished by the "laurel-leaf point," carefully worked on both sides.

In the Late Solutrean this form gradually degenerates, while the characteristic form is the "Solutrean shouldered

specimens with sharply angulate barbs and by precursors
of the Azilian harpoon, broad and large (Figure 45).
Among Late Magdalenian implements are often found

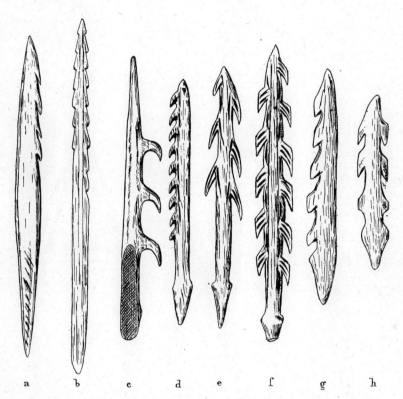

Fig. 45. Evolution of the harpoon during Magdalenian times. After
H. Breuil. *a, b* Archaic prototypes. *c, d* Harpoons with a single
row of barbs. *e, f* Harpoons with a double row of barbs. *g, h* Degenerate types of the final Magdalenian.
From three-fifths to two-thirds actual size.

points with the upper end terminating in a double bevel in
which a point was set but not fastened (Figure 46). The
designs adorning these implements have been, in part, taken
directly from an animal model, and show a series of heads,
conventionalized horns, etc. (Figure 99). Noteworthy also
is the revival of certain Aurignacian types in flint, such

as the pseudo points of La Gravette, pseudo planing tools, and atypical pseudo shouldered points. This apparent revival is due only to the accident of convergence.

Finally, among the products of Magdalenian industry are

Fig. 46. Combined spear points of stag horn from the cave of La Paloma, Asturias. After E. Hernández-Pacheco.
Two-thirds actual size.

found fine needles, delicate bracelets, cylindrical chisels, awls, polishers, and furthermore the "propulseurs" or dart throwers (Figure 47). Of the commander's or ceremonial staff (bâton de commandement) we shall speak later (Figure 58).

Fig. 47. Dart thrower (*propulseur*) of reindeer horn, the upper end fashioned into the head of an anthropomorph, from the cave of Lorthet, Ariège, France. After a photograph.

One-half actual size.

While the Early Palæolithic extended over the entire earth, it would appear that the Late Palæolithic was no more than a Mediterraneo-European civilization. (The Late Palæolithic in Spain is treated in Chapter VI.) Moreover, even within these geographic limits the Late Palæolithic presents wide variations, while outside them its existence has not yet been clearly and definitely established.

The commencement of this new culture was undoubtedly owing to an invasion of Aurignacian tribes who destroyed the Neanderthal race in Europe, thus effecting a revolution of great importance to human culture. Very tempting is the supposition which places the center of formation for these new elements in the Mediterranean region, but this is no more than a hypothesis, the truth of which can be demonstrated only by means of thorough investigations in the eastern Mediterranean.

So far as our present knowledge goes, there seem to be two distinct centers of Aurignacian culture: the first in western and central Europe, and the second in the Mediterranean region.

The Aurignacian region of western and central Europe includes, besides France, the northern part of Spain, Belgium (A. Rutot names this phase "Montaiglian"), and England, where Aurignacian industry has been found in the cave of Paviland, Glamorganshire, on the west coast of Wales. This region extends east of the Rhine through all central Germany, where the Aurignacian is admirably represented in the cave of Wildscheuer, near Steeten on the Lahn, Rhine Province; in the caves of Sirgenstein, near Schelklingen (pp. 384, 385), and of Bockstein, near Langenau, in Würtemberg; and in the cave of Ofnet, Bavaria. There are also many Aurignacian stations in the loess of Lower Austria in the valley of the Danube between Melk and Vienna. Mention may be made of the station of Willendorf, excavated by me in 1908, where a section of loess twenty meters thick was found to contain no less than nine archæologic strata, embracing the entire evolution of the Aurignacian industry and separated one from another by sterile strata. The fauna included the woolly mammoth (frequent), woolly rhinoceros, cave lion, lynx, wolf, fox, Arctic fox, bear, wolverine, hare,

wild boar, bison, ibex, chamois, Saiga antelope (?), reindeer, stag, giant deer, and horse. The upper stratum, belonging to the Late Aurignacian, contained a figurine eleven
centimeters in height, made of porous limestone, well preserved and with traces of pink color. It represents a nude
woman with largely developed breasts and hips but no true

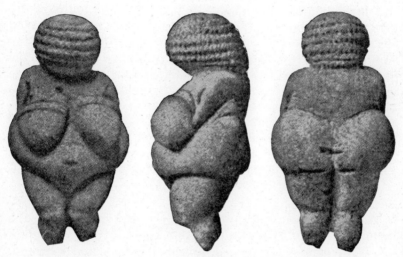

Fig. 48. Stone statuette from Willendorf, Lower Austria. After a
photograph.
About two-thirds actual size.

steatopygy. The hair is arranged in concentric circles around
the head; the face, on the other hand, is quite ignored. The
legs and arms are very meager, being of secondary interest
to the artist. The only ornament represented is a sort of
bracelet indicated by coarse dots on the forearm (Figure
48). At Krems, a market town near Willendorf, on the road
called "Hundssteig," only the Middle Aurignacian is found,
but that is very abundant. Farther eastward this phase is
found in Hungary at the stations of Magyarbodza near
Brassó, the cave of Pálffy near Detrekö-Szentmiklós, and
the cave of Istállóskö in the Bükk Mountains; and it also
extends as far as Poland.

It is probable that the slight traces found at the cave of

Malkata Peschtera near Tirnova, and at the cave of Morovitza near Teteven—both in Bulgaria—are also of Aurignacian age.

The Aurignacian of the Mediterranean region seems to have its center of distribution in the northwestern part of Africa—a region comparatively well known, thanks to the labors of Pallary, Gobert, Breuil, de Morgan, and Boudy—and there can be no doubt that this culture also extended into Spain (Chapter VI).

The Aurignacian of Africa is known as the Capsian, a name derived from Gafsa in Tunis. It immediately succeeds the Mousterian, which here also is absolutely identical with that of Europe.

Subdivisions of the Capsian are as follows:

a Early Capsian—corresponding to the Aurignacian of Europe.

b Late Capsian—a post-Aurignacian which represents an evolution independent of the Solutreo-Magdalenian of Europe, but parallel to and synchronous with it. This is again divided into two regional groups, the Ibero-Mauretanian of western Algeria (called the "Ibero-Maurusien" by French specialists) and the Getulian of eastern Algeria and southern Tunis.

The Early Capsian strongly resembles the typical Aurignacian of Europe, and consists of an admixture of Early and Late Aurignacian industries together with types of Châtelperron and Gravette; whereas it is known that in central Europe these industries are separated from each other by deposits of the Middle Aurignacian.

From this industry is evolved the Late Capsian with its extraordinary geometric stone implements, large bone needles, and curved blades made of ostrich eggs, passing thus into the Azilian and Proto-Neolithic. Commencing with these phases may be observed indications of a dry climate, which from then on become more and more pronounced, while the bones of mammals begin to occur but rarely. The principal food supply consists of molluscs, similar to those now found in the same country, which appear in great numbers after a rainy winter.

Traces of Late Palæolithic man are also found in Egypt.
M. Blanckenhorn believes he has met with such in various
flint workshops on the middle terrace of the Nile; and P.
Sarasin and H. S. Cowper attribute to the same origin the
series of geometric stone implements which they collected
from the surface of the desert near Heluan. Although as yet
little definite is known in regard to the separate discoveries,
it should also be mentioned that in South Africa there has
recently been found an industry of blades, of Late Palæo-

Fig. 49. Bone harpoon from the Palæolithic breccias of Antelias,
Syria. After R. Describes.
Three-fourths actual size.

lithic aspect, associated with skeletal remains of two extinct
species of antelope, related to the gnu and to Pallas's antelope (*Antilope Pallas*).

A second Mediterranean center of dispersal seems to have
been in Syria, the scientific exploration of which is due
chiefly to Father G. Zumoffen. The cave of Nahr el Kelb
and that of Antelias near Beyrut contained a well-developed
Aurignacian of Early Capsian type. This industry includes
keeled planing tools, lateral gravers, La Gravette points,
and primitive implements of bone. The accompanying fauna

—stag, horse, Dama deer, roe deer, bison, panther, bear, wild boar, wild goat, and antelopes—is essentially of forest type, which leads to the supposition that at that time great forests extended from Lebanon to the coast. It is surprising to find here large and rather coarse harpoons of somewhat more recent date (Figure 49). The cave of Muraret el-Abed, not far from Dibl in upper Galilee, discovered by P. Karge, also belongs to the Early Capsian. To the close of the Capsian are assigned various stations in the open with small geometric forms of flints which cannot be considered as belonging to the true Neolithic, and which often lie in deposits completely separate from those of the age of polished stone.

A third and important Mediterranean center of dispersal was Italy. In the south, typical Aurignacian deposits are found in the cave of Romanelli, Otranto, and in the Grotta all' Onda near Camajore, Lucca. In the north is the classic locality of Grimaldi near Mentone, a district very rich in caves. The grottos "Des Enfants," of "Cavillon," of "Barma Grande," and of "Baousso da Torre" contain in their abundant deposits a typical Aurignacian with a great number of sepultures (see the palæo-ethnological résumé in this chapter). The fauna is characteristic of a cool climate and includes the woolly mammoth (?), horse, wild boar, wild ox, bison, stag, roe deer, Dama deer (?) [*Cervus* (*Dama*) *somonensis*], moose, reindeer, ibex, chamois, wolf, bear, cave bear, cave hyena, cave lion, leopard, lynx, hare, beaver, and Alpine marmot. At the base is still found Merck's rhinoceros (see pp. 399 and 408). The associated industry in the aggregate is unquestionably Late Aurignacian. H. Breuil very properly draws attention to the fact that to it must be added certain geometric forms in flint, and some small circular planing tools which tend to become Azilian in type, or are at least evolving in that direction.

The discoveries in southern Russia should be regarded with caution. The Palæolithic stations in the loess of Kiev and Mezine, on the banks of the Desna (Tchernigov), and in other places, correspond to a prolonged and degenerate Aurignacian which, in reference to northern Africa, might be termed Late Capsian. The fauna includes the reindeer, musk ox, wolverine, Arctic fox, woolly mammoth, and woolly rhinoceros. If we also take into account the extraordinary artistic features of which we shall presently speak (Chapter VII), there would be nothing singular in the existence of a Late Palæolithic peculiar to eastern Europe, which appears to be related to that of the Mediterranean region rather than to that of central and western Europe.

As an isolated discovery in Asia belonging to the Late Palæolithic, mention may be made of the station of the "Mammoth Hunters" at Tomsk with its industry of atypical blades. The remarkable discoveries of hand axes in India do not exclude the hypothesis that no true Late Palæolithic industry existed here, and that the partly polished, Proto-Neolithic hand axes of this region were directly evolved from the hand axes of the Early Palæolithic.

Thus we assign to the Aurignacian only a very restricted area of distribution, while, on the other hand, the Mediterranean phase—without evolving through the stages of the Solutrean and Magdalenian—follows its own course towards the Azilian. Of this culture we shall speak in Chapter X. From all this it follows that the extension of the succeeding cultures of the Solutrean and Magdalenian was even more limited.

Thanks to the fortunate discoveries made by E. Hillebrand in Hungary, there can be no doubt that the Solutrean originated in eastern Europe. In the caves of Szeleta, Balla, Kiskevély, and Pálffy is found a "Primitive Solutrean" with crude and poorly developed precursors of the laurel-leaf point. In the cave of Pálffy below this Early Solutrean lies a typical Aurignacian; and in the caves of Szeleta, Jankovich, and Puskaporos above this "Primitive Solutrean" lies a typical Solutrean with typical laurel-leaf points. These facts prove that it was here that the evolution of the Solutrean took place. Shouldered points were as yet unknown. From Hungary the Solutrean culture extended into Poland (Cave of Wierzchow), Austria (Zeltsch-Ondratitz and Millowitz), and Moravia, where especial interest attaches to the station of the "Mammoth hunters of Předmost." The list of fauna from this site is given elsewhere (p. 388). In the loess together with this fauna there was found a very abun-

where not the slightest authentic trace of it has been found —a fact confirmed by H. Breuil. In northern France it is of rare occurrence, and Belgium and England[1] seem to have been little influenced by this culture. It should here be emphasized that even in the region of the typical Solutrean industry in France its aspect of an alien origin is so striking that there can be no doubt why the natural evolution of the Late Aurignacian is interrupted. The "atypical" shouldered point disappears for a time, to reappear subsequently to the Early Solutrean, transformed by the Solutrean retouch into the "typical" shouldered point.[2]

In contrast to the distribution of the Solutrean, which it has been shown took place from the east westward, that of the Magdalenian seems to have progressed from the west eastward. Its extension is approximately the same as that of the Solutrean. H. Breuil feels convinced that the appearance of this culture is due to the advent of new peoples. Be this as it may, any idea of Mediterranean origin may be dismissed, since it is much more probable that the Magdalenian had its rise in the French Pyrenees. From this center it advanced into Périgord, extending its branches into the Catalonian and Cantabrian regions of northern Spain. This stage is well represented in central and southern France, but occurs less frequently in northern France, as also in Belgium and England.[3]

Central Europe played an important part in this civilization. In Switzerland three geographic districts can be distinguished. The first is in the southwest near Lake Geneva, its most notable site being that of Veyrier with five perforated ceremonial staves ("bâtons de commandement") ornamented in part with designs of plants. The second district, in the northwest, includes the valley of the Birs between Basle and Delsberg, where six caves have been found with deposits of Late and final Magdalenian. The industry is simple and the fauna embraces the Arctic fox, bear, cave bear, tailless hare, banded lemming, horse, wild ox, wild boar, reindeer, stag, roe deer, ibex, Arctic hare, Alpine marmot, and others. There is not the slightest sign of the woolly mammoth and woolly rhinoceros. Also of great importance are the stations in the third district, in the northeast near Schaffhausen. These are the caves of Freudental, Schweizersbild, and Kesslerloch. The deposits at Schweizersbild, which unfortunately were not excavated by the best method, have afforded a great number of implements of flint, horn, and bone, among them two perforated ceremonial staves and fifteen fragments of such, ornamented with designs representing the reindeer, wild horse, and wild ass. More abundant are the instances of representative art in the cave of Kesslerloch near Thaingen. (For the fauna, see p. 384.) The "Grazing Reindeer" is a masterpiece, and worthy companion pieces are the designs of the wild horse and some sculptures, among which is one representing the head of a musk ox (Figure 11).

In Germany up to the present time some thirty Magdalenian sites are known, almost all of them in caves. Stations in the open are very rare, but among them may be named that of Obercassel with two sepultures and some carvings in bone, and that of Andernach near Coblenz, where the deposits were found above a stream of congealed lava. Fine bone implements were found here and also the representa-

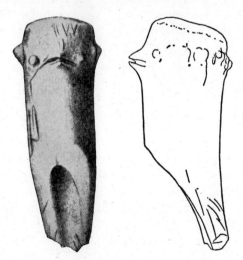

Fig. 51. Bird carved out of stag horn, from Andernach on the Rhine.
After R. R. Schmidt.
Two-thirds actual size.

tion of a bird carved in stag horn (Figure 51). Worth mention is the site of Schussenquelle in Würtemberg, which was embedded in tuff. In Bavaria the caves of Klause at Essing, near Ratisbon, contained an abundance of beautiful imple-

Fig. 52. A flat piece of limestone with designs painted in red, from the cave of Klause near Neu-Essing, Bavaria. From a photograph. *Two-thirds actual size.*

ments of stone and horn, and also painted tablets of stone (Figure 52). In addition there are excellent designs in outline, and especially remarkable is a perforated ceremonial staff on which is carved an extraordinary mask, half animal and half human.

Austria is not very rich in Magdalenian sites; nevertheless, mention must be made of the scanty inventory of the cave of Gudenus, near Krems, on the banks of the Danube. In Moravia are the caves of Kostelik and Kulna with some obscure designs. In Hungary various caves with rare Magdalenian deposits have recently been described. From the

Fig. 53. Men's headdresses, from the Palæolithic rock paintings of eastern Spain. (Compare Figs. 54 and 55.) *a* From Val del Charco del Agua Amarga, Teruel. *b* From Alpera, Albacete. *c* From Cueva de los Caballos, Castellón. *d* From Alpera, Albacete. *e* From Cueva Rull, Castellón.

Reduced in size.

cave of Maszycka in Poland comes a remarkable series of awls with geometric ornamentation very similar to the Late Magdalenian ornamentation of France.

From the inventory of forms, and from the works of art, it is possible to recognize several regional groups. Thus the Magdalenian of northern Spain contains harpoons and etchings on shoulder blades which are peculiar to this district; the designs with incised outlines are very rare except in their center of evolution in southern France; and finally, certain engravings from Moravia have no parallels in the west.

Even though we admit a striking psychologic resemblance between Late Palæolithic man and primitive people of the present; and although it is true that the modern shafted

Fig. 54. Men's body adornments shown in Palæolithic rock paintings in the province of Castellón. After H. Obermaier and P. Wernert. *a* From the cave of Saltadora. A hunter with adornments on head, middle, and legs. *b* From the Cueva del Mas d'en Josep. A hunter with adornments on the back, middle, and one knee. *c* From the cave of Saltadora. A hunter with knee ornaments. *d* From the Cueva del Mas d'en Josep. A hunter with adornments on head, middle, and knees.

Reduced in size.

lances, the implements of carved wood, the many-colored shields, the strange idols, the mural paintings, the extraordinary ornaments, and the rare masks found in ethnological collections do indeed, to a certain extent, resemble the products of the culture and art of Late Palæolithic man; it is none the less evident, notwithstanding, that this division of the Palæolithic, both in art and in industry (referring especially to the exquisite workmanship in stone, and to the work in horn and bone), shows such an advanced stage of development that its equal would be sought in vain among primitive tribes of the present.

Fig. 55. Archers shown in the Palæolithic rock paintings of eastern Spain. After H. Obermaier and P. Wernert. *Above:* From the cave of Saltadora, Castellón. *Below:* From Alpera, Albacete.
Reduced in size.

Much light is thrown upon the subject of personal ornament and dress by the mural paintings of eastern Spain (Chapter VII) and by various artefacts found in the sepultures. The "ladies" of Cogul and Alpera (Figure 110 and Plate XII) wear singular caps and bell-shaped kirtles. The

Fig. 56. Quiver with bow and arrows, a basket and a staff, painted in rose on the rock of the cave of Saltadora, Castellón. After H. Obermaier and P. Wernert.

Actual size.

hunters represented in the shelters of Barranco de Valltorta and Alpera show varying forms of headgear. Some consist merely of ornaments of feathers, shells, or perforated teeth; others are genuine caps, sometimes with tassel or side flaps; and again there are headdresses in the form of animals' ears (Figure 53).The ornaments shown on the arms are generally in the shape of clumsy rings, and those on the legs are often in the shape of thick twisted wheels or of flowing ribbons (Figure 54). Wide bands, sometimes fringed, are also seen depending from the neck or shoulders of various warriors. More frequent is an adornment of the hips, which was certainly worn in the form of a large girdle, sometimes double, and hanging down in front and back (Figure 54).

The many pictures of archers show that they made bows and arrows of different sizes and shapes, as well as quivers, pails, and baskets (Figures 55, 56).

A picture very similar is offered by the sepultures of the

same stage. Some of the skeletons interred in the caves of
Grimaldi had upon their heads caps or nets on which shells
had been sewn. Other ornaments were collars, very elaborate
stomachers, bracelets, and decorative bands around the
knees. In the same place two children had been interred with
apron-like garments over them on which shells had been
sewn. Similar funeral regalia, as well as bracelets of ivory
and the use of coloring matters, were also found at other
57).

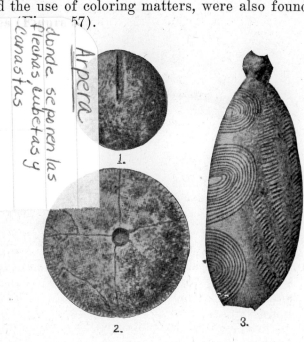

Fig. 57. Ornaments of ivory, perhaps used for body adornment,
from photographs. 1, 2 From the Solutrean sepulture at Brünn,
Moravia. 3 From the Solutrean site of Předmost, Moravia.
Three-fourths actual size.

Throughout this stage there continued the enthusiasm for
"collecting curiosities" already mentioned among the customs of the Early Palæolithic. These treasures consisted of
round pebbles, variegated stones, beautiful minerals, fossils,
etc. This does not exclude the fact that many perforated
pendants, thin flakes of bone and stone, the perforated
teeth of animals, and the statuettes of animals were exclu-

sively used as ornaments. Also primitive man in the present time cumbers himself with amulets, means of witchcraft and of protection of all kinds. A similar interpretation should doubtless be given to a great part of these Palæolithic absurdities. It is also possible that the drawings and engravings on harpoons and awls were not always simply for ornament or to mark ownership, but may have been magic

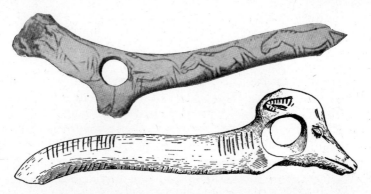

Fig. 58. Perforated staves (bâtons de commandement) of reindeer horn. *Above:* A specimen from the cave of La Madeleine, Dordogne, France, with engravings of wild horses. After Lartet and Christy. *Below:* A specimen from the cave of Placard, Dordogne, with the carving of a fox's head. After H. Breuil.

Reduced in size.

signs, protective against adverse influences and designed to insure success.

An extraordinary feature is the occurrence of ceremonial staves (bâtons de commandement) made of the antlers of stag or reindeer and adapted to the shape of these organs (Figure 58). These objects have a hole—sometimes several—in the lower end. They are found in the Aurignacian, but those of the Magdalenian are of better workmanship and often decorated with engravings or carvings. They have been explained as insignia of dignity or office, as handles of slings, as tent pegs, as shaft or arrow straighteners, etc. It is not impossible that the earlier forms may have had some practical use, but later, as the type became more deli-

slightly inclined toward the right or left, and, finally, the masculine skeleton from the cave of Paviland, Glamorganshire, England.

Fig. 61. Double sepulture at the base of the Grotte des Enfants near Mentone. After R. Verneau.

To the Proto-Solutrean belongs the skeleton of a crippled individual found at Laugerie Haute, Dordogne.[6] The individual in crouching position lying face down, found at Laugerie-Basse, belongs to the Magdalenian (Figure 62).

Another Magdalenian sepulture in Dordogne is that of Ray-monden near Chancelade, the skeleton found there being in crouching position and covered with ocher. To complete the list there must be added the sepulture of Duruthy near Sordes, Landes, the skeleton of Les Hôteaux, Ain, interred upon its back, and the skeleton of Cap-Blanc, Dordogne.

These remains were sometimes placed in made trenches; in other cases the bodies were laid upon the ground and some of them directly upon the hearth. Here the dead took up his habitation, and accordingly the survivors departed. In many cases stones were placed around the remains; and very often devoted offerings of ornaments, weapons, and tools bear witness to the belief of the Palæolithic cave men that these would be of use to the departed in the life beyond. It is noteworthy that the women—at least in many cases— enjoyed equal consideration with the men, and also that tender affection is evinced toward the children.

In contrast to the bodies laid out in the position of peace-ful sleep are those in the forced crouching position which has already been noted in the Early Palæolithic (p. 96). This leads to the supposition that these people believed that at least a part of their dead departed this mortal life with disgust, that they found the life beyond sorrowful, and were full of affliction and of inappeasable envy of those who had had the good fortune to survive them, in consequence of which the spirits of the dead were able to molest or hurt their survivors.

The forced flexing and binding of the dead is practiced by many primitive peoples of present times in order to prevent forever the return of the dead or of his spirit to earth; and there can be no doubt that it was partly or entirely owing to similar ideas that some of the Palæolithic skeletons were bound in crouching position, and that others were loaded down with great stones or, as a special precaution, placed upside down. Given this marked ethnographic similarity between Palæolithic man and primitive peoples of the pres-ent—the recognition of which similarity is due to modern ethnography—it appears very possible that various funeral customs were practiced during the Late Palæolithic in the same region and by the same people, and that the mode of

Penck, Quelle, Rérolle, Schmieder, and others have also contributed their efforts toward throwing light on the very important question of the geology of Spain during the Glacial Epoch.

The glaciation of the Pyrenees was notable, even though the glaciers did not extend beyond the mountain range, as they did in the Alps, where the glaciers covered all the surrounding country. On the northern (French) slope of the range the limit of perpetual snow was then from 1300 to 1500 meters above sea level in the west, 1700 meters in the central region, and 2000 to 2200 meters in the east.

The extent of the glaciers was considerably greater on the northern slope than on the southern (Spanish) slope, where, however, traces of glaciers have been found by M. Braun, M. Chevalier, C. Depéret, L. Gaurier, M. Gourdon, L. Mallada, O. Mengel, A. Penck, Roussel, L. M. Vidal, and others.

The earliest report on the glaciation of the Spanish Pyrenees is that of Angelot (1840). For later and more extensive studies we are indebted to A. Penck (4), whose investigations covered the western part of the central mass of these mountains. According to him there is evidence of the former existence of the following large glaciers:

Glacier of the Gállego River—its foot reaching to about a mile and a quarter below Biescas, about 800 meters above sea level.

Glacier of the Ara River—foot reaching to about a mile and a quarter below Broto, about 850 meters above sea level.

Glacier of the Cinca River—foot approximately below the "Paso de las Debotas," about 700 meters above sea level.

In the summer of 1918 I myself had occasion to visit the principal adjoining valleys to the eastward, and obtained the following results:

Glacier of the Esera River—foot reaching about to Sahún, about 1000 meters elevation.

Glacier of the Noguera Ribagorzana (Noguera de Barrabés) River—foot to the south of Vilaller, at an elevation of 1000 meters.

Glacier of the Noguera de Tor River—foot to the south of Barruerra, at an elevation of 1100 meters.

Glacier of the Flamisell River—foot to the south of Torre de Capdella, at an elevation of 1060 meters.

From the place now known as Andorra flowed the *Valira Glacier*—its foot extending not far from Santa Coloma and to the south of Andorra la Vieja, at an elevation of 1000 meters.

No positive data are as yet obtainable for the region farther eastward. In the central region above referred to, the snow line during the Glacial Epoch has been estimated at 1700 to 1800 meters.

In contrast to these, the Cantabrian Mountains, on account of the neighboring ocean, experience much greater humidity and precipitation, which is also evidenced in the study of their glacial geology.

Their greatest elevation is the group known as the Picos de Europa (2642 meters), which, together with P. Wernert, I studied in 1914 (5). In the eastern massif in the region of Andara, in addition to a number of small hanging glaciers there was the notable *Glacier of Urdón,* which ended not far from the village of Tresviso, at a height of 750 meters. From the wild ravines and gorges of the central massif, the *Deva Glacier* flowed out to the south, with its terminal moraines not far from Pido at an elevation of 930 meters; while to the north flowed the united *Duje* and *Lloroza Glaciers,* ending not far from Sotres at a height of 900 meters, as well as the steep *Bulnes Glacier.* The latter flowed into the ice-filled gorge of the Cares Brook and ended near Arenas de Cabrales not far from Poncebos, at about 250 meters. Naturally, in addition to these main ice-flows, there were also a number of small hanging glaciers.

Heavy glaciation occurred also in the western massif, known as the Picos de Cornión, which I studied thoroughly during the summers of 1919 and 1920. The coastward slope of the mountains, crowned by the towering peak of Peña Santa de Enol (2479 meters), was covered by a solid sheet of ice from which the following glaciers branched out: in the northeast the *Casaño Glacier,* ending at 850 meters; to the north and northwest the *Escalero Glacier,* with the Lake of Enol and the Lake of Ercina, ending at 820 meters, the *Abeyera Glacier,* ending at 930 meters, the *Redemoña Glacier,*

Bed of the Pleistocene glacier of Bulnes, Picos de Europa, Spanish Pyrenees. A U-shaped valley further eroded and deepened into the present gorge of the river Bulnes.

An erratic block. Peñalara in the Sierra de Guadarrama, Spain.

PLATE V

ending at 950 meters, and the *Busteguerra Glacier,* ending at 900 meters. The southern slope, dominated by the Peña Santa de Cain, gave rise to the westward-flowing *Dobra Glacier,* which ended at a height of 650 meters in the valley of Angón near the village of Amieba, shortly after uniting with the extensive *Joulloengo Glacier* on the right, at the Majadas de Cedemal, at an elevation of 760 meters. The principal sources of the Dobra Glacier were from the Garritas, the Torre del Torco, the Peña Santa de Cain, the Cueto Albo, and the Peña Bermeja (2391 meters), but it was also fed from the Pico de Samaya and the Pico Jarrio, lying farther to the south and properly not included among the Picos de Cornión.

The snow limit of the latest glaciation must have stood at 1400 to 1500 meters above sea level. Traces of an earlier and severer glaciation are found in the former lake basin of Comeya, which was dammed back by a more ancient Escalero Glacier, the water-washed moraines of which can be traced as far as the entrance of the present gorge of Mestas (about 750 meters).

The branch of the Cantabrian Cordillera running parallel with the northern coast includes a whole series of peaks over 2000 meters high, which in the main must certainly have been ancient centers of glaciation. Especially important for future investigations in this respect are the Sierra de Isar and the Peña Labra, as well as the Peña Curavacas, Peña Prieta, Espigüete, and Pico de Mampodre, lying to the east and south of the Picos de Europa; and the Braña Caballo, Canto Cabronero, Peña Ubiña, Peña Rubia, and Pico de Cuiña, lying westward from the same. Such high peaks are not again encountered until we reach the southern limits of our boundary mountains, as in the Sierra Segundera (1793 meters) and the Sierra Cabrera, on the glacial conditions of which W. Halbfass, F. Aragón, and J. Taboada Tundidor (6) have published brief reports. The mighty frontal moraines of the *Tera Glacier* surround the Lake of Castañeda and lie at a height of about 1000 meters above sea level, which, in estimating the snow limit of glacial times, should be regarded as a maximum rather than an average figure.

The glaciation of the Iberian Mountains has been recently studied by my pupils, J. Carandell and J. Gómez de Llarena (7). Traces of glaciation are very slight in the Sierra de Neila, but somewhat more pronounced in the Sierra de la Demanda (2134 meters), where the former limit of perpetual snow may be estimated at some 1950 meters. The most important center was that of the Sierra de Urbión (Pico de Urbión, 2246 meters), from whose summits the following glaciers descended: that of Lake Urbión to 1550 meters, of Lake Larga to 1680 meters, and of Lakes Helada and Negra to 1650 meters; which shows that the snow limit must have been about 1850 meters. We cannot as yet venture to give an opinion upon the traces of glaciation in the isolated Sierra de Moncayo (2315 meters) reported by M. Vicente and J. Gómez de Llarena.

Actual investigations in regard to glaciation in the middle latitudes of the Peninsula were made in 1883 in the Serra da Estrella, Portugal. It is noteworthy that, although the greatest heights in this range do not exceed 1991 meters, nevertheless it was possible for F. A. de Vasconcellos to verify traces of glaciation consisting of many polished stones found in the valley of Lake Comprida, of erratic blocks like those in the valley of Conde (at a height of 1500 meters) and also in the upper valley of the Zezere near Apertado (1200 meters), and finally of typical moraines near Manteigas (700 meters), which indicate the presence in that valley of a glacier over nine and a quarter miles wide. In 1895 Nery Delgado announced the existence of other glacial deposits in the valley of Ceira, which extended as far as the plain of Mondego (8).

This extensive glaciation is explained by the nearness of the ocean and the humid climate of the mountains, circumstances which lowered the limit of perpetual snow to an altitude of from 1400 to 1500 meters (provisional estimate). Vasconcellos also speaks of traces of glaciation at the foot of these mountains, but these indications need further study, already undertaken, as it happens, by E. Fleury.

As regards the Cordillera Central, C. de Prado in 1864 had already indicated incidentally the glaciation of the Sierras of Béjar and Hervás, and he also spoke with cer-

The valley of Ordesa in the Spanish Pyrenees. Its U-shape is due to the action of the Pleistocene glacier of the river Ordesa, which flows from Mont Perdu.

The postglacial recessional moraine at the eastern foot of Peña Vieja in the Picos de Europa, Spanish Pyrenees.

PLATE VI

tainty in 1862 of the existence of glaciers in the Sierra de Gredos. According to O. Schmieder (1915) there were several valley glaciers in the Sierra del Trampal (2404 meters), such as those of Garganta de Solana and Garganta del Trampal, as well as those of Garganta del Barco and Garganta de los Caballeros south of Barco de Ávila. Although all this region still needs a more detailed study, nevertheless it may safely be asserted that there were a considerable number of glaciers throughout the mountainous district lying between the Sierra de Béjar and the Picos de Gredos. In the last-named group, the highest of the range (Almanzor, 2592 meters), I was able in 1915, in company with H. del Villar and J. Carandell, to show the former existence of extensive glaciers in Garganta de Gredos and Garganta del Pinar (or Cinco Lagunas), which ended respectively at altitudes of 1450 and 1415 meters (Plates VII and III). With these data the height of the snow limit here during the Glacial Epoch may be estimated at 1800 to 1900 meters (9).

As to the Pleistocene glaciers of the Sierra de Guadarrama, opinions differ widely. They have been treated by C. de Prado (1864), Baysselance (1883), D. de Cortázar (1890), J. Macpherson (1893), A. Penck (1894), G. de Mazarredo (1910), and others (10). According to indications reported by the two last-named authors, the existence of valley glaciers would be impossible here, and still less possible the uniting of such supposed glaciers at the foot of the mountains in a huge ice-sheet covering the northern border of the plain of New Castile. Thanks to the researches of L. Fernández-Navarro (1915), we know that there were a number of small hanging glaciers on the northern slopes of the valley of the Lozoya. In the same group of Peñalara (2406 meters) were three other glaciers of the same type. The most extensive descended the southeast slope of Peñalara from west-north-west to east-south-east, and in its bed to the left lies the Lake of Peñalara. This glacier, earlier noted by A. Penck (1894), ended at an altitude of 1910 meters. The second glacier, the flow of which covered the present site of Hoyo de Pepe Hernando, ended at a height of 1830 meters. The third descended the eastern slope of the same massif.

Its moraines commenced somewhat below and south of the Lake of Birds, and ended at a height of 2050 meters. These figures enable us to estimate the perpetual snow limit during the Pleistocene at 2050 to 2100 meters (Plate V, b).

On parts of the slope below these glaciers I have met with more ancient moraine deposits at altitudes of 1750, 1720, and 1900 meters, which indicate the existence of a previous glaciation during which the snow limit must have reached 2000 meters, which is 100 meters lower than that of the

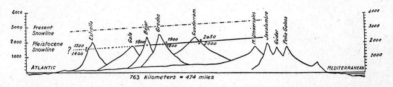

Fig. 64. Transverse section through the Iberian Peninsula showing the respective limits of perpetual snow at the present time and during the Glacial Epoch. Heights are given in meters.

latest glaciation. There are also clear indications of various phases of retrocession.

This shows that the limit of perpetual snow during the Pleistocene increased in height from the Atlantic coast in the west, toward the interior, where the climate becomes gradually more continental—as is also the case with the Pyrenees during the Pleistocene, or with Norway at the present time (Figure 64).

Of great importance is the question of Pleistocene glaciation in the loftiest mountain range of Spain, the Sierra Nevada (Mulhacén, 3481 meters). According to Schimper (1849) the glaciers descended from here as far as Granada (Alhambra, 770 meters), and also, in the opinion of J. Macpherson, the moraines are found almost everywhere around this range at heights of from 600 to 700 meters. On the other hand, the conclusions of A. Penck, E. Richter, A. Benrath, and O. Quelle (1908) are entirely opposed to this hypothesis of a regional glaciation in the Sierra Nevada. It may now be asserted that the glaciers of the southern slopes were almost exclusively hanging glaciers (11). In 1915, in collabo-

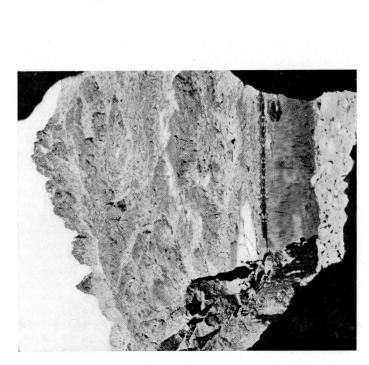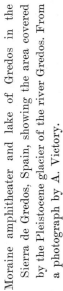

Moraine amphitheater and lake of Gredos in the Sierra de Gredos, Spain, showing the area covered by the Pleistocene glacier of the river Gredos. From a photograph by A. Victory.

Moraine of the Pleistocene glacier of Mulhacén, in the Sierra Nevada, Spain. From a photograph by J. Carandell.

PLATE VII

The Alpine marmot (*Arctomys marmotta*), so far, has been found in the deepest deposits of the cave of Castillo near Puente Viesgo (excavations of 1914), and also in the (Solutrean?) fauna of the cave of La Peña, near San Román de Candamo, Asturias.

In this list the fauna of the Early Pleistocene is typically represented only by the southern elephant, the hippopotamus, and the Etruscan rhinoceros. The last-named was indigenous to Europe. The hippopotamus came from Africa into Europe, and the same course seems to have been followed by the southern elephant. As stated previously (p. 35), it is certain that at the commencement of the Pleistocene Epoch the Strait of Gibraltar was already open, but the two continents were then united by a land bridge which connected northern Africa with Italy through Sicily.

The remaining species in this list are typical of the latter half of the Pleistocene, and belong for the most part to its close. This fauna shows that during the Pleistocene, with the rare exceptions above referred to, Spain was entirely dependent upon Europe and had no relation whatever with Africa. Such families as the Hyænidæ, Felidæ, Canidæ, Ursidæ, Suidæ, Cervidæ, and others, all had European precursors in Tertiary times.

The list of Spanish fauna consists almost exclusively of representatives of moderate or warm climates. The so-called "cold faunas" which play such an important part in other regions, are found here only in the *north of the Peninsula*. Even there they are of infrequent occurrence, nor is it likely that later investigations will greatly change the present known limits of their distribution. The principal route open to these northern types was the narrow strip of coast east of the Pyrenees, by which the mammoth, woolly rhinoceros, and reindeer made their way into Catalonia. Another route lay along the coast of Gascony toward the Basque Provinces, and through it the above-named animals, together with the marmot, entered the Cantabrian region.

As to the Alpine species, it would seem that the Alpine marmot had already disappeared before the close of the Pleistocene. The Pyrenean ibex and chamois existed in great numbers and spread not only into the valleys, but also almost as far as the coast plain.[5] Maritime immigrants from the north were the Arctic molluscs, *Cyprina islandica* and *Pecten islandicus* (p. 35).

The reported discovery of remains of the lemming in a cave of Athuguia in Portugal is quite inadmissible, since it has been shown that these remains consist of modern mummified specimens (16). Up to the present, typical steppe forms are entirely lacking. The Corsican pika (*Prolagus corsicanus*) or tailless hare above referred to, as well as the Cape pika (*Prolagus calpensis*) or tailless hare of Gibraltar, so far as known, have nothing in common with the steppe forms of pika (*Lagomys*).

Among the graphic protrayals of animals made by Pleistocene man are excellent representations of the wild ox, bison (Figure 17), stag, roe deer, and Dama deer. There are also a few representations of moose at Alpera and at Minateda—both in the Province of Albacete. In the numerous pictures of horses it is possible to recognize a number of types, as has been shown by H. F. Osborn. There are many pictures of the diminutive plateau, desert, or Celtic horse (related to the Arab type), and others of the heavy type of the forest or Nordic horse. Representations of the steppe horse (*Equus przewalski*) are abundant in France but very rare in Spain (Figure 16). The wild ass is also found (Figure 119). The ibex is frequently shown, there are several good pictures of the chamois in Cantabria, and also what is probably a representation of the same animal at Tortosillas near Ayora, Valencia. Quite remarkable are the various pictures of elephants in the caves of Pindal and Castillo, Cantabria. It should be noted that these animals are shown without tusks and with scanty hair (Figure 19). There is a picture of the rhinoceros at Minateda, and another (somewhat doubtful) representation of it in the cave of La Pileta, Málaga.

It should be kept in mind that in many cases the fauna of the Iberian Peninsula does not show distinct climatic phases. In consequence it is not only difficult, but often impossible, to determine the age of many of the Spanish sites, especially those belonging to the close of the Palæolithic, since the bones found there belong to species still existing in the same region.

On the other hand, it is certain that many species characteristic of a warm climate—such as the southern and straight-tusked elephants, the Etruscan and Merck's rhinoceroses, the hippopotamus, the striped hyena, and others —survived much longer in Spain than in France. This makes it necessary to proceed with great caution in any estimates of the relative antiquity of archæologic deposits in Spain that are based on the associated fauna. In Chapter VIII we recur to the consequences involved by this fact. Pleistocene human remains in Spain are treated in Chapter IX.

Little is known of the Pleistocene fauna of the Balearic Islands. Nevertheless, the excavations of Miss Dorothea Bate (17) have resulted in the surprising discovery of an absolutely new genus, *Myotragus*. *Myotragus balearicus* was a mammal about the size of a fox, with limbs of short, stocky build, adapted to climbing among rocks, its food consisting of tough plants. It was an excessively specialized ruminant, and had horns. In skull and dentition it has many points of resemblance to the Capridæ, but instead of three lower incisors and one canine on either side of the lower jaw, as is usual among hollow-horned ruminants, the canines and the two outside incisors are entirely absent. Only the median incisors remain, greatly developed and with persistent pulp, as in the rodents. The premolars are also reduced in number, while the molars are high. The dental formula is as follows:

$$i\frac{?}{1}; \quad p\frac{2}{1}; \quad m\frac{3}{3}$$

Remains of *Myotragus* occur both in Majorca and Minorca. The discovery sites of Majorca are the Cueva de la Barxa, Fuente de la Cala, near Capdepera; the Cuevas de los Colombs, Cap Faruch, Bay of Alcudia; and the Cueva des Bous, near Santueri. On Minorca Miss Bate reports the following: Cueva de los Extranjeros, near Santa Galdana Barranco, Bay of Marcaria; and the small fissure near Sestrucarias, Bajoli.

C. W. Andrews thinks it not impossible that certain mammal remains discovered by M. Dehaut in a cave breccia at Cap Figari, in the north of Sardinia, may belong to *Myotragus*. The animal, which was named *Antilope melonii,* has been doubtfully referred to *Nemorhœdus* by M. Dehaut, but it seems to have been very similar to *Myotragus* and may prove to be identical. The horns are similarly rounded in section and run straight back in a line with the forehead; the orbit also seems to have been similarly situated.

In the same level with *Myotragus* there was also found a new genus of the family Muscardinidæ, which Bate has named *Hypnomys,* with two species, *H. morpheus* of Majorca, and *H. mahonensis* of Minorca. This genus shows many points of resemblance to *Eliomys* and *Leithia,* although perfectly distinct from either.

Bate has also discovered in two fissures containing fossils in the island of Minorca, the remains of a gigantic tortoise, *Testudo gymnesicus.* The presence of these species shows that the Balearic Islands were separated from the mainland *before the Glacial Epoch.* Their fauna, corresponding to the Late Tertiary, evolved independently after the separation, which thus tended to the formation of specialized types.[6]

Theories concerning climatic conditions during the Pleistocene are based on the supposition that the formation of the Spanish coast and the conditions of the Gulf Stream were then essentially the same as now. And, since we are not able to make detailed investigations, our deductions must be more or less hypothetical in regard to the fauna—as yet little known—of the central and southern part of the Peninsula.

It can now be positively affirmed that the extent of surface actually covered by glaciers in the Peninsula was, comparatively speaking, very restricted. They did not extend beyond the highlands and the high mountain regions, so that their direct effect upon the lowlands was but slight.

The climate of northern Spain—that is, the Cantabrian region—was probably a very moist coast climate, similar to the present climate of Scotland and northern Ireland.

Central Spain had a dry continental climate, with a long severe winter and a short rainy summer, as at present. The "meseta" of Old Castile probably had a climate similar to

Bona—a cave near Mirones, discovered by L. Sierra, which contains a small deposit of the Late Solutrean with typical shouldered points, and laurel-leaf points with concave base.

Fuente del Francés—a cave near Hoznayo-Entrambasaguas in the jurisdiction of Santoña, discovered in 1880 by E. de la Pedraja. The archæologic deposit—containing industrial remains belonging to the Magdalenian, Solutrean, and Mousterian—has been entirely removed.

San Vitores—a cave near Solares, discovered by J. Carballo and I. Salguero, with traces of the Mousterian (?).

Cueva del Mar—a cave near Rivamontán al Monte in the jurisdiction of Santoña, discovered in 1903 by L. Sierra, containing industrial remains which are probably Aurignacian.

Truchiro—a cave near Rivamontán al Monte, discovered by L. Sierra in 1903, which contains Magdalenian deposits.

Environs of *Astillero*—near Santander. Acheulean hand axes in quartzite, discovered in the open by Robert Shallcross.

Nuestra Señora de Loreto (*Peña Castillo*)—a cave near Peña Castillo, within the city limits of Santander, which contains abundant Magdalenian deposits, discovered by M. de Olavarría.

Ciriego—a station in the open, within the city limits of Santander, behind the cemetery, where quartzite hand axes of Acheuleo-Mousterian type were found. Its discovery was announced in 1919 by J. Carballo and Count de la Vega del Sella (also Asturian industry).

In the region of the river Pas, southwestern Santander, are found the following:

Castillo—a cave near Puente Viesgo in the jurisdiction of Villacarriedo.

Entrance of the cave.—The existence of archæologic deposits here was announced by H. Alcalde del Rio. Their exploration was undertaken by the Institut de Paléontologie Humaine, Paris (1910-1914), and accomplished under the scientific direction of H. Obermaier assisted by P. Wernert. From time to time during the course of the excavations assistance in the scientific work was ably rendered by H. Breuil (26), Paris; Baron A. Blanc, Rome; P. Teilhard, Paris;

Miles Burkitt, Cambridge; N. C. Nelson, New York; F. Birkner, Munich; and R. Mallet, Paris (Plate VIII).

The stratigraphic succession found here is one of the most complete known among deposits with direct superposition of various industries. The section, which has an average thickness of 16-18 meters, includes the following strata:

Fig. 69. A perforated staff or bâton de commandement from the cave of Castillo, Puente Viesgo, on which the figure of a stag is deeply engraved. The engraved lines were formerly filled with red coloring matter.

Two-thirds actual size.

z Recent detritus.
y Stalagmitic deposit.
x Eneolithic industry.
w Azilian industry with flattened harpoons (Chapter X).
v Stalagmitic deposit.
u Late Magdalenian industry, including harpoons with a single row of barbs and perforated base, and a perforated bâton de commandement with a stag (Figure 69) depicted in deeply engraved lines which were formerly filled with ocher. Chief among the accompanying fauna is the stag.
t Clay layer, almost sterile.
s Early Magdalenian. An enormous deposit of ashes, nearly six feet deep. The flint implements are poor, but there are many artefacts in bone and horn, including numerous fragments of ceremonial staves or bâtons, generally unadorned, and a number of hind shoulder blades engraved with heads of hinds (Figure 70). There are also scattered human remains (Chapter

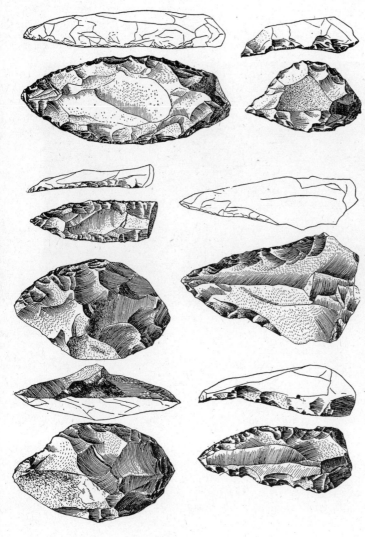

Fig. 72. Implements from the Late Mousterian level (*d*) in the cave of Castillo, consisting of a small hand ax (coup de poing), hand points, and a borer, all of worked flint.

Three-fourths actual size.

In the first large chamber inside the cave, industrial remains of Acheulean and Mousterian type were discovered by H. Obermaier and H. Breuil, including hand axes of quartzite and serpentine (Figure 74).

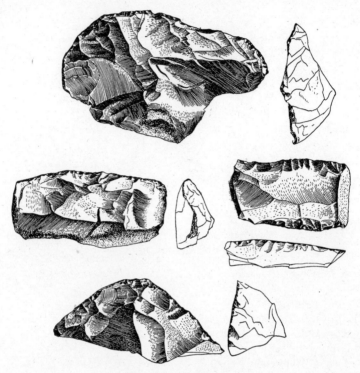

Fig. 73. Flint scrapers from the Late Mousterian level (*d*) in the cave of Castillo. Face and side views.
Three-fourths actual size.

On the slope of the mountain, just below the cave, Acheulean implements of quartzite were found in the open, and also in pockets of clay, by H. Breuil, H. Obermaier, and L. de Rozas.

Morín (Villanueva)—a cave near Villaescusa within the municipal limits of Villanueva, discovered by H. Obermaier and P. Wernert (1911). The existence of industrial remains was also announced by O. Cendrero (1914) and J. Carballo

(1915), and the deposit was systematically excavated (1918-1920) by Count de la Vega del Sella together with H. Obermaier. The stratigraphic succession is as follows:

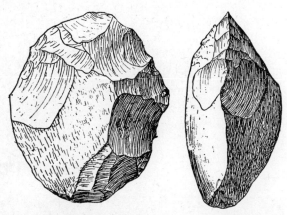

Fig. 74. An Acheulean discoidal hand ax (coup de poing) of serpentine, from the "Cave Bear loam" in the large inner chamber in the cave of Castillo. After H. Breuil and H. Obermaier.

Three-fifths actual size.

k Recent detritus.
i Middle (?) Tardenoisian industry.
h Azilian industry, with flattened harpoons.
g Magdalenian, with harpoons with a single row of barbs.
f Traces of Late Solutrean, with shouldered points of Cantabrian type.
e Final Aurignacian, with a point of Font-Robert type.
d Middle Aurignacian, with bone points with cleft base.
c Middle Aurignacian, more primitive in type.
b Sterile layer.
a Late Mousterian, with many large implements of serpentine and quartzite, identical in type with those of level *f* in the neighboring cave of Castillo. Fauna—Merck's rhinoceros.

Pendo (San Pantaleón)—a cave near Escobedo-Camargo in the jurisdiction of Santander, contains an enormous deposit discovered (1878-1880) by M. de Sautuola. It includes Azilian, Magdalenian, Solutrean, and Aurignacian industries, as I was able to demonstrate through investigations made during the years 1919-1921. Of especial interest is a ceremonial staff (bâton de commandement) found in 1914 by O. Cendrero, engraved with a number of deeply incised lines. Fauna—Merck's rhinoceros.

Cobalejos (*Puente Arce*)—a cave near Puente Arce-Valle de Piélagos in the jurisdiction of Santander, discovered by E. de la Pedraja, which contains deposits of Magdalenian, Solutrean, and Mousterian. In 1914 the author, together with L. de Rozas, found here in Late Magdalenian deposits a decorated awl and a human molar. At the base were found small implements of Mousterian type, made of quartzite. The rhinoceros molar noted by E. Harlé appears to belong to Merck's rhinoceros.

Camargo (*Peña del Mazo*)—a cave near Revilla-Camargo in the jurisdiction of Santander. This grotto was studied by M. de Sautuola, but has since been destroyed in consequence of the exploitation of a stone quarry. The latest investigations were made by J. Carballo and L. Sierra, and to the latter we owe the determination of the various levels, as follows:

e Neolithic and Copper Age artefacts.

d Traces of Azilian industry.

c Magdalenian deposits. J. Carballo owns a ceremonial staff found here, engraved with serpentine designs.

b Solutrean deposits.

a Aurignacian deposits. From this level came the human skull now in the Museum of Limpias, Santander (Chapter IX).

In the region of the rivers Besaya and Saja (neighborhood of Torrelavega) are found the following:

Hornos de la Peña—a cave near San Felices de Buelna in the jurisdiction of Torrelavega, containing deposits discovered in 1903 by L. Sierra and H. Alcalde del Río, and excavated in 1909-1910 for the Institut de Paléontologie Humaine, Paris, under the scientific direction of H. Obermaier, H. Breuil, and J. Bouyssonie (27). The stratification is as follows:

e Indications of Neolithic culture.

d Magdalenian deposit, in gray clay, containing a meager number of specimens. Among these are javelins and typical flints, and several articles in stag horn, ornamented with spiral designs.

c Early Solutrean industry, in yellow clay, with fragments of laurel-leaf points.

b Middle Aurignacian industry, in yellow clay, with abundant flints; also the frontal bone of a horse with the posterior part of the same animal engraved upon it.

a Mousterian artefacts embedded in a sandy deposit, which are made chiefly of quartzite.

The maximum thickness of the whole deposit is two meters. The strata were rather complicated.

San Felices de Buelna—in this neighborhood Acheulean deposits were found in the open, with hand axes of quartzite collected by H. Alcalde del Río and H. Breuil.

Peña de Carranceja—near Carranceja-Reocín in the jurisdiction of Torrelavega, visited in 1903 by H. Alcalde del Río, contains indications of Magdalenian and Solutrean industry.

Altamira—a cave near Santillana del Mar in the jurisdiction of Torrelavega. This great cave was studied during the years 1878-1880 by M. de Sautuola. Its entrance contains a most notable deposit of Solutrean and Magdalenian, which has been investigated by M. de Sautuola, E. de la Pedraja, Botín, E. Harlé, F. Quiroga, Taylor Ballota, H. Alcalde del Río, and L. Sierra (28).

The stag's shoulder blades found here, ornamented with engravings, cannot possibly belong to the Late Solutrean, as suggested by H. Alcalde del Río, but should be attributed to the Early Magdalenian as indicated by the excavations at Castillo. The Late Solutrean of Altamira is characterized by Solutrean shouldered points and laurel-leaf points with concave base.

El Cuco—a cave near Ubiarco-Santillana in the jurisdiction of Torrelavega, discovered by M. de Sautuola, which contains a Magdalenian deposit.

In the region of the river Deva in the extreme west of the province are found the following:

Unquera—near San Vicente de la Barquera, where H. Breuil and H. Alcalde del Río discovered a Mousterian deposit in the open, beneath a thick layer of clay with remains of the woolly rhinoceros.

La Hermida—in the gorge of the river Deva between Panes and Potes, where H. Breuil and H. Alcalde del Río discovered a deposit in the open which contained Late Magdalenian and Azilian artefacts.

ASTURIAS

In the region of Panes are found the following:

Panes—according to investigations made by H. Breuil, H. Obermaier, and H. Alcalde del Río, affords these industrial remains, namely:

1. At the rock-shelters to the southeast of the town—Magdalenian (or Azilian) flints.
2. At the foot of these shelters—a great Acheulean deposit in the open, with many hand axes in quartzite.
3. In the direction of Peña Mellera between Panes and the cave called Cueva del Sel—Acheulean deposits of the same character.

La Loja (*El Mazo*)—near Panes, a grotto at the entrance of which H. Breuil and H. Obermaier discovered vestiges of industrial remains which are probably Magdalenian.

In the region of Llanes are found the following:

Balmori (*Quintana*)—a cave near Balmori, Llanes, explored by Count de la Vega del Sella, 1914-1917, a part of the time in collaboration with H. Obermaier. The stratification is as follows:

d Asturian industry.
c Azilian industry.
b Early Magdalenian remains, with awls with rectangular cross section. The accompanying fauna consists of the moose, cave lion, and the Arctic mollusc, *Cyprina islandica*.
a Indications of Solutrean industry, with a shouldered point.

Arnero—a cave near Posada, Llanes, discovered by Count de la Vega del Sella in 1914, and explored by the same, together with H. Obermaier, in 1919. The stratification is as follows:

b Stalagmitic deposit and abundant Asturian industrial remains.

a Reddish clay with Middle Aurignacian artefacts, characterized by bone points with cleft base. The accompanying fauna consists of Merck's rhinoceros, wild ox, horse, stag, roe deer, ibex, and chamois.

There are also indications of Mousterian (?) industrial remains, much disturbed and not in their original intact state.

Cueto de la Mina—near Posada, Llanes, discovered and explored (1914-1915) by Count de la Vega del Sella (29). The stratification of this important rock shelter is as follows:

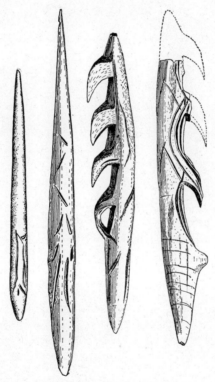

Fig. 75. Bone awls, or points, and harpoons from Late Magdalenian deposits in the cave shelter of Cueto de la Mina, now in the collection of Count de la Vega del Sella.

Four-fifths actual size.

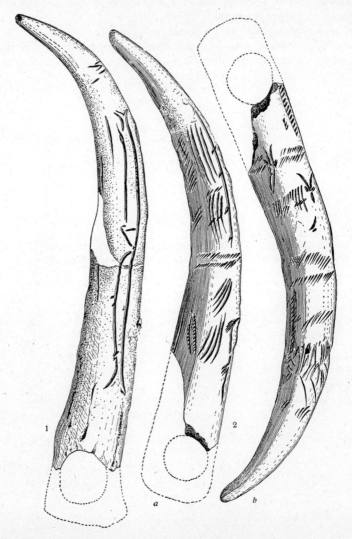

Fig. 76. Perforated staves (bâtons de commandement) from Late Magdalenian deposits at Cueto de la Mina, now in the collection of Count de la Vega del Sella. 1 Engraved with designs of fishes. 2 Engraved with conventionalized ibex heads and other decorative designs.

One-half actual size.

m Traces of Asturian industry—5 cm.

l Traces of Azilian industry—5 cm.

k Late Magdalenian—50 cm.—a rich and varied industry in flint and quartzite. Harpoons with a single row of barbs, and an awl engraved with a much conventionalized ibex head (Figure 75); also several ceremonial staves of stag horn, among them

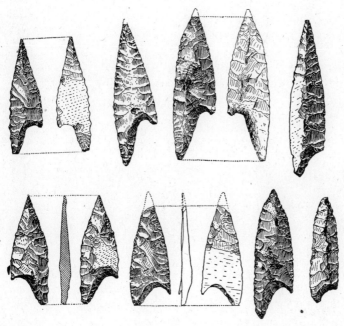

Fig. 77. Shouldered points of worked flint, in varying forms, from Cueto de la Mina, now in the collection of Count de la Vega del Sella.

Actual size.

one engraved with two fishes (Figure 76, 1), and another with conventionalized ibex heads and various linear designs (Figure 76, 2). Shells of *Cyprina islandica*.

i Middle Magdalenian—55 cm.—a reddish deposit without harpoons. Shells of *Pecten islandicus*.

h Early Magdalenian—40 cm.—with many simple bone implements (spatulas, awls, javelin points, fine needles), some of which are ornamented. Shells of *Cyprina islandica*.

g Late Solutrean—60 cm.—divided into four strata, which, however, according to the character of implements are essentially the same. Numerous typical shouldered points, short-pointed and with a well-defined barb at the side (Figure 77); also laurel-leaf points, most of them with concave base (Figure 78). The fauna includes the stag (very abundant), horse, Pyrenean ibex, chamois, and cave hyena. There are also molars of the woolly mammoth.

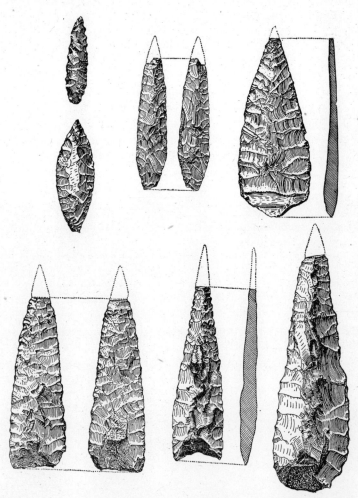

Fig. 78. Leaf points of worked flint belonging to the Late Solutrean, from Cueto de la Mina, now in the collection of Count de la Vega del Sella.

Three-fifths actual size.

f Red loam and sand—30-40 cm.
e Early Solutrean—30 cm.—with simple laurel-leaf points.
d Sterile layer—25 cm.
c Late Aurignacian—10 cm.—with awls of ivory and points of "La Gravette" type.
b Sterile loam—20 cm.
a Late Aurignacian—10 cm.—with unimportant industry and remains of the cave hyena.

At the base of the Late Magdalenian deposit (*k*) were found a few oval hand axes of quartzite of the same type as those from the Late Mousterian deposit (layer *f*) in the cave of Castillo. These doubtless fell from the edge of the plateau overhanging the cave during Magdalenian times.

La Riera—a cave near Posada, Llanes, discovered in 1916 by Count de la Vega del Sella, and explored by the same together with H. Obermaier. The stratification is as follows:

g Asturian industry, very abundant.
f Azilian deposit, with harpoons.
e Azilio-Magdalenian.
d Late Magdalenian, with harpoons with a double row of barbs.
c A layer of red loam which originally lay on the plateau above the grotto, and fell during Magdalenian times. It contained a number of hand axes of quartzite, belonging to the Acheulean.
b Late Solutrean.
a The base, which has not yet (1919) been explored.

Fonfría—a cave near Barro, Llanes, discovered and explored in 1915 by Count de la Vega del Sella, whose account has not yet been published. The stratification is as follows:

e Superficial stalagmitic deposit.
d A layer of molluscs adhering to the stalagmitic covering.
c A black deposit with quartzite implements of Asturian type.
b Sterile layer of red clay.
a A small Magdalenian deposit.

In the region of Ribadesella are found the following:

La Cuevona—in Ribadesella, which contains Early Magdalenian deposits, was excavated in 1915 by E. Hernández-Pacheco and P. Wernert. Later researches were made in 1916 by Count de la Vega del Sella and H. Obermaier.

Viesca—a cave in Ribadesella containing industrial remains which probably belong to the late Magdalenian, was excavated in 1915 by E. Hernández-Pacheco and P. Wernert.

Cueva del Río—a cave in Ardines near Ribadesella, excavated by E. Hernández-Pacheco and P. Wernert in 1915, contains industrial remains belonging to the Azilian (?) and probably to the Early Magdalenian.

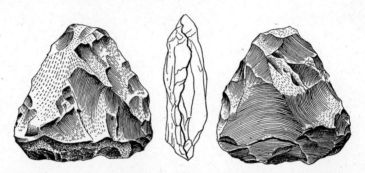

Fig. 79. Triangular hand ax of quartzite from the Cueva del Conde, Tuñón, now in the collection of Count de la Vega del Sella.
One-half actual size.

Ferrán (Peña de Ferrán)—a cave near Infiesto explored by A. Argüelles, which contains a Magdalenian deposit with harpoons of Cantabrian type with one row of barbs.

Cueva del Conde (Cueva del Forno)—a cave near Tuñón, Santo Adriano, discovered and explored in 1915 by Count de la Vega del Sella, whose results are as yet unpublished. The stratification reported is as follows:

c Dark earth, recently disturbed—25 cm.—containing abundant implements of quartzite and a few of flint, some of which are forms typical of the Late Aurignacian.

b Dark reddish layer—25 cm.—containing numerous implements of coarsely worked quartzite, also flint implements, scarce but typical, some plain bone awls, and fragments of bone points with cleft base, belonging to the Middle Aurignacian. One molar of Merck's rhinoceros. In the same layer were found implements typical of the Early Mousterian, generally much weathered, characterized by a thin and narrow hand ax of triangular form

(Figure 79) and by small implements. These are doubtless due
to some early disturbance of the deposit.

a Sterile layer of red clay.

Collubil—a cave near Cangas de Onís, in the district of
Amieba, discovered and explored by Count de la Vega del
Sella, whose results are as yet unpublished, which contains
a Magdalenian industry consisting exclusively of implements of quartzite.

In the region of Oviedo are found the following:

Sofoxó—a cave in the district of San Pedro de Nora,
near Trubia, discovered and explored (1915-1916) by Count
de la Vega del Sella in collaboration with H. Obermaier. It
contains a Magdalenian deposit with a harpoon with one
row of barbs, and an awl ornamented with a conventionalized
ibex head.

Soto de las Regueras—Grado, in the zone of high alluvial
deposits lying between Valduno and Soto de las Regueras,
has afforded Acheulean hand axes in quartzite, discovered
in 1915 by J. Cabré.

Cueva de la Paloma—near Soto de las Regueras, Grado,
explored in 1914-1915 for the Comisión de Investigaciones
Paleontológicas y Prehistóricas under the direction of
E. Hernández-Pacheco with the coöperation of Count de la
Vega del Sella both years, of J. Cabré in 1914, and of
P. Wernert in 1915. A treasure seeker had so completely disturbed the deposits that in no single spot was it possible to
establish a clear and trustworthy stratigraphic succession.
The following grouping, therefore, must be considered as a
purely arbitrary restoration, and as correcting our earlier
expressed views, founded on the report of others.

d Recent detritus containing remains from the Age of Metals and
from Neolithic times, apparently with numerous Neolithic
sepultures.

c Azilian industry, abundant in typical flints and various bone
awls, also one flat harpoon.

b Late Magdalenian, including harpoons with one and two rows of
barbs (some with the base perforated laterally), various engravings, and a number of bone implements such as awls, spatulas,
and javelin points (Figure 46).

a Early Magdalenian, including an undecorated ceremonial staff, various engravings on bone and bosses of stone, fine needles, and a quantity of other bone implements.

Peña de Candamo—a cave near San Román de Candamo, which contains a scanty Solutrean deposit with remains of cave hyena and marmot, found in 1916, in a small cave directly adjoining the above, by E. Hernández-Pacheco and P. Wernert, and explored by them.

BURGOS

Aceña—a rock shelter near Santo Domingo de Silos, discovered in 1910 by J. Carballo and Saturio González, which contains Late Palæolithic deposits, probably Aurignacian, with points of La Gravette type.

Barranco del Río Lobo—a rock shelter near Montoria del Pinar, containing a deposit which is probably Mousterian, discovered by H. Breuil and Saturio González.

Cueva del Caballón—a cave near Oña, discovered and explored in 1915 by J. M. Rodríguez Fernández, which contains a Magdalenian deposit with a ceremonial staff (bâton de commandement) ornamented with a conventionalized ibex head.

La Blanca—a cave near Oña, discovered and explored by J. M. Rodríguez Fernández, which contains traces of Aurignacian (?) and Mousterian industry with remains of the beaver.

LOGROÑO

Peña de la Miel—the lower cave, on the bank of the river Iregua, discovered by L. Zubia and explored by L. Lartet in 1865, containing Late Palæolithic deposits.

The Palæolithic stations so far discovered in central Spain are found in the following provinces:

SALAMANCA

Salamanca and environs—numerous indications of Acheulean and Mousterian occupation, found partly *upon,* and partly embedded *in* the diluvial shotter terraces of the river Tormes. The discovery sites occur both on the left bank (Matadero, Fuente de Carpihuelo, Teso de la Feria) and on the right (Toma de Aguas), and have afforded finely worked hand axes and similar implements of quartz and quartzite. They were discovered in 1921 by H. Obermaier, and their investigation has been carried on by César Morán.

SORIA

Barranco del Río Ucero—a scanty Mousterian deposit in the open, discovered in 1912 by H. Breuil and Saturio González.

Cerrada de la Solana—a rock shelter near Carrascosa de Arriba, Caraceña, discovered in 1912 by J. Cabré, whose results are as yet unpublished. It contains an Acheulean deposit with very characteristic hand axes in quartzite.

Torralba—near Fuencaliente de Medinaceli. This station is situated on the northern slope of the Sierra Ministra at a height of 1112 meters above sea level, and at the junction of the Soria railroad with the line from Madrid to Saragossa. This Palæolithic industry is found embedded in the shore of an ancient lake and constitutes an absolutely uniform deposit of clay sediment, 50 to 90 cm. in depth. The fauna and industry are remarkably homogeneous, from which it would seem impossible that there has been any secondary intermixture with elements belonging to later ages. Above this deposit lies sterile marl, over three feet in depth, and above that is a layer of weathered red clay.

This deposit was discovered through digging a trench in the course of railroad construction, in 1888, and numerous remains of elephants were collected at the time, part of which were acquired by the School of Mines in Madrid. But our knowledge of its nature is due to the systematic study and exploration of the site by the Marquis of Cerralbo, who has devoted himself to this work ever since 1907 (30).

The fauna includes the straight-tusked elephant, a few specimens of which somewhat resemble the southern elephant, and also the rhinoceros, wild ox, stag, and horse.[3] The industry is a well-advanced Chellean, as shown by a series of hand axes in quartzite and chalcedony. The worked hand axes of limestone are exceedingly primitive in type, doubtless because of the difficulty of working such unpromising material (Figures 21, 24, 25, and 80). The small artefacts associated with these are variable in type, some being primitive and others quite well developed, as is also the case with contemporary deposits in France.

It is very probable that other deposits of the same nature will be found in the neighboring territory close to the same ancient lake. This seems to be indicated by the remains of fossil animals recently discovered near Ambrona.

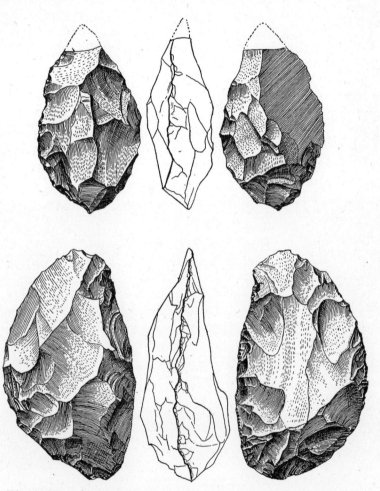

Fig. 80. Two Chellean hand axes, one of quartzite and one of chalcedony, from Torralba, now in the collection of the Marquis de Cerralbo.

Two-fifths actual size.

SARAGOSSA

In the environs of *Saragossa*—traces of Chellean and Acheulean industry were found in the alluvial deposits of the river Ebro, according to preliminary investigations made by H. Obermaier in 1918 and 1919.

GUADALAJARA

Environs of *Aguilar de Anguita* and *Alcolea del Pinar*—deposits in the open which probably include Late Palæolithic industry, and certainly Tardenoisian. (Collections of the Marquis of Cerralbo.)

Casas de Uceda—near Cogolludo, with Mousterian industrial remains in the open, along the Jarama River, discovered in 1921 by J. Pérez de Barradas.

MADRID

The sites described below are all in the neighborhood of the city of Madrid. The following are found on the right bank of the river Manzanares:

Casa de Campo—with Mousterian industry discovered by J. Pérez de Barradas at a depth of two meters, embedded in red loam (31).

San Isidro—a site exceedingly rich in Palæolithic material, served for many years as a source of sand and gravel for the neighboring city. More than fifty years ago the geologist, Casiano de Prado (32), aroused great scientific interest in the place, and following him a number of specialists explored it, but, unfortunately, no systematic observation and research were made in regard to the stratification, fauna, and industry. The sand pit is now worked out and destroyed, and we are therefore reduced to reconstructing the following arbitrary industrial stratification, based on the indications given by early investigators and on the traces still visible in what remains of the section.

e Sand with clay and vegetable mould	1.5 m.
d Reddish gray sand, almost all coarse, part with horizontal stratification, part contorted, containing some beds of clay	7–8 m.
c Dark bluish gray clay with elephant remains and pockets of fine white sand, indicating former pools of water	.3–3 m.

b Gravel formed by swift-flowing water   3 m.

C. de Prado and other early investigators refer to the
fact that there was in this deposit an archæologic
horizon with faunal remains (elephant). In truth,
and in view of the specimens in the Anthropological
Museum of Madrid, which consist of a small series
of typical Chellean implements more or less worn
and rounded, we consider that they could be derived only from this level (Figures 22, 23).

a Base—Middle Miocene deposits with remains of *Anchi-
therium* and *Mastodon angustidens*. These deposits
form the actual bed of the Manzanares in which the
river flows.

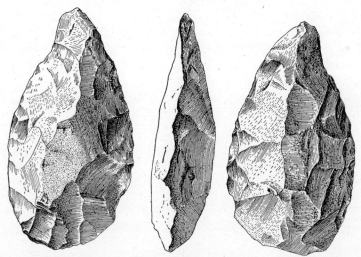

Fig. 81. A sandstone hand ax (coup de poing) of Early Acheulean
type from San Isidro.
One-third actual size.

Layer *c* and especially layer *d* comprise the Acheulean
deposits, which appear to have been quite prolific in industrial remains. These include magnificent types of Early
Acheulean implements which have not been waterworn
(Figures 27-30 and 81). From the various indications
it may be gathered that this industry was distributed
throughout the deposit of sand—not uniformly, however,

e Vegetable mould.
d White earth, with Palæolithic industry of indeterminate character.
c Clay.
b Gravel, with Mousterian industry.
a Tertiary deposit.

Los Rosales—discovered by the same, contains loam and sand with Mousterian industry.

Villaverde Bajo (section by the railway station)—discovered by the same, contains loam with an exceedingly fine Acheulean industry.

Olivar de la Granja—in the valley of the Culebro Brook, within the municipal limits of Getafe, discovered by the same. Stratification as follows:

f	Vegetable mould	10 cm.
e	Loam	90 cm.
d	Reddish sand	270 cm.
c	White sand	
b	Whitish sand with Mousterian industry	30 cm.
a	Reddish sand with Mousterian industry	80 cm.

Stations situated on the left bank of the Manzanares, and also within the neighborhood of the city of Madrid, are the following:

Las Delicias—situated in the district of Las Delicias and actually within the limits of the railway station of the line from Madrid to Cáceres, was discovered in 1917 by Alejandro Guinea Unzaga, and explored by H. Obermaier and P. Wernert (35). Stratification as follows:

d	Vegetable mould mixed with clay, with indications of Palæolithic industry	120 cm.
c	Dense clay	150 cm.
b	Sandy deposit	5–8 cm.
a	Tertiary clay.	

At the base of layer *c*, in layer *b*, and on the surface of layer *a* was found an industry typical of the final Acheulean, with exceedingly fine and thin hand axes, so perfect as almost to recall the Solutrean types (Figure 32).

Cerro Negro—within the municipal limits of Vallecas, dis-

covered by P. Wernert and J. Pérez de Barradas, contains
an Acheulean industry in a deposit of greenish clay.

El Almendro—within the municipal limits of Villaverde
and about six and a quarter miles south of the site of San

Fig. 83. Discovery site of El Almendro, Villaverde, in the neighborhood of Madrid. These deposits, which contain an Early Mousterian industry with numerous hand axes, are about 50 feet above
the present river bed of the Manzanares. The place is shaded by a
large solitary almond tree (in Spanish, "almendro") from which
the site receives its name.

Isidro (Figure 83), discovered by the same (36). Stratification as follows:

b Gravel, not very coarse, with Early Mousterian industry which
    includes numerous hand axes. At the base an industry which
    may possibly be Chellean.
a Gypseous marl of the Tertiary.

La Gavia—within the municipal limits of Villaverde, discovered by the same (37), contains sand with Mousterian
industry.

Stone Quarries of Vallecas—discovered (1919) and described by H. Obermaier, P. Wernert, and J. Pérez de Barradas (38). The railway cutting at this site shows the following stratification:

f Humus.
e Loam.
d Loamy sand with abundant Mousterian industry.
c White sandy marl.
b Red sand, with an industry transitional from Acheulean to Mousterian.
a Grayish green marl with a scanty Acheulean industry.

Besides these, a number of discoveries of secondary importance have also been made in this region, chiefly in the open and scattered over the surface.

Algete—near Alcalá de Henares, a Chellean site lying between the village of Algete and the Jarama River, discovered in 1921 by J. Pérez de Barradas.

Las Zorreras—near Alcobendas (Colmenar Viejo), an Acheulean site, discovered in 1921 by the same.

TOLEDO

Illescas—a station in the open, with indications of industrial remains suggestive of the Mousterian and Late Palæolithic cultures, discovered by L. Fernández-Navarro and P. Wernert in 1917.

Toledo—Quaternary shotter on the right bank of the Tagus, with atypical implements of the Early Palæolithic, discovered in 1920 by J. Pérez de Barradas (39).

CIUDAD REAL

La Tabernera (Hoz del Río Frío)—a rock shelter near Solanilla del Tamaral, containing a Late Palæolithic deposit with atypical quartzites, discovered by H. Breuil and H. Obermaier in 1912.

Chillón—near Almadén, a deposit in the open, probably Chellean and Mousterian, discovered by H. Breuil in 1916.

CÁCERES

Alia—an important Mousterian deposit in the open, discovered by H. Breuil in 1916.

BADAJOZ

All the stations in this province were discovered and described by H. Breuil (40).

Albuquerque-Codosera—a site in the open on the bank of the river Gevora, containing a Chelleo-Acheulean deposit.

Mérida—a site in the open, in the alluvial deposits of the river Guadiana, containing Chellean implements of quartzite and sandstone.

San Serván (*Calamonte*)—a site in the open, south of Mérida, containing Mousterian industry in quartzite.

Alange—a site in the open, south of Mérida, containing an Acheulean (?) industry.

Muro de Helechosa—a site in the open, with an Early Palæolithic industry in quartzite.

Fuenlabrada de los Montes—an important site in the open, containing Acheulean industry in quartzite.

Peñalsordo—near Capilla, containing Mousterian industry in the open, and Chellean (?) in the terraces of the river Zujar.

Tamurejo Baterno—a site in the open, with Acheulean and Mousterian industry in quartzite.

SOUTHERN SPAIN

CORDOVA

Posadas-Almodóvar del Río—on the shores of the Guadalquivir near the city of Cordova, containing Chellean industry associated with remains of the straight-tusked elephant, according to Salvador Calderón and J. Vilanova.

JAÉN

Aldeaquemada—a site in the open, near Santisteban del Puerto, with a Mousterian industry in quartzite, discovered by H. Breuil and J. Cabré in 1913.

Despeñaperros—near Santa Elena, which contains implements of quartzite belonging to the Early Palæolithic. According to J. Calvo and J. Cabré (1916) they were found in the open in the "Atajo de los Arcos."

La Puerta—a site in the open on the shores of the Guadalimar, discovered by H. Breuil and J. Cabré, which contains Mousterian industry in quartzite.

Puente Mocho—archæologic deposits in the open in the olive gardens on the banks of the Guadalimar between the bridge of Beas as far as the slope of the Botos de Campillo, and containing Chellean, Acheulean, and Mousterian implements in quartzite. The most important site extends about a third of a mile on either side of the Puente Mocho. Discovered by H. Breuil and J. Cabré in 1913, and described by J. Cabré and P. Wernert (41).

CADIZ

Arcos de la Frontera—where traces of Palæolithic industry were found in the sulphur mine ''Señor del Perdón'' by Claudio Sanz Arizmendi in 1908. The implements—made mostly of flint, more rarely of quartzite—were found *in situ* in the conglomerate which lies, almost horizontally, directly above the sulphur lode. I have seen the originals (eleven specimens), and they impressed me as belonging to a well-developed Mousterian.

Lake Janda—where deposits in the open, mostly in contact with the ''tierras negras'' (black earth), have been found to the south and east of the lake. They belong to the Chellean, Acheulean, and Mousterian cultures, and were discovered, some in 1913 by E. Hernández-Pacheco and J. Cabré, and others in 1914 by H. Breuil (42). The presence of any Late Palæolithic industry is very doubtful.

Los Barrios and *Castellar de la Frontera*—north of Algeciras, where H. Breuil discovered, in 1916, Chellean and Acheulean implements of quartzite, very much worn, embedded in Pleistocene gravels.

The *Rock of Gibraltar*—until very recently has yielded only fossil remains, nor did the latest excavations of W. L. H. Duckworth show any traces of Palæolithic industry. In 1919, however, H. Breuil discovered a rock shelter at the foot of Rock-Gun and opposite the Devil Tower, which contained hearths of Pleistocene age. Stone implements were very scarce, but unmistakably of Mousterian type. The fauna included the horse, wild ox, brown bear, wild boar, stag, ibex, and rabbit, with remains of tortoise and numerous molluscs (43). The human skull of Pleistocene age found in Forbes Quarry is described on page 288.

MÁLAGA

Bobadilla—a site in the open, with Mousterian industry, in part beneath a layer of clay, discovered in 1912 by H. Breuil, H. Obermaier, and J. Cabré.

Hoyo de la Mina—a cave near La Cala del Moral in the environs of the city of Málaga, discovered by M. Such in 1917, which contains abundant Neolithic material and also a Palæolithic deposit. The excavations, which are but just begun, have yielded numerous implements of flint—including various kinds of graving tools, small planing tools, and a few Tardenoisian forms—which give the impression that the industry should be assigned to the final phase of the Palæolithic. The fauna consists of wild ox, horse, hare, and stag (44).

GRANADA

Explorations conducted in 1916 by H. Obermaier resulted in the discovery of the Palæolithic stations described below.

In the region of Moreda are found the following:

Puntal—a cave in the foothills of the Sierra de Harana and within the municipal limits of Darro, which contains breccias with Mousterian industry and indications of Late Palæolithic industry. Fauna—horse.

Horá—a cave, also within the municipal limits of Darro, with breccia containing a fine Mousterian industry with remains of stag and horse (Figure 84, *c* and *d*). In the open at the very foot of this cave were found indications of Mousterian and Aurignacian industry.

Llano de Huélago—a site in the open, west of the railway station of Huélago, where were found Palæolithic flints of Mousterian (?) and Aurignacian age.

In the region of Piñar are found the following:

Cerillo de Orea—in the Barranco del Carrizal about a mile and a quarter north of Piñar, a deposit in the open, with Late Palæolithic industry.

Fuente de la Zarza—about one-third of a mile east of Piñar, a station in the open with typical Mousterian industry and vestiges of a scanty Capsian (Figure 84, *a* and *b*).

In the region of Iznalloz are found the following deposits,

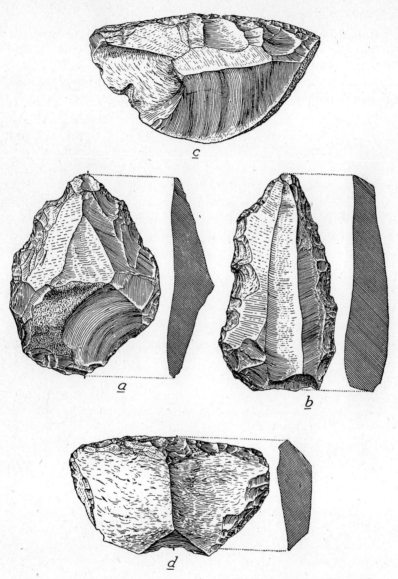

Fig. 84. Fine Mousterian scrapers (*c*, *d*) from Cueva Horá, Granada.
Fine Mousterian point and flake (*a*, *b*) from the Fuente de la
Zarza, Granada.

Actual size.

all of which occur in the open, to the west and northwest of Iznalloz.

Loma del Rubio—with indications of Mousterian (?) and Early Capsian industry, and perhaps also Late Capsian.

Llano de la Venta de las Navas—with Mousterian and Aurignacian industry.

Venta de las Navas—with Mousterian and Aurignacian industry.

Haza de la Cabaña—with Mousterian, Proto-Aurignacian, and Capsian industry.

ALMERÍA

In the environs of Vélez Blanco the three following sites were discovered by F. de Motos and H. Breuil.

Ambrosio—a cave containing Late Capsian industry.

La Cueva Chiquita de los Treinta—a rock shelter near Chirivel, with Capsian industry and a Solutrean (?) arrow-point.

Fuente de los Molinos—a rock shelter with Late Capsian industry.

In the neighborhood of Cuevas de Vera are the following:

Serrón—a cave with Capsian industry, discovered by L. Siret.

Caves of Zájara—two caves with Capsian industry, discovered by L. Siret.

Cueva Humosa—a cave near Albox, with Capsian industry, discovered by L. Siret.

EASTERN AND NORTHEASTERN SPAIN

MURCIA

In the region of Mazarrón-Lorca are the seven caves named below, with Palæolithic deposits, all of which were discovered by L. Siret (Figures 88 and 89).

Palomarico—with Mousterian and Capsian industry.

Las Perneras—with Mousterian and Capsian and a Solutrean (?) laurel-leaf point.

La Bermeja—with Mousterian, and Early, Late, and final phases of Capsian industry.

Las Palomas—with Capsian industry.

La Tazona—with Capsian industry.

Cueva de los Tollos—with Capsian industry.

Cueva del Tesoro—with Capsian industry.

There is also the rock shelter of *Monte El Arabi,* near Yecla, discovered by H. Breuil in 1914, with Capsian industry and one laurel-leaf point (?).

ALBACETE

Montealegre—a station in the open near the "Cortijo del Conde," discovered by H. Obermaier in 1916, with Late Palæolithic industry.

Minateda—a station in the open near Hellín, in the Barranco del Canalizo, with Mousterian industry, discovered by H. Breuil in 1916.

ALICANTE

Aspe—a station in the open, with Mousterian industry, discovered by D. Jiménez de Cisneros.

Los Calaveres de Benidoleig—a cave near Denia, with Early Palæolithic industry (one hand ax), and an atypical Late Palæolithic industry, discovered by H. Breuil in 1913.

Cueva del Cuervo—a cave near Ondara, with typical Mousterian industry, discovered by H. Breuil in 1913.

VALENCIA

Cueva del Parpalló—a cave near Gandía, explored by J. Vilanova, E. Boscá, and H. Breuil, containing Capsian industry and a flat stone with the head of a lynx (?) engraved upon it, discovered by Breuil (45) in 1913 (Figure 85).

Las Maravillas (Cova de les Maravelles)—a cave near Gandía, with Capsian industry, discovered by J. Vilanova and H. Breuil.

San Nicolás—a cave near Ollería, explored by E. Boscá, which contains Aurignacian industry.

Cova Negra—a cave near Játiva, explored by J. Vilanova, E. Boscá, and M. Juan, which contains Early Aurignacian industry.

El Collado—a deposit in the open, near Oliva, which contains an atypical Late Palæolithic industry, discovered by E. Boscá.

La Truche (Turche)—a rock shelter near Buñol, with Capsian industry, discovered by H. Breuil in 1913.

TERUEL

Cocinilla del Obispo—a station in the open, near Albarracín, with Capsian industry, discovered by H. Breuil and J. Cabré.

Calapatá—a rock shelter near Cretas, with Late Palæolithic industry, discovered by H. Breuil and J. Cabré.

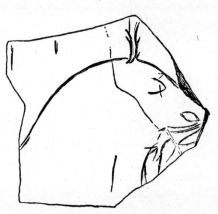

Fig. 85. A flat piece of limestone from the Cueva del Parpalló, engraved with the head of a lynx(?). After H. Breuil.
Actual size.

El Charco del Agua Amarga—a rock shelter near Alcañiz, with Late Palæolithic deposits investigated by J. Cabré in 1914, and by H. Obermaier and P. Wernert in 1919.

Dels Secans—a rock shelter on the Matarraña Brook near Mazaleón. Near this shelter, in 1917, L. Pérez Temprado and J. Cabré found a number of stone implements which seem to be Palæolithic and suggest the Solutrean.

Alcañiz—stations in the open, with traces of the final phases of Late Palæolithic industry, judging from the collection of V. Bardaviu Ponz.

Albalate del Arzobispo—stations in the open, with traces of Palæolithic industry, judging from the collection named above.

TARRAGONA

Constanti (?)—near Tarragona, reported as the discovery site of an Acheulean hand ax, but this is doubtful.

Cogul—a station in the open, near Lérida, with Late Capsian industry, discovered by Ramond Huguet.

Romaní (*Bauma del Fossar Vell*)—a rock shelter near Capellades-Igualada, discovered by Amador Romaní Guerra in 1909, and explored by the same and by L. M. Vidal (46). Stratification as follows:

b Magdalenian deposit, with many implements of flint and a few of bone. The presence of a human thigh bone and of a great number of perforated marine shells (*Cyprœa pyrum, Nassa reticulata, Nassa mutabilis, Neritula neritea, Pleurotoma, Mitra striatula*) gives ground for the supposition that these may be the remains of a Palæolithic sepulture that has been subsequently destroyed. Accompanying fauna—bear, cave hyena, wolf, stag, horse, ibex, wild boar, and rabbit.

a Mousterian deposit which we consider as probably of the Abri Audi type, a cultural phase intermediate between the final Mousterian and the Early Aurignacian. Accompanying fauna —cave hyena, stag, horse, and a species of lynx.

Agut—a site near Capellades-Igualada, discovered by J. Agut in 1910 and explored by A. Romaní Guerra and L. M. Vidal. Part of the material found here appears to be Palæolithic but hardly typical, possibly an atypical Aurignacian (?). Among the specimens are four human teeth of uncertain age.

Caus de les Goyes (*Caus de las Gojas*)—on the river Ter near San Julián de Ramís are two Palæolithic caves which we shall term San Julián de Ramís I and II (47).

No. I, explored in 1898 by M. Palol and F. Viñas, contains rather atypical artefacts, belonging probably to the final Magdalenian and to the Azilian.

No. II, explored in 1916 by M. Pallarés and P. Bosch Gimpera, has been studied by P. Wernert, whose conclusions are as yet unpublished. It contains an important Solutrean industry with laurel-leaf points, typical shouldered points, and also a new regional variant of the shouldered point (Figure 91, *b*). Associated fauna—woolly mammoth, stag, horse, rabbit, and a species of lynx (*pardellus*).

Serinyá (*Bora Gran d'en Carreres*)—near Serinyá-Besalú, discovered in 1866 by J. Catá, and excavated by Pedro Alsius del Torrent (1871), E. Harlé (1881), and others (48), which contains traces of Azilian and, in particular, a fine Magdalenian industry, including a considerable number of bone implements. Among these are harpoons, both with single and double row of barbs, and an awl engraved with conventionalized ibex heads. There are also several modern forgeries in bone. The fauna includes wolf, horse, wild ox, Pyrenean ibex, chamois, stag, reindeer, roe deer, Dama deer, rabbit, wild boar, and a species of lynx (*pardellus*).

Bañolas—where an isolated human lower jaw was discovered, but without any accompanying Palæolithic artefacts (page 288).

PORTUGAL

Up to the present time the Palæolithic stations discovered in Portugal (49) belong almost exclusively to the Early Palæolithic, which seems to be very abundant. The material employed in making the implements is generally quartzite, which makes it often difficult to determine the exact cultural stage. The most important sites are here enumerated.

In Lisbon and its environs are found the stations of *Casal do Monte, Monsanto, Casal das Osgas, Amoreira, Agonia, Boticaria, Estrada de Aguda-Queluz, Minho das Cruces, Bica, Pedreiras, Casal da Serra, Peñas Alvas, Alto do Duque, Santo-Antão-do-Tojal, Zambujal,* and others, containing typical Chellean, Acheulean, and abundant Mousterian implements, according to C. Ribeiro, P. Choffat, Mesquita de Figueiredo, V. Correia, J. Fontes, P. Bouvier-Lapierre, H. Breuil, and other investigators.

The implements are generally found in the open, on the surface of the ground, but in some cases they have been found *in situ*, as, for instance, in the trenches of "Calçada dos Mestres" at Monsanto.

Rabicha—in the valley of Alcantara in the district of

Lisbon, discovered by A. A. da Fonseca Cardoso, contains Chellean (and Acheulean?) industry.

Caldas da Rainha D. Leonor-Obidos—in the district of Leiria, has yielded, according to F. Alves Pereira, both Chellean and Acheulean implements found in the open.

Furninha—a cave in Peniche, Cabo Carvoeiro, in the district of Leiria, explored by N. Delgado. The fauna, according to E. Harlé, includes remains of bear, striped hyena, wildcat, lynx, leopard, and Merck's rhinoceros. Traces of Mousterian industry were found at a depth of thirteen feet, and at twenty-three feet a hand ax of Chellean aspect.

Leiria—where Chellean hand axes have been found by C. Ribeiro, E. Cartailhac, and Tavares Proença.

Mealhada—in the district of Aveiro near Coimbra, discovered by Costa Simoes and studied by C. Ribeiro, N. Delgado, P. Choffat, and J. Fontes, which contains Chellean (Acheulean) hand axes scattered through the alluvial deposits and associated with remains of the straight-tusked elephant, stag, and horse.

In Oporto and its environs—namely, at *Oporto, Paços, Ervilha,* and *Castello do Queijo*—industrial remains of Chellean, Acheulean, and Mousterian type have been found, according to F. de Vasconcellos, C. Ribeiro, and F. Fontes.

Arronches—in the district of Portalegre, where Chellean and Acheulean implements, found for the most part *in situ* embedded in the ancient terrace of the river Caya, were discovered in 1916 by H. Breuil.

Only scanty vestiges of Late Palæolithic industry have been found in Portugal, barely sufficient "to justify the assertion of its existence" (H. Breuil). Certain "indications" of such are found at sites in the open near Lisbon, which might be attributed to an "Aurignacio-Capsian" industry.

Serra dos Molianos—a grotto near Alcobaça, also contains blades of "Late Palæolithic aspect," according to Breuil.

Casa da Moura—grottos near Cesareda which are still more interesting. Here Breuil reports finding, in deposits with fossilized remains of rabbits, fragments of stag horn javelins together with blades, flakes, planing tools, blades

with blunted back, etc., which "seem decidedly Magdalenian." This last word signifies, of course, for this region,
the Late Capsian.

The stations of *Mugem*—in the valley of the Tagus, may
be considered as Tardenoisian (pp. 324-326).

Glancing over the discoveries so far known, we are impressed by the fact that the Early Palæolithic culture was
certainly abundantly distributed throughout the whole
Iberian Peninsula. It is true that, as yet, no Pre-Chellean
deposits have been found, but it is none the less certain that
the presence of typical Chellean industry has been already
demonstrated in the south, at Lake Janda, in the region of
Algeciras, on the banks of the Guadalimar near Puente
Mocho, and at Posadas; in the center, in the region of
Madrid, and at Torralba; and in the west, in Estremadura,
and in Portugal. It is, doubtless, an accident that as yet this
culture has not been found in northern Spain; and it is to
be expected that before long its presence here also will be
demonstrated.

Moreover, there are numerous deposits with Acheulean
industry, and it is not always possible definitely to distinguish this at all the sites from the preceding Chellean
stage. This difficulty is partly due to the fact that at most
of the stations in the open—such as Lake Janda and Puente
Mocho—human occupation has been continuous, resulting
in an intermixture of materials. In other cases the material
chiefly used for the manufacture of artefacts is quartzite,
which is hard to work and often results in coarse and clumsy
forms which are very difficult to distinguish and classify.

Acheulean industry is found in the south in the same
places named above for the Chellean; in the center, in the
environs of Madrid and at the rock shelter of Cerrada de la
Solana; in the west, in Estremadura and in Portugal; and
in the east, at Constanti and at the cave of Benidoleig. In
the north there are the two deposits at Castillo, as well as
Astillero, San Felices de Buelna, Panes, and Posada—their
industry characterized by implements generally large,
clumsy, and more or less either amygdaloid or disc-like in
form.

The Mousterian industry is found in all parts of Spain,

and when it has been investigated and studied in detail it will be possible, in all probability, to distinguish various local phases of its evolution. As a local form we have already drawn attention to the Mousterian quartzite implements at Castillo (Figure 71) and at the cave of Morín—both in the province of Santander—which are not in any sense hand axes, but rather large and comparatively narrow flakes with the under side unworked.

If we consider that the true Chellean is entirely wanting in central Europe, we are driven to the conclusion that this culture reached France and England, not from the east, but from the south. As connecting links between these countries and northern Africa we find Italy and—still more important—Spain. The Strait of Gibraltar was by no means an impassable barrier, as it would have been quite possible to cross it on some primitive kind of raft. The same route was followed by the Acheulean culture, while the Mousterian —in our opinion—reached Spain by way of northern Europe, as has been previously set forth (see pp. 88-90 and Figure 37). This explains why, in many cases, a typical Mousterian industry is found actually intermixed with types of the Late Acheulean, so that here (as also at Saint-Acheul in northern France) the triangular hand ax occurs frequently in Mousterian deposits.

Of special importance in this connection is the fact that the Mousterian industry of Madrid—which has already been the subject of expert and detailed investigation at the sand pit of Sotillo and other sites—presents in certain strata, in addition to the ordinary types of implements found in all Mousterian deposits, fine flint blades and other similar types, such as blades with blunted backs, scrapers, etc. These show a surprising similarity to Late Palæolithic work, although their stratigraphic position indicates that they are much older. This suggests the hypothesis that, on the introduction of the typical Mousterian and contemporary with it, another cultural phase, essentially different from the Acheulean and Mousterian, was already established, at least in certain parts of central and southern Spain. Perhaps it originated in Africa, and it might be designated—provisionally—as "Pre-Capsian," since its typical forms might easily be considered as precursors of the Capsian industry.

Far more complicated, especially in Spain, is the succession of the Late Palæolithic industries. As we have already had occasion to insist (page 114), the Mousterian in northern Africa is followed by the Early Capsian. This Capsian phase is characterized by a mixture of forms belonging to the Early Aurignacian (Châtelperron point) and to the Late Aurignacian (La Gravette point)—forms which in France are found separated by a Middle Aurignacian industry (Figure 86).

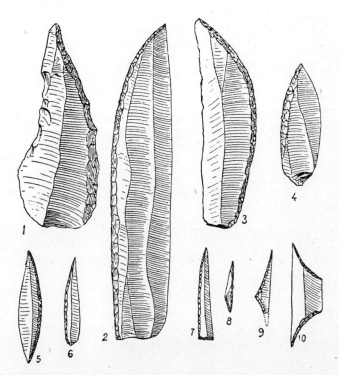

Fig. 86. Capsian implements from Tunis, Africa, showing their course of evolution from the primitive flake with blunted back (1) through forms resembling the types of Châtelperron and La Gravette into the final geometric types. After H. Breuil. Localities: 2, 9 El Mekta. 4, 6 Ain Kerma. 3, 7, 8, 10 Bir Khamfus. 5 Sidi Mansour.

Three-fifths actual size.

13)—a type which also occurs in Spain in the cave of Morín, Asturias. It has a broad, flat, central stem or peduncle, while to the right and left of where this joins the body of the implement the edges are worked into carefully finished points or barbs (Figure 91, *b*). The age and stratigraphic position of this remarkable type are established beyond doubt, although as yet only a few specimens are known.

These two new variants of the shouldered point (pointe à cran), to which we can find only vague resemblances in the industry of southern France, add special interest to the Solutrean industry of Spain, which does not seem to have extended in any marked degree into the center of the Iberian Peninsula. It is true that H. Breuil has reported a few isolated specimens of Solutrean aspect found in Almería at the Cueva Chiquita de los Treinta, and in Murcia at Monte Arabí and the cave of Las Perneras. We do not deny the possibility of occasional infiltrations of Solutrean culture, especially along the Mediterranean coast, but for the present we incline to a cautious scepticism in this respect, since the specimens in question might just as well belong to a Neolithic culture (Figure 90).

The geographic extension of the Magdalenian culture in Spain is practically the same as that of the Solutrean: that is to say, it also was derived from southern France, and extended only into the northern part of the Peninsula. It has been found in the provinces of Guipuzcoa, Vizcaya, Santander, and Asturias. Traces of it have also been found on the southern slope of the Cantabrian Mountains in the cave of La Blanca near Oña, Burgos, and in Catalonia at the cave of Serinyá, Gerona.

The homogeneity of the Magdalenian culture of Spain with that of France is very great, in regard to both the stratigraphic succession and the types of artefacts—including implements of both stone and bone and small objects of primitive art. Naturalistic designs are found in deposits containing harpoons with a single row of barbs at Castillo, and further developed conventionalized designs are found associated with harpoons with a double row of barbs at Cueto de la Mina and Serinyá. Nevertheless, specialized local forms are not lacking. The general use of quartzite is responsible for a number of special forms of stone implements. Of still more importance is the existence of harpoons of Cantabrian type with a lateral perforation at the base (Figures 68 and 75).

Occasion may here be taken to correct the widely accepted but erroneous opinion that the Magdalenian harpoons (of France) were cylindrical in form because they were fashioned of reindeer horn, which is exceedingly dense and compact in texture, and that the Azilian harpoons were necessarily flat because they were made of stag horn, which is too porous and spongy in texture to be fashioned into the rounded cylindrical form. In Spain both the rounded cylindrical harpoons of the Magdalenian and the flattened harpoons of the Azilian are made exclusively of stag horn—a proof that the change of form had nothing to do with the material used in manufacture.

The investigations accomplished in the Cantabrian region have already made it possible to establish a series of stratigraphic subdivisions of the Magdalenian deposits found here (50), which are as follows:

f Layer with no harpoons, and a much impoverished industry in bone. Besides the conical planing tools there are also small round planing tools which might be precursors of the Azilian types.

e Layer containing harpoons with a double row of barbs.

d Layer containing harpoons with a single row of barbs.

c Layer containing large awls, mostly round in cross section.

b Layer containing numerous awls with triangular or quadrangular cross section.

a Layer with primitive industry, including bone points slightly curved and with a *slight* lateral flattening (Figure 92). A similar type is found in the Solutrean, but with a *pronounced* lateral flattening.

Day by day it becomes clearer that Spain is destined to play a most interesting rôle in all that concerns the study of Palæolithic Man. As regards number and riches, its industrial deposits are in no respect inferior to those of France. Its importance increases as we realize the fact that the Iberian Peninsula was a highway and connecting link be-

tween two continents. Here was the meeting place of the two
streams of civilization, from the south and from the north,
where they intermixed and underwent a further evolution.
These facts give ground for the hope that future research
here may achieve results of the highest importance, such as

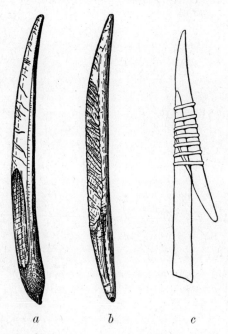

Fig. 92. Curved points of horn with a flattened place on one side. *a*
Solutrean type. *b* Magdalenian type. *c* Supposed manner of use.
Four-fifths actual size.

have already been attained in the domain of Palæolithic Art,
where Spain—with her incomparable treasures in this field
—is well assured of a preëminent place in Europe.

To a description of this art, the following chapter is
devoted.

CHAPTER VII

PALÆOLITHIC ART

IF there is any fact worthy to command the interest of people of culture, it is surely that of the existence of Palæolithic art—an art that, by reason of its antiquity, surpasses in interest the far more recent prehistoric or pro- tohistoric art of both the Orient and the Occident. And this interest is still further enhanced when we consider the high degree of perfection in execution which it often reached, and the fidelity with which it reproduced what was observed in actual life. Moreover, the artistic productions of these re- mote ancestors of ours reveal an advanced artistic senti- ment, in spite of their rudimentary psychology and the poverty of their technical resources and materials.

The first rough sketches indicative of genuine art are found in the late Palæolithic at the beginning of the Auri- gnacian. None the less, judging from the elegance and symmetry of the finest Acheulean hand axes, we can recognize a well-developed sense of proportion even at this early date. Since in Early Palæolithic times man had not yet learned to fashion horn and bone, we cannot hope for the discovery of works of art carved in these materials. But the highly finished execution of the Aurignacian sculptures suggests the idea that during some earlier phase—perhaps outside Europe— wood was worked and sculptures made in some fairly pliant material, possibly modeled in clay. It would, perhaps, not be too venturesome to assume a still earlier phase than the modeling of inorganic material, such as plastic work with the hides or guts of animals.

From the Aurignacian on (page 126) we have evidence of a lavish use of body ornaments, and of the important rôle played by the coiffure. The fact that certain coloring materials (red and yellow ocher) have been found in the most ancient Mousterian deposits, and that various coloring materials have been found in almost all stations of later date, affords reasonable ground for the supposition that these were probably used for the most part in painting the body, and perhaps for tattooing. Judging from the example afforded by primitive peoples now existing, we may assume that this paint was sometimes used purely for adornment, and sometimes as a tribal symbol, as a protective charm to prevent forced migration or kidnaping, or in token of war or mourning.

If we should further seek to investigate other forms of artistic expression, such as song, dance, and music, it will easily be understood that the excavations offer no certain information. Nevertheless, the sketches of dances and masks previously mentioned (pp. 129, 130, and Figure 59) make it probable that some sort of music was produced by very primitive instruments.

The subject here considered, however, is limited to the artistic representations of the Late Palæolithic, with the subdivisions of "mobiliary" and "mural" art—the former including small movable objects bearing ornament or design, and the latter decorations applied to the walls and roofs of caves, rock shelters, and cliffs. This is more or less a distinction without a difference, as the two groups are intimately related (1).

Under the term "mobiliary art" ("art mobilier" of the French) are included sculptures, reliefs, and designs in outline made on stone, horn, bone, or ivory, as well as decorations applied to industrial or ceremonial articles, such as the ceremonial staffs ("bâtons de commandement"), dart throwers, and weapons.

These articles are found, together with faunal remains and the débris of cooking, in undisturbed Palæolithic deposits. Their age is thus established beyond question, rendering unnecessary all discussion in regard to their authenticity and antiquity. Moreover, a great number of these art products bear the stamp of Palæolithic origin in the fact that they are completely fossilized, and that the representations of animals include those which by the close of the Palæolithic had either migrated elsewhere or become extinct, such as the mammoth, reindeer, ibex, Saiga antelope, and others (Figure 11).

This proves that these animals could have been portrayed only when they were still living in the regions of the discovery sites during the Glacial Epoch. Confirming this is the fact that representations of these animals have been found embedded in hearth ashes and detritus associated with skeletal remains of animals of the same species. It is further to be noted that often those very animals that are now extinct or migrated elsewhere, afforded the material for the manufacture of these works of art, this material including even reindeer horn and mammoth ivory, which can be worked to advantage only when fresh. Moreover, it can be shown that in none of the prehistoric or protohistoric periods was there any art development which would present the slightest relationship to this. This entire mass of evidence, both internal and external, goes to prove beyond question the Palæolithic age of this art.

Edouard Piette was the first to demonstrate that sculpture was first to appear during the Late Palæolithic and remained dominant for a considerable period; that somewhat later began the bas-reliefs and figures of animals in outline; while during the Magdalenian stage, engravings

PLATE IX

Reliefs cut in stone, discovered at the rock shelter of Laussel, Dordogne, France. From original photographs by Dr. G. Lalanne. *Left:* Figure of a woman with the horn of a bison in her right hand. *Right:* Figure of a man, apparently in the act of shooting with bow and arrow.

Reduced in size.

were generally the most numerous. This classification, however, must not be understood as absolute. Outline figures are by no means completely lacking in the Late Aurignacian, and both sculptures and reliefs occur in the Magdalenian (2). The universal implement for outlining and engraving was the graving tool (burin) of flint.

The earliest works of mobiliary art in Palæolithic times are human statuettes and reliefs made of stone, which are confined almost exclusively to the Aurignacian (3). The exception consists of the idols of Brünn and Předmost, which belong to the Early Solutrean but nevertheless present strong analogies to the Aurignacian (Figure 50). The plastic representations of animals, however, are found throughout the Late Palæolithic from the Late Aurignacian on. The valuable discoveries made by E. Piette in the Grotte du Pape, Brassempouy, Landes, belong to an early phase of the Aurignacian. Unfortunately they consist only of fragments. Nevertheless, among them is the miniature human head in ivory shown here (Figure 93), which is distinguished by a remarkable headdress, apparently intended to portray either a coiffure or a hood. As to the face, the nose and brows are indicated, and perhaps the eyes and mouth were painted in color. No less remarkable are certain steatopygous feminine figures carved in soapstone, found at Baoussé-Roussé (Grottes de Grimaldi, Mentone), but none of these equals in artistic merit the statuette of Willendorf previously described (Figure 48).

Extraordinary importance attaches to the large reliefs carved in stone, discovered in 1909 by G. Lalanne, in Late Aurignacian deposits at the rock shelter of Laussel, near Marquay, Dordogne. The best represents a nude female form about eighteen inches high, with pronounced steatopygy, which was carved on the side of a huge isolated block of stone. The face is barely indicated, while the body—which was formerly colored red—is portrayed in careful detail. In its right hand the figure holds what looks like the horn of a bison (Plate IX). Two other fragmentary reliefs also portray women, and a third is perhaps intended to show the act of childbirth. As all these reliefs represent women of extreme corpulence, it is quite a contrast to find another figure, eighteen and a half inches in height, representing a tall, well-proportioned man, in which—in spite of the imperfect preservation of the relief—may be recognized the

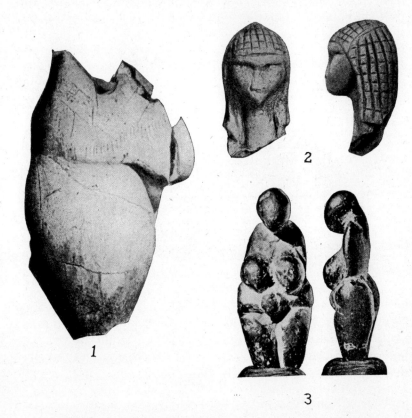

Fig. 93. Human statuettes of Aurignacian age. Torso of a woman (1) and a woman's head (2), both carved in ivory and found at Brassempouy. After E. Piette. Statuette of a woman (3) carved in soapstone, from Mentone. After S. Reinach.
Actual size.

pose of an archer. Of secondary importance is another bas-relief representing two persons, which belongs to the Aurignacian deposits of Terme Pialat near Combe-Capelle, Dordogne.

Almost all the human representations of Aurignacian

may perhaps represent a tattooing of the face; the breasts are pendent and indicated by a number of oval lines; the arms are but meager, as in the idol of Willendorf; the navel is clearly defined, the hips and waist exaggerated, and the

Fig. 100. Geometrically conventionalized female figure engraved on ivory, from the loess discovery site of Předmost. After M. Kříž.
Two-thirds actual size.

two legs much conventionalized in form. The first exact interpretation of this design was given by the present writer.

The extraordinary abundance and development of design attained during this period suggests the idea that the artists of Late Palæolithic times might have produced more ambitious works of art, depicted on the walls of the caves and rock shelters. As a matter of fact, the discoveries of the last twenty years have afforded a great number of instances of this mural art—the "art parietal" of the French. This art consisted of sculptures, fine engravings, and—most important of all—representations in colors which included black, made of carbon or manganese ore, light and deep yellow, orange, red, reddish gray, violet, and terra cotta, made of ocher. Of rare occurrence is white, made of calcined marl, while blue and green are altogether unknown.

The engravings were done partly with fine points and partly with stouter graving tools (burins). The deep contours of the large reliefs in stone seem to have been scraped or hewn out by means of massive stone chisels. Colors were applied either by means of a sharpened pencil of ocher or charcoal, or with a paintbrush. The necessary colors were always ground and were probably blended with fat. This explains why they are frequently found to have actually united with the rock in a chemical combination—a sort of "fossilization"—which has contributed most favorably to their preservation.

The sites where this Palæolithic mural art is to be found, so far as our present knowledge goes, are limited exclusively to western Europe. The credit of the discoveries in France will be imperishably associated with the names of Bégouen, Breuil, Capitan, Cartailhac, Lalanne, Peyrony, Regnault, and Rivière. In Spain, where this art is even more abundant and of greater importance, the principal explorations have been made by Alcalde del Río, H. Breuil, J. Cabré, J. Carballo, E. Hernández-Pacheco, F. de Motos, H. Obermaier, M. de Sautuola, P. Serrano, L. Sierra, Count de la Vega del Sella, W. Verner, and P. Wernert. The first systematic and scientific investigation of these discoveries—both in France and Spain—is due to H. Breuil, whose splendid work, most effectively supported by the munificence of Prince Albert of Monaco, has supplied a solid foundation for future investigations.

The following list enumerates those caves and rock

shelters in France where examples of this mural art have been found.‡

DORDOGNE

*La Mouthe—discovered in 1894 by E. and G. Berthou-meyrou; studied by E. Rivière (7).

***Les Combarelles—discovered in 1901 by D. Peyrony; studied by H. Breuil, L. Capitan, and D. Peyrony (8) (Figures 14, 15, 59, d and e).

***Font-de-Gaume—discovered in 1901 by D. Peyrony; fully described by H. Breuil in an exhaustive monograph (9) (Figures 9, 12, 19, c, 104, m and n).

*Bernifal ⎫ —discovered in 1903 by D. Peyrony, and de-
Calévie ⎬   scribed by H. Breuil, L. Capitan, and D.
*Teyjat ⎭   Peyrony (10).

*La Grèze—reported in 1904 by M. Ampoulange; studied by H. Breuil and L. Capitan (11).

La Croze de Gontran—discovered in 1908 by the Abbé Vidal; verified by H. Breuil.

***Cap-Blanc—discovered in 1909 by G. Lalanne (12) (Figure 106).

Gorge d'Enfer—1912.

*Grotte de Comarque—discovered in 1915 by H. Breuil and P. Paris (13).

*Grotte Nancy—idem.

Grotte de Beyssac—discovered in 1915 by H. Breuil.

GIRONDE

Pair-non-Pair—discovered in 1883; its scientific value recognized in 1896 by F. Daleau (14).

HAUTE-GARONNE

**Marsoulas—discovered in 1897 by F. Regnault and L. Jammes; studied by E. Cartailhac and H. Breuil (15).

HAUTES-PYRÉNÉES

**Gargas—discovered in 1906 by F. Regnault; a new gallery discovered in 1910 by H. Breuil; studied by H. Breuil and E. Cartailhac (16).

‡ The relative importance is indicated as follows: *** a site of the foremost importance; ** a site of considerable importance; * a site of secondary importance. Unimportant sites are not starred.

Mas d'Azil—discovered in 1902 by H. Breuil; further investigated by E. Cartailhac in 1908, and by Count Bégouen in 1912 (17).

***Niaux*—discovered in 1906 by L. Molard; studied by E. Cartailhac and H. Breuil (18) (Figures 104, *d, e,* and 120).

Bédeilhac and *Pradières*—both discovered in 1907 by E. Cartailhac, H. Breuil, and H. Obermaier.

**Le Portel*—discovered in 1908 by R. Jeannel and L. Jammes; studied by H. Breuil (19).

***Tuc d'Audoubert*—discovered by Count Bégouen in 1912 (20).

***Caverne des Trois Frères*—discovered in 1914 by Count Bégouen (21) (Figure 103).

Isturitz—discovered in 1913 by E. Passemard.

Chabot—discovered in 1878; reported by L. Chiron in 1889; further investigated by the same, together with L. Capitan, in 1910.

In Spain (22) the mural art of Palæolithic times is widely distributed. In the Cantabrian region—in the northwest—it is found at the following sites.

**Basondo* (*Santimamiñe*)—a cave near Cortézubi in the district of Guernica, discovered in 1917 by Jesus Guridi.

Venta de la Perra—a cave near Molinar de Carranza, discovered in 1904 by L. Sierra.

La Sotarriza—a cave near Molinar de Carranza, discovered in 1906 by L. Sierra.

La Haza—a cave near Ramales, discovered in 1903 by L. Sierra and H. Alcalde del Río.

**Covalanas*—a cave near Ramales, discovered in 1903 by L. Sierra and H. Alcalde del Río (23).

Salitre—a cave near Ajanedo in the district of Miera, discovered in 1903 by L. Sierra.

PLATE X

The "Cueva de los Caballos" (—>) or "Horses'
Cave" in the Barranco de Valltorta near Albocácer, Castellón. From an original photograph by
the author.

species of animals pictured during certain phases. His view is chiefly based on the evidence afforded by the Spanish sites—where, for instance, at Altamira ibexes are most frequent in the oldest pictures and stags are shown only very occasionally in the latest, while the skeletal remains of both species are most abundant in archæologic deposits belonging to the very close of the Palæolithic. In making their pictures, the artists of these caves certainly exercised a choice of subjects which may be explained through the motive of a magic propitious to the hunt. It would thus be a more probable conclusion to infer that the species pictured comprised exactly those whose scarcity at the time—at least in certain localities—was a matter for concern.

Among the most important sites of France is the cave of Font-de-Gaume, near Les Eyzies, Dordogne. It contains many fine paintings of the highest order, most of which, unfortunately, are badly damaged or faded. Pictures of bison, reindeer, ibex, wild horse, and mammoth are abundant, and there are also occasional pictures of rhinoceros, bear, wolf, and cave lion (Figures 9, 12, 19, and 104). In contrast to this, the neighboring cave of Combarelles is devoted almost exclusively to engravings. These comprise chiefly representations of mammoth, wild horse, reindeer, bison, and ibex; but there are also a few showing the cave lion, wolf, and bear (Figure 14, 15, 59). Besides these there are a number of anthropomorphic figures which are strikingly grotesque (48). Equally important with these sites are the two caves of Tuc d'Audoubert (Figure 97) and the Caverne des Trois Frères, both near Saint-Girons, Ariège, and not far from Montesquieu-Avantès. The Caverne des Trois Frères —in addition to hand silhouettes, finger tracings, and primitive engravings of the Aurignacian time—contains extensive ensembles of Magdalenian engraving, which depict chiefly bison and wild horse, but which also include cave lion, rhinoceros, mammoth, cave bear, and reindeer. Among the anthropomorphic designs is one resembling a human figure with a rather long tail and stag's antlers on its head (Figure 103).

The mural art at the rock shelter of Cap-Blanc, not far from Les Eyzies, bears witness to the existence of truly monumental sculpture. On a face of rock that has been excavated for a length of about fifty feet, there are a number of high reliefs hewn in the limestone, which include a reindeer, several bison, and some splendid wild horses, life size (Figure 106).

In no wise inferior in importance to the art stations of southern France are those of northern Spain. Here, near Santillana del Mar, Santander, is the cave of Altamira, which has been not inaptly termed the "Sistine Chapel of Palæolithic Art." The great "hall" near the entrance contains—besides a number of older pictures—a whole series of polychrome paintings of bison, horses, hinds, and wild boars, most of which are in an excellent state of preservation and bear witness to a truly remarkable art development. A number of the bison pictures have been painted, with striking effect, on the natural curves and bosses of the low stone roof of the cave—a daring device which gives a lifelike relief to the figures (Plate I).

A visitor to the cave of Pasiega, near Puente Viesgo, Santander, is impressed—more than in most other caves— by the conviction that Palæolithic mural art was certainly not designed to serve purposes of decoration or mere amusement. This cave consists of a labyrinth of low and generally narrow clefts, and contains over two hundred and fifty paintings and engravings, which include stag and hind, wild horse, wild cattle, bison, ibex, and chamois, with tectiforms and similar designs. These belong, almost entirely, to Aurignacian and Early Magdalenian time, and therefore, for the most part, are simple outline pictures. They are placed by preference in the remotest clefts and crannies of a cave that, itself, is most difficult of access. One of the few larger chambers has a sort of "throne"—quite unmistakable—hewn out of the rock, and on it was found a worked stone implement. All this serves to deepen the impression that the rites of some secret, mysterious cult must have been celebrated here (Plate XI, Figure 104).

The region of eastern and southeastern Spain presents an equally realistic style of art, its peculiar characteristic being the occurrence of human representations (Figures 53-55, 107-112, 114-118, and Plates XII-XV). These show a

action. This type we have styled the "nematomorphic" type (Figures 108, 115, 117). Approaching this is the "cestoso-matic" type, in which the head is more or less ovaloid and rests on a broad, almost triangular breast extended into a long and very slender torso. The legs are long and stout,

Fig. 108. Human figures of the "nematomorphic" type, from the shelter of Los Caballos, Castellón, painted in dark red.
Reduced in size.

Fig. 109. Human figures of the "pachypodal" (?) type, from the
shelter of Los Caballos, Castellón, painted in dark red.
Reduced in size.

with calves prominent and carefully defined (Plate XIII). Finally, we may note the "pachypodal" type with comparatively short figure, large and generally angular head, short slender torso, and legs stout but not excessively long (Figures 109, 118).

The majority of the figures are naked and portray male figures with the body form, arms, and ornaments clearly indicated. It is only occasionally that figures are found showing very short "breeches" reaching barely to the knee (Els Secans). Female figures are of very rare occurrence, and are almost invariably clad in skirts (Plate XII, Figure 110). It is evident that the Palæolithic artists sought to

Fig. 110. Female figures from the principal shelter at Alpera, Albacete, painted in dark red.
One-third actual size.

portray typical human figures, but, nevertheless, they made no effort to portray the individual details, especially the features of head and face. One of the rare exceptions to this rule is reproduced in Figure 111. It is therefore impossible to base on these paintings any definite idea of the appearance and physical peculiarities of these Capsian peoples,

Fig. 111. Human figure from the shelter of Saltadora, Castellón, painted in dark red.
Actual size.

and it would be still more ill-judged to draw conclusions therefrom in regard to their skull form and other racial characteristics.

The animal pictures of this region are, for the most part, equally small, and comprise the following species. Representations of the stag (Plates XII, XIV, XV; Figure 113), ibex (Plate XII), and wild ox (Plate XII, Figure 17, *a*) are very abundant; less frequent are those of the wild horse, wild boar (Figure 112), and various Canidæ (jackals?); while those of the Dama deer and moose (both at Alpera and Minateda), of the rhinoceros (at Minateda), of the chamois (at Tortosillas), and of the wild ass (at Albarracín —Figure 119) are exceedingly rare. In addition there are pictures of geese and cranes (or storks?) as well as one of a fish—all at Minateda. The occurrence of the bison (at Cogul), and of bear, lion, reindeer, and Saiga antelope (at Minateda) seems rather doubtful.

Of especial interest is the painted rock shelter of Cogul, Lérida, where—besides several realistic animal figures and a number of geometrically conventionalized Epipalæolithic paintings—there is a group representing nine women. The

PLATE XII

Ensemble painting on the walls of the rock shelter of Cogul, Lérida. After J. Cabré.
About one-twelfth actual size.

are buzzing around the intruder, and are represented on a much larger scale than that of the human figure.

Finally, there are the numerous painted rock shelters of the Barranco de Valltorta, a wild, romantic gorge lying

Fig. 116. Rock-painting in red at the Cuevas de la Araña, Bicorp, representing a gatherer of wild honey. After an original copy made by W. K. (1921).

Actual size.

between Albocácer and Tirig, Castellón, which are of prime importance. In the Abrigo del Civil there are various human figures that attract special notice, being little more than linear indications (''nematomorphic'' type—Figure 117). Two of these are waving bundles of bows and arrows above their heads; the legs are wide apart; and the beholder is strongly impressed with the idea that this picture portrays

a weapon or war dance. Another interesting ensemble picture is reproduced in Plate XIII. It consists of numerous
figures of warriors or hunters, belonging chiefly to the
"cestosomatic" type. The figures, which apparently are
quite unrelated and do not form a group composition, present a really remarkable variety of pose and action. Somewhat farther south, in the same Barranco de Valltorta, is

Fig. 117. "War dance" of archers of "nematomorphic" type, painted
in black in the principal shelter of the Cuevas del Civil, Castellón.
Three-fifths actual size.

the small cave known as Cueva dels Tolls, with representations of animal tracks; and also the important Cueva de los
Caballos (Plate X). This last contains a notable number of
interesting paintings, among them numerous hunters of the
"nematomorphic" type (Figure 108) and others of the
"pachypodal" type (Figure 109). Very lifelike is the representation of a stag hunt (Plate XIV), the right-hand part
of which, however, is obscured by a stalagmitic deposit. To
the left, four hunters in various poses are seen showering
arrows upon a herd of stags and hinds with two young ones.
The fact that the animals are running toward their pursuers
leads to the conclusion that behind the herd—at least sup-
posably—there must be a number of armed beaters, a conclusion confirmed by the fact that there are several arrows
sticking in the hind parts of the animals.

An equally interesting hunting scene is that painted in
the neighboring cave of Mas d'en Josep (Plate XV). The

shown in our chronologic tables (pp. 237, 238, see also pp. 258, 259), the earliest art of both regions consists of rather clumsy and primitive figures, followed by monochrome linear designs. Later come paintings in uniform plain color, or partly in line shading; and, finally, the semipolychrome and polychrome representations.

The Palæolithic age of the realistic paintings of eastern Spain is further confirmed by the fact that among the animals portrayed there are many species which, ever since then, have been entirely extinct in France and the Iberian Peninsula. Among these are the moose,[1] of which there are a number of pictures in the Cueva del Queso at Alpera, and at Minateda; the wild ass, portrayed in the rock shelter of Fuente del Cabrerizo, Albarracín (Figure 119); and the rhinoceros, at Minateda. On the other hand, the identification of certain paintings at Cogul as two bison is probable but not certain (Plate XII). Besides these, pictures of the ibex are very frequent, a fact to be attributed to the cool climate of post-glacial times.

It cannot be denied that this list of extinct species is very short; but then, even in the Cantabrian region—which presents an absolute uniformity with southern France—species that are exclusively Pleistocene (except the bison, which is abundant everywhere) are of very rare occurrence, although the mammoth, woolly rhinoceros, and reindeer are known to have existed there. It is, therefore, not very surprising to find a similar scarcity in eastern Spain. Moreover, it must not be forgotten that the object of these Palæolithic artists was certainly not to supply a complete compendium of contemporary mammals pictured for the benefit of future ages. The animal pictures found in the caves of France very rarely include beasts of prey, but chiefly portray the most preferred animals of the chase. Even among these—especially in the various regions of Spain—there seems to have been a rather limited selection of subjects, determined apparently by psychologic motives which will be discussed later.

Further evidence of the indubitable Palæolithic age of these paintings is furnished by various palæoethnical considerations. Thus, any suggestion of the peaceful life of Neolithic herdsmen and agriculturists is conspicuously lacking. Their entire scenic scope is primitive, and very typical of the life of Palæolithic hunters and nomads. Except for a few "dances," the groups pictured portray only hunting and battle scenes. The men are shown nude, with bow and arrow for their only weapons; and it is surely through no mere chance that the arrows pictured at Alpera have points slanting out from one side of the shaft, unmistakably similar to the flattened points of stag horn found exclusively in Solutrean and Magdalenian deposits in Santander and Asturias (Figures 55, 92). In certain rock recesses of eastern Spain—such as the Cueva dels Tolls in the Barranco de Valltorta and the rock shelter of Morella la Vella, both in Castellón (Figure 114)—there are pictures of animal tracks. Similar ones are found in the cave of La Pileta, Málaga, and—a point of special importance—among those very pictures which, beyond question, are of Palæolithic age.

The adornment pictured in the realistic human figures on head, neck, back, and middle, as well as on arms and legs (Figures 53, 55), is typically Palæolithic (50). It is also essentially similar to the remains of ornaments of shells, horn, etc., found embedded by the head, middle, and extremities of the Palæolithic skeletons discovered at Laugerie-Basse, the Grotte des Enfants, the Grotte du Cavillon, and other sites.

Since these rock shelters are only shallow recesses, their floor almost always consists only of bare rock where no archæologic deposits have been made, or preserved. But in the exceptional cases when flint implements have been found within or directly at the foot of such shelters, they are almost always of Palæolithic type, as, for instance, at Cogul, Charco del Agua Amarga, Calapatá, the Barranco de Valltorta, and Els Secans.

Conclusive evidence of the Palæolithic age of these paintings is furnished by the direct stratigraphic succession of the pictures themselves. As previously noted, both in the north and in the east of the Iberian Peninsula it is not uncommon to find, in one and the same spot, successive layers of pictures painted one on top of another, which in many cases has made it possible to subdivide them into chronologic phases. It is a fact of no small importance that in

PLATE XIV

The stag hunt—a mural painting in dark red (restored), in the "Cueva de los
Caballos" (see Plate X), near Albocácer, Castellón.
Reduced in size.

signs common in the north, such as the "tectiforms" and the hand silhouettes, should be entirely lacking here. This lack is more than balanced by the important representations of the human figure, and the surprising scenic compositions— both entirely lacking in the Franco-Cantabrian region.

It has already been remarked what surprising similarities are found between these Capsian paintings and those in South Africa which are commonly ascribed to the Bushmen, and which certainly, for the most part, are very old.

This Capsian art, too, passed through a long course of evolution, as is clearly shown by numerous "palimpsests" —namely, by means of the direct superposition of successive layers of pictures.

Profiting by private data supplied through the courtesy of H. Breuil, it is possible, in the light of our present knowledge, to distinguish six evolutionary phases which show an unmistakable parallelism with the evolutionary phases of the Franco-Cantabrian region.

I. EARLY CAPSIAN—*First Phase,* equivalent to the Aurignacian.

Characterized by small figures, very primitive and incorrect, some realistic and some linear and with a tendency to conventionalism.

II. EARLY CAPSIAN—*Second Phase,* equivalent to the Solutrean (?).

Principally monochrome, linear paintings, of a decidedly realistic conception.

III. LATE CAPSIAN—*First Phase,* equivalent to the Early Magdalenian.

Principally full-length pictures in a uniform monochrome of very good style and technique. Later: Linear drawings, sometimes with interior line-shading.

IV. LATE CAPSIAN—*Second Phase,* equivalent to the Middle Magdalenian.

Monochrome pictures, partly shaded.

V. LATE CAPSIAN—*Third Phase,* equivalent to the Late Magdalenian.

Semipolychrome and polychrome paintings (Cogul, Albarracín, Minateda, Lavederos de Tello).

PLATE XV

The stag hunt—a mural painting in dark red, in the "Cueva del Mas d'en Josep" near Albocácer, Castellón.
Reduced in size.

VI. LATE CAPSIAN—*Fourth Phase,* equivalent to the Transition to
the Epipalæolithic.
Decadence to more and more geometrically conventionalized
pictures.

As yet, no sites with paintings of certain Palæolithic age
are known in western Spain.

In southern Spain, however, there is a most instructive
and important site—the cave of Pileta near Benaoján,
Málaga. It is very difficult of access, and its widely branching
passages contain realistic pictures of animals—among them
being wild horses, stags, ibexes, wild oxen, and fishes, as
well as a bison and, possibly, a rhinoceros. They show striking similarity to the zoömorphic paintings of the Cantabrian
region, in part resembling the Aurignacian style found
there, and in part an archaic Magdalenian. The tectiforms
and similar signs and dotted forms sometimes coincide with
typical northern designs, and sometimes are original and
new. Especially noteworthy are certain pictures that appear
to represent traps, with clearly defined animal tracks inside
them (Figure 114). There are other minor correspondences
with the style of eastern Spain—a number of details that
lead to the inference that Andalusia was the center of a truly
remarkable "hybrid" form of mural art, and awaken the
hope that later discoveries may afford grounds for deter-
mining its importance and significance. Passing mention
may be made of the most recent layer of pictures in this cave,
with their purely geometrically conventionalized designs of
Neolithic or Eneolithic age. An extended description of
these, however, does not fall within the scope of the present
chapter.

In proceeding to discuss the psychologic background of
Palæolithic art we are forced to abandon the domain of exact
scientific investigation and to venture into the realm of
theory and hypothesis.

It is obvious that among the producers of these works—
both of mobiliary and of mural art—there were a number of
true artists who were not only sharp observers and splendid
draughtsmen, but were also gifted with a deep sense of
beauty and with the skill to portray it. Nevertheless, we

cannot suppose that they followed "art for art's sake." This applies equally to a considerable number of the objects of mobiliary art which arouse the conviction that some must be idols or fetiches, and that others, again, were fashioned to serve purposes near akin, connected with beliefs in magic or totemism. A number of writers have entertained this theory, among them Bernardin (1876), Andrew Lang (1882), S. Reinach, E. Cartailhac, H. Breuil, and others. (See also page 129.) The study of the mural art of the caves leads to similar conclusions. The mural paintings are by no means to be found in all the caves inhabited during the Glacial Epoch, even though they may offer surfaces excellently adapted for decoration. On the contrary, the painted caves are, comparatively speaking, few in number, and most of them are not habitable, or at least are very difficult of access, as, for instance, Combarelles, Font-de-Gaume, Portel, La Pasiega, and Buxu. Others, again, were indeed inhabited near the entrance, but paintings of the same age were hidden in dark and remote recesses, as, for example, in the cave of Castillo. The entrance chamber of the cave of Altamira contains abundant deposits of Solutrean and Early Magdalenian industry, while the imposing polychrome paintings in the great hall close by belong to the Late Magdalenian. The cave, therefore, was not inhabited at the time when the famous ceiling received its principal decoration. In other caves also it has been found that the mural paintings are not contemporary with the industrial deposits, but are of either earlier or later date. Thus the industrial deposit at Marsoulas—to cite but one instance—contains chiefly the bones of reindeer, an animal not once portrayed in the various animal pictures of this cave.

We must therefore dismiss any idea that the purpose and character of these paintings are merely decorative, and this conclusion is further strengthened by the fact that in many cases they are limited to the remotest crannies and clefts, wrapped in utter darkness, and only to be found with the greatest pains. Of many of the engravings it may be said without exaggeration that they are actually invisible and were designed by their makers for the eyes, not of men, but of gods.

CHAPTER VIII

GEOLOGIC CHRONOLOGY OF PALÆOLITHIC INDUSTRIES IN EUROPE

Introduction—Systems of chronology for the Alpine region—Chronologic system of A. Penck—Chronologic table of A. Penck—Critique of Penck's system of chronology—Chronologic system of H. Obermaier—Chronologic table of H. Obermaier—Systems of chronology for northern Germany—Chronologic system of F. Wiegers—Chronologic table of F. Wiegers—Critique of Wieger's system of chronology—Stratigraphy and chronology of southern Europe—Spain—Stratigraphic succession of industries and fauna at Castillo—"Cold" fauna at other sites in Spain— "Cold" fauna in the Riviera—Conclusions.

HAVING studied the order of succession of the various stages of Palæolithic industry—from Pre-Chellean to Magdalenian—we now find ourselves obliged to seek a solution of the interesting problem of synchronizing these stages with the geologic stages of the Glacial Epoch. In this we make no pretense of discussing the "geologic age of man," since the scope of this inquiry is limited to Europe—a continent which, in the light of careful research, can hardly be considered as the possible cradle of humanity. As yet, however, it is only here that our knowledge of the glacial deposits and the archæologic stratigraphy of the Glacial Epoch is sufficient to justify an attempt at geologic chronology. In those regions where there are no glacial deposits, the character of the fauna of the archæologic deposits is in many cases sufficient to afford a trustworthy conclusion in regard to the climate, and thus to connect them with certain glacial or interglacial stages. (See Chapter II and pp. 378-403, especially the chronologic systems on pp. 27, 28, 29, 381.) It is clear that in this undertaking we need consider only the most recent theories, based upon modern geologic stratigraphy.

We will first consider those chronologic systems based upon a study of the Alpine region. The first important attempt at a systematic chronology of this region is due to

A. Penck (1903, 1909). Starting with the fact that a considerable number of Magdalenian deposits—such as those at Schussenquelle, Kesslerloch, Schweizersbild, Veyrier, Les Hôteaux, and others—are within the terminal moraines of the final great glaciation (Würm), he rightly claimed that the Magdalenian belongs to the Post-glacial Stage. And since, up to the present time, Mousterian deposits have been found only outside the Riss moraines, which are much farther from the Alpine "massif," he concludes that the Mousterian industry was synchronous with the Third Glacial Stage. According to him, this applies only to the Mousterian with cold fauna, for he admits that there was also a more recent Mousterian with warm fauna, which is represented in the gravels of Villefranche, beyond Lyons, by flints of Mousterian type associated with remains of Merck's rhinoceros. This latter phase he places in the first (warm) half of the last Interglacial Stage, while in the second (cool) half—the steppe phase—he places the Aurignacian and Solutrean, which are well represented in the loess of Lower Austria and Moravia. In consequence, this loess would be only of interglacial age. Thus the Chellean would have to be placed at least as far back as the Second Interglacial Stage, which results in the following table.

CHRONOLOGIC TABLE OF A. PENCK

Post-glacial Stage	
b Bühl Advance ⎫ *a* Achen Retreat ⎭	Magdalenian
IV. Fourth Glacial Stage (Würm)	
3 Third Interglacial Stage	
b Steppe phase ⎫ *a* Forest phase ⎭	Aurignacian and Solutrean Warm Mousterian
III. Third Glacial Stage (Riss) 2 Second Interglacial Stage	Cold Mousterian Chellean
II. Second Glacial Stage (Mindel) 1 First Interglacial Stage ⎫ I. First Glacial Stage (Günz) ⎭	No vestiges of Palæolithic industry

This system of chronology was accepted—either wholly or with certain reservations—by J. Geikie, H. Menzel, J. Bayer, and others.[1]

From the table above reproduced we must first eliminate

the "warm Mousterian" of Villefranche-sur-Saône. The
present author, after a careful examination made at the site,
is convinced that the remains of Merck's rhinoceros found
here are extremely fossilized and, for the most part, waterworn, thus showing that they must have been transported
hither; while the remains of mammoth, reindeer, and bison
are much better preserved and not eroded, as is also the case
with the Mousterian implements found here. It follows that
these latter were indeed contemporary, and therefore that
the industry of Villefranche is simply a "cold" Mousterian,
whose geologic age cannot be exactly determined from its
location on the banks of the Saône. We must strongly insist
that in western and central Europe there is no true Mousterian with warm fauna. Such a fauna is found only in the
Pre-Chellean, Chellean, and Early Acheulean (pp. 66, 68,
69, 72, 78), for, from the Late Acheulean on, we find a cold
fauna which lasts through the final Magdalenian. Indubitable Mousterian with warm fauna is found only in
southern Europe—as in Italy (Mentone) and Spain—where
then and ever since the climate and fauna naturally would
be different.[2]

As we have remarked, the post-glacial age of the Magdalenian is proved beyond question in the Alpine region,
where, on the other hand, absolutely no deposits of Solutrean or Aurignacian are known. As to the Mousterian, it is
with pleasure that we record a very recent discovery in the
caves of Cotencher in the gorges of the Areuse, Neuchâtel,
Switzerland, where H. G. Stehlin and A. Dubois have found
an early (?) Mousterian deposit in direct contact with the
moraines of the last glaciation of Rodano, about five-eighths
of a mile within the limits of the terminal moraine. With
these new data, it becomes possible to connect the Mousterian of central Europe definitely with the Fourth (Würm)
Glacial Stage, and to assign a date for the Mousterian culture anterior in part to the maximum of that glaciation. (In
regard to the deposit at Wildkirchli, which is not in contact
with any glacial deposits, see page 85.)

Two Acheulean deposits are also known—one at Conliège,
near Lons-le-Saulnier, Jura, where two hand axes, described
by M. Boule, were found within the glacial area. They were

embedded in a clay which is certainly more recent than the glacial deposits of the district, which are attributed by A. Penck to the Third (Riss) Glacial Stage.

In 1887 C. Tardy described a lanceolate hand ax corresponding to the type of the Late Acheulean. It was found in the neighborhood of Challes de Bohan, near Hautecour, Ain, where indeed there must have been a veritable workshop, as five others, which have since been lost, were found at the same site. It was found *in situ,* embedded in red clay, beneath which was glacial detritus belonging—according to the investigations of A. Penck—to the Riss glaciation. It is, therefore, impossible to assign the Acheulean to a date previous to the Third (Riss) Glacial Stage, and consequently it must be placed in the Third Interglacial Stage.

To this same interglacial stage must be assigned the fauna in which the straight-tusked elephant appears for the last time, such as that of Flurlingen with Merck's rhinoceros, and that of Dürnten with Merck's rhinoceros and the straight-tusked elephant (page 399).

This fauna agrees absolutely with that characteristic of the climate of the Chellean and of the Early Acheulean (pp. 68, 69, 72). On this account we place those two industries in the early and warm phase of the Third Interglacial Stage. The Pre-Chellean is excluded from this stage by the characteristic occurrence of the trogontherian mammoth, Etruscan rhinoceros, saber-tooth tiger (*Elephas trogontherii, Rhinoceros etruscus, Machairodus*), and others (page 66), a fauna which agrees surprisingly with that of the Second Interglacial Stage (page 396).

These correspondences indicate, we believe, the chronologic position which should be assigned to the Pre-Chellean, Chellean, and Acheulean industries of central and western Europe. Here, as already shown, the "cold fauna" begins with the Late Acheulean and lasts through the Magdalenian —that is to say, into the Post-glacial Stage. Studies by E. Koken, based on the excavations of R. R. Schmidt, go to show that two phases of maximum cold may be distinguished in this cold fauna, during which an Arctic microfauna—with the lemming as its principal element—appears in the caves of Swabia. The latest maximum of cold coincides with Early

Magdalenian deposits which are certainly post-glacial, and consequently must be identified with the Bühl advance (page 28). The first maximum is indicated in these caves by deposits intervening between Late Mousterian and Early Aurignacian industrial deposits, and can therefore be identified with the Fourth (Würm) Glacial Stage. From all this may be deduced the following chronologic table, the principal features of which were established some time ago by the present author.

CHRONOLOGIC TABLE OF H. OBERMAIER

Post-glacial Stage	
b Bühl Advance	Magdalenian
a Achen Retreat	{ Solutrean { Late Aurignacian
IV. Fourth Glacial Stage (Würm)	{ Early Aurignacian { Late Mousterian
3 Third Interglacial Stage	
c Steppe phase	{ Early Mousterian { Late Acheulean
b Forest phase	{ Early Acheulean { Late Chellean
a Steppe phase	?
III. Third Glacial Stage (Riss)	Early Chellean?
2 Second Interglacial Stage	Pre-Chellean
II. Second Glacial Stage (Mindel)	
1 First Interglacial Stage	No indications of man's presence
I. First Glacial Stage (Günz)	

As a result of this classification, and in opposition to Penck's view, we must consider the latest loess deposit to be wholly post-glacial in age. This is indicated by the fact that various loess deposits in the Alpine region—such as those near Berg and Fischbach in the valley of the Inn—are found within the limits of the Würm moraines. Furthermore, there are the industrial stations of Munzingen in Baden and of Gobelsburg in Lower Austria. Both of these are situated in the "recent loess" and belong to the Magdalenian, an industry which is unquestionably much more recent than the Fourth Glacial Stage (pp. 34, 35). E. Koken has come to a similar conclusion, based on his studies of the loess deposits of Würtemberg and its vicinity.

STRATIGRAPHIC SUCCESSION OF INDUSTRIES AND FAUNA AT CASTILLO

4 Most recent prehistoric deposits and
   Neolithic
   Azilian
   Late Magdalenian
	With present fauna

3 Early Magdalenian
   Solutrean
   Late Aurignacian
	With reindeer, although rare

2 Early Aurignacian
   Mousterian
   Acheulean
	With warm fauna. Of characteristic
	and frequent occurrence is Merck's
	rhinoceros

1 Atypical industry Base	Clay of the caves with cave bear and reindeer occurring rarely

The presence of the northern reindeer on the Cantabrian coast is convincing proof of the contemporary existence of a glacial stage. According to the investigations made in the Alpine region, the upper levels with reindeer remains in the cave of Castillo should coincide with the latest glacial stage (Würm) and, in part, with the post-glacial Bühl Advance. It follows, consequently, that those deposits with warm fauna that lie below—namely, the Early Aurignacian, Mousterian, and Acheulean—must belong to the latest interglacial stage, and the still earlier deposits with reindeer remains would correspond to the Third (Riss) Glacial Stage. Unfortunately, the stage of human industry which corresponds to these deposits cannot be positively identified. All we can say is that it is "pre-Acheulean" and not improbably contemporary with the Chellean culture (Figure 122).

In full agreement with these conclusions from the stratigraphic succession of deposits at the cave of Castillo, is the occurrence of mammoth remains in Solutrean deposits at San Julián de Ramís, Gerona (page 198, Ch. VI), and at Cueto de la Mina, Asturias (page 174, Ch. VI). In Solutrean and Magdalenian deposits at this latter site there are also found shells of the Arctic molluscs *Pecten islandicus* (Figure 121) and *Cyprina islandica*. We may also note the comparative frequency of reindeer remains in the Magdalenian deposits of Valle in Santander, Armiña in Vizcaya, Aïtzbitarte in Guipuzcoa, and Serinyá in Gerona (page 148).

CHAPTER IX

FOSSIL MAN

THE investigations of the last few years have greatly
increased the number of human remains dating from
the Glacial Epoch known in Europe; while, on the
other hand, the number accepted as authentic in other continents has been much reduced. In spite of this, it is believed
that the cradle of humanity is to be found outside Europe—
where far fewer investigations have been made—and that it
is there that we may hope for the discovery of remains of
the true ancestors of man.

Even the European discoveries require a severely critical discrimination, for in earlier times skeletal remains of man were reported as embedded in deposits of the Glacial Epoch when, in reality, they belonged to sepultures of later date excavated in such deposits, or else to discoveries made in disturbed ground. We will first enumerate all those skeletal remains which are proved beyond question to belong to the Glacial Epoch, and will discuss later the date which should be assigned to them. Even though we feel obliged to eliminate a number of discoveries as "uncertain," this does not mean that it is impossible that they belong to the Glacial Epoch. The further study of anthropology may make it possible—if not now, then at some future time—to reëstablish more than one of these fossils as Palæolithic, although at present what is known of their situation and stratigraphic position is not sufficient to determine their age.

Of the countries of western Europe, it is France that has the greatest number of human fossils, although so far none are known belonging to the Pre-Chellean, Chellean, or Acheulean industrial stages. The oldest skeleton would be that of Le Moustier, Dordogne, provided that it really was embedded in the Early Mousterian deposits of this site, and not in the layers with the "Abri Audi" type of industry (p. 95, Chapter IV). This latter industry was also present in the deposits at Le Moustier, although apparently O. Hauser failed to recognize it. The skeleton—poorly preserved—is that of an individual about sixteen years old, and belongs to the Museum of Ethnology in Berlin. The skull is somewhat more satisfactory since its latest restoration, but it would seem that only the lower jaw is in such a state as to be valuable for scientific study. It has the interesting peculiarity of containing seventeen teeth.

From their position, associated with industry typical of the climax of the Mousterian, it is easy to determine the age of the four sepultures at La Ferrassie, Dordogne. D. Peyrony has demonstrated the following succession of strata:

8	Recent detritus (humus and stones)	120 cm.
7	Late Aurignacian	65 cm.
6	Layer of detritus due to an ancient fall from the roof	35 cm.

Les Eyzies, Dordogne, various fragments (Lartet, Cartailhac, and
    Capitan).
La Mouthe, Dordogne, one tooth, one vertebra (E. Rivière).
Limeuil, Dordogne, skull fragments (J. Bouyssonie).
Grotte des Fées, Gironde, fragments of upper and lower jaw
    (Daleau).
Brassempouy, Landes, two teeth (Breuil).
Sordes, Landes, various fragments (Breuil).
Grotte des Forges, Bruniquel, Tarn-et-Garonne, skull fragments.
Aurensan, Hautes-Pyrénées, various fragments (Hamy).
Espélugues, Hautes-Pyrénées, various fragments (Nelli).
Montconfort, Haute-Garonne, skull fragments (L. Darbas).
Gourdan, Haute-Garonne, skull fragments (Piette).
Caverne des Trois Frères, Montesquieu-Avantès, Ariège, one ulna
    (Count Bégouen).

Final Palæolithic.
La Balme, Savoie, fragment of skull top and femur (G. Blanc).

The skull from Egisheim near Colmar, Alsace, is considerably fossilized. It was found in 1865, at a depth of two
and a half meters, in a deposit of loess and associated with
remains of woolly mammoth, bison, etc., on which account
we feel justified in assigning this skull—which has no Neanderthaloid characters—to the Late Palæolithic.

Of much greater importance is a discovery made by Paul
Wernert in January, 1914, at Enzheim near Strasbourg. It
consists of an incomplete human skeleton embedded in
ocher, presumably a sepulture. It was found in the lower
terrace of the Rhine, the deposits being intermixed with
pebbles from the Breusch Brook and, at various places,
yielding remains of the woolly mammoth. No doubt can be
entertained as to the Palæolithic age of this sepulture, excavated with the skill of a specialist. Moreover, the bones
themselves are extremely fossilized. Certain primitive characters in the skull support the assumption that the remains
are of Aurignacian age.

There are also a number of human remains of "uncertain" age, so that much caution must be exercised in drawing
conclusions from them. Such is the case with the skull of
Bréchamps, Eure-et-Loir, apparently derived from a loess
deposit containing Mousterian implements. The same is

true of the frontal, found in 1883 by Doré-Delente at Mar-
cilly-sur-Eure, Eure, at a depth of seven meters, which
cannot be definitely classified. The data concerning the lower
jaw of a child from Estelas near Cazavet, Ariège; the lower
jaw from Aubert, Ariège; the frontal from Sallèles-Ca-
bardès, Aude; the skeletal fragments from the Grotte des
Cottés, Vienne; and those from the Grotte du Fournet near
Die, Drôme, are all insufficient.

The skeleton of a woman, from Le Moustier, brought to
scientific notice by E. Rivière, is not authentic. It is also
necessary to reject the skeletal remains of Denise, Haute-
Loire; those of Gravenoire; the skulls of Resson, Aube; and
those of La Truchère, Saône-et-Loire; the lower jaw from
Moulin-Quignon, Somme; and that of Isturitz, Basses-
Pyrénées. Finally, it is deplorable that serious scientific consideration has been given to the skulls of Levallois-Clichy
and of Grenelle near Paris, the age of which cannot possibly
be determined.

Belgium possesses two human fossils of extraordinary
value in the two skeletons from Spy, Namur—both fairly
well preserved and belonging to the Late Mousterian (associated fauna listed on p. 96). There can be no doubt that
the lower jaw from the cave of La Naulette, near Dinant,
also belongs to the Early Palæolithic. The floor of the cave
consisted of a clay deposit eleven meters deep, in which there
were seven interlying layers of stalagmitic deposit. The jaw
was found between the second and third layers from the
bottom, associated with other human remains and bones of
the mammoth, woolly rhinoceros, giant deer, reindeer, and
others. No industrial remains were found. The other human
remains found in Belgium—such as those from Engis in the
province of Liège, from the Trou du Frontal near Furfooz
(which seems to be Neolithic), from Maestricht, and from
Wyere—are of uncertain age.

England has recently (1911-1913) become a center of
interest in regard to fossil man on account of the discovery
of the skull and lower jaw of Piltdown, Sussex, by C. Dawson
and A. Smith Woodward. Unfortunately, only nine fragments of the skull were found, including the top and a large
part of the occipital and temporal bones, but not enough to

indicate the form of the entire skull, which makes a trust-worthy restoration very difficult, particularly so in regard to the forehead and the face. There are also the nasal bones and a large part of the right lower jaw showing the two foremost molars and the socket of the third, but the articulation of the jaw is lacking, and so is the middle part—that is to say, the chin (Figure 125). Somewhat later, a canine tooth was discovered by P. Teilhard du Chardin, which at first was supposed to belong to the lower jaw, but which has

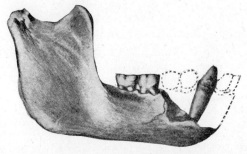

Fig. 125. Lower jaw from Piltdown, England. After C. Dawson and
A. Smith Woodward.
One-half actual size.

more recently been considered as an upper tooth. Finally, in the winter of 1915, C. Dawson discovered in a ploughed field about a mile distant from the original spot, the inner supraorbital part of a frontal bone, the middle of an occipital bone, and a left lower first molar tooth, all evidently human. These are rolled fragments which certainly agree in thickness and extent of fossilization with the earlier find, but which give ground for belief that at Piltdown there are the remains of at least two individuals. Except for the fragments discovered in 1915, the Piltdown remains lay at the base of a bed of reddish brown gravel impregnated with iron and twenty-five meters above the present level of the river Ouse. They are fossilized to the same extent, more or less, as the remains of fauna from the same site. The fauna falls into two groups, distinguished by their state of preservation. The more ancient remains—worn and rounded—

include the mastodon, stegodon, and rhinoceros. The comparatively recent ones are not worn, and include beaver, hippopotamus, horse, and deer. The bone of a proboscidean shows unmistakable traces of clumsy workmanship by the hand of man. A small number of flint flakes also have certainly been shaped, but none of the forms are typical. It may be said that they belong to the Early Palæolithic in the widest sense of the term. According to the latest reports, these implements lay somewhat higher than the human remains of *"Eoanthropos dawsoni,"* the importance of which will be discussed later on in this chapter.

Our own personal opinion is that Piltdown, geologically speaking, is an ancient discovery site with two separate faunas of differing age which later became intermixed. The worn and rounded remains of mastodon, stegodon, and rhinoceros—which have been displaced and redeposited—belong to the Pliocene, as well as the numerous natural eoliths associated with them. The unworn remains of beaver, horse, deer, and hippopotamus belong to the Pleistocene; and the human remains are doubtless contemporary, as they also are much fossilized and show no signs of being disturbed and redeposited, as witnessed by the sharp angular edges of the skull fragments. Although it is not impossible that they are of Pre-Chellean age, it seems to us more probable that they belong to Chellean or Early Acheulean times, when, as is well known, the hippopotamus appeared for the last time in western Europe.

In the cave of La Cotte de Saint-Brelade, in the island of Jersey, which contains a typical Late Mousterian industry, thirteen isolated human teeth were discovered by R. R. Marett.

The human sepulture at Paviland, Glamorganshire (p. 133), discovered by Buckland in 1823, belongs to the Aurignacian. The skeleton, together with mortuary offerings of shells of *Nerita littoralis,* spindles of ivory, and a bone needle, lay embedded in ocher, on which account it was misleadingly termed the "red lady" in spite of its being plainly the skeleton of a man. The associated fauna includes the woolly mammoth, woolly rhinoceros, horse, wild boar, bear, cave hyena, and wolf.

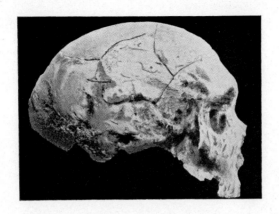

PLATE XVI

The skull of Gibraltar—Neanderthal type. After
A. Hrdlička.

Also of Palæolithic age are the human remains—consisting of a lower jaw and various other bones—found in 1867 at Kent's Hole near Torquay, Devonshire, associated with remains of cave bear, giant deer, mammoth, and reindeer.

The skeleton from Tilbury, near London, which is very incomplete, is apparently of Pleistocene age, as it was found about ten and a half meters deep in the gravel deposits of the Thames. Of the same age, in all probability, are the

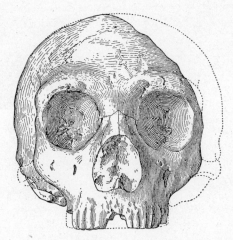

Fig. 126. The skull of Gibraltar, the best female specimen of the Neanderthal type of man. After M. Boule.

human skeleton discovered in 1912 in the valley of the Medway Creek not far from the railway station of Halling, Kent, and the badly preserved skulls found at Bury Saint Edmunds, Suffolk, and at Manor Hamilton, Sligo, Ireland. The skeleton from Gough's Cave near Cheddar, Somerset, is classed as Magdalenian, but its stratigraphic position is not exactly determined.

The skeleton from Galley Hill, Kent, has been much discussed, but in any case shows no such extent of fossilization as the remains of Pleistocene fauna found associated with it. These also appear to be much intermixed and include typical representatives of both warm and cold climates. Since the order of stratigraphic succession and other cir-

cumstances of the discovery are unknown, no positive conclusions can be drawn in regard to the age of the human
remains, which John Evans and others consider to be of
early prehistoric age.

The skeleton from Ipswich, Suffolk, brought to scientific
notice by Reid Moir, is inauthentic, as the discoverer himself
has since declared. Of uncertain age also is the jaw bone
found in 1855 at Foxhall near Ipswich, which was not seen
in situ by any competent person.

In Spain the most complete of Palæolithic human remains
is unquestionably the skull taken from Forbes's Quarry on
the northern slope of the Rock of Gibraltar, which has no
record of definite stratigraphic position or of associated
fossils. It was discovered by Lieutenant Flint in 1848 and
brought to the attention of the scientific world in 1864.
Since the recent examination made by M. Boule there can
be no doubt that this fossil belongs to the ancient Neanderthaloid type (Figure 126, Plate XVI).

Approximately of Mousterian age is the lower jaw found
at Bañolas, Gerona, in 1887 by P. Alsius del Torrent. It was
embedded in a very hard travertine, is extensively fossilized,
and shows primitive racial characters (Figure 127).

The rather defective skull from Camargo, Santander, discovered by L. Sierra (Plate XVII), belongs to the Aurignacian; and so also do the lower jaw of a child and the
molar of an adult found in the cave of Castillo, Santander.
In the Magdalenian deposits of this cave were found fairly
large pieces of two skulls which had been fashioned into
bowls.

The following are also of Magdalenian age, namely: a
single molar from the cave of Cobalejos, Santander; a milk
molar from the cave of Morín near Villaescusa, Santander;
and a few small fragments of limb bones from the cave of
Serinyá, Gerona. It is also not impossible that the scanty
human remains found at the rock shelter of Romaní, Barcelona—consisting of a thigh bone and a few molars—represent what is left of a destroyed sepulture of Late Palæolithic age (p. 197).

On account of indeterminate stratigraphic position or
other uncertainties connected with their discovery, it is

votive offerings. No flint implements were found, but in close association with the human remains were one tooth each of reindeer and bison. According to R. Bonnet, one of the skeletons is that of a woman from twenty to twenty-five years old, about 147 centimeters in height, with a dolichocephalic skull and a cranial capacity of about 1370 cubic centimeters. The second skeleton is that of a man some sixty years old, about 172 centimeters in height, the skull also dolichocephalic and with a cranial capacity of about 1500 cubic centimeters.

In the same region is the Magdalenian site of Andernach, on the Rhine, where human remains have been found consisting of two child's teeth and seven rib fragments (p. 121). A human skull top was found in the sands of Fühlingen near Cologne, which is certainly of Late Palæolithic, and probably of Aurignacian age.

The reports of Rautert and Klaatsch in regard to a "second Man of Neanderthal," found near the old Feldhofer Cave, are without foundation, since nothing is known concerning the age of these remains. It is also necessary to exclude certain remains found in southwestern Germany, namely, the skeletal remains from Mosbach near Wiesbaden, and the two skulls from Mannheim, which deserve some consideration on account of their being found at a depth of six meters. No scientific certainty attaches to the remains found at Lahr on the banks of the Schutter, Baden, nor to the skull of Cannstatt, Würtemberg, which is not Neanderthaloid, although fairly well fossilized. It would seem that it was discovered in 1700, but not until 1835 did it appear in print as an object associated with a Roman vase. Other discoveries have been claimed for sites in Würtemberg, Bavaria, and northern Germany, but these also are not admissible.

Up to the present time, only fragmentary Palæolithic human remains are known in Switzerland, all of which belong to the Magdalenian. In the cave of Freudental, near Schaffhausen, there were found one parietal and a lower jaw belonging to a person about seventeen years old, together with a few fragments of the skull and pelvis, according to J. Karsten. In the cave of Kesslerloch, also near Schaffhausen, a collar bone was found, according to K. Merk. In the cave of Büsserach, Jura, was found a fragment of a small leg bone (fibula), according to G. Frey. At the grotto of Scé, Jura, some skull fragments and a hand bone (metacarpal) were found, according to H. de Saussure.

In Jugo-Slavia a site of commanding importance is that of Krapina in Croatia (pp. 87, 97), where K. Gorjanovič-Kramberger discovered an industrial deposit—probably

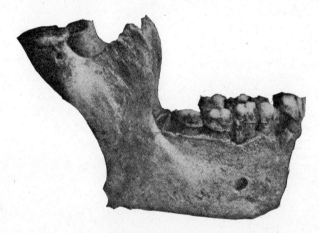

Fig. 130. Lower jaw ("J") from Krapina, Croatia. After K. Gorjanovič-Kramberger.
Three-fifths actual size.

Pre-Mousterian — containing remains of warm fauna (Merck's rhinoceros) and about five hundred human skeletal fragments, all broken and some of them burned. They represent at least eleven individuals, both children and adults.[1]

Important discoveries have also been made in Czecho-Slovakia. The fragment of lower jaw found in the cave of Šipka, Moravia, is certainly Mousterian. It was discovered by K. Maška in the farthest recess of the cave, 1.40 meters below the surface, in the deepest industrial deposit, embedded in a layer of ashes (pp. 86, 385, 386).

The sepulture in the loess of Brünn, Moravia (p. 118),

so lavishly provided with mortuary offerings, must be credited to the Solutrean culture, and also the group sepulture known as the "Mammoth hunters" at Předmost, Moravia (pp. 117, 118). At this last-named site K. Maška discovered fourteen complete skeletons and remains of six others, surrounded by a circle of stones. In addition H. Wankel found here a lower jaw fragment, and M. Kříž the skull of a child, two lower jaw fragments, and other skeletal remains belonging to at least six individuals.

The incomplete lower jaw—generally known as the Ochos jaw—from the Schwedentisch grotto in the Hadecker Valley, Moravia, is certainly of Palæolithic age. The deposit in which it lay contained also remains of a Pleistocene cold fauna with traces of ashes and charcoal, but nothing that would connect the jaw with a definite cultural stage.

Among the discoveries of doubtful authenticity are the skulls found at Brüx, Podhaba, Lieben, and Strebichowitz, all in Bohemia, and also the remains found at Schlappanitz and Hussowitz, at the cave of Fürst Johann near Lautsch, at Kostelik, Byčiskala, Jachymka, and Balcarova-skala, all in Moravia.

Human remains belonging to the Late Palæolithic found in Austria include some fragments of thigh bone, of upper arm bone, and of upper and lower jaws, discovered in the Aurignacian deposits at Willendorf, Lower Austria (pp. 112, 113); and also the tooth of a child, found in the Magdalenian deposit at the cave of Gudenus, Lower Austria.

In Hungary E. Hillebrand reported the discovery of a complete child's skull—also of Magdalenian age—found 1.30 meters below the surface in the cave of Balla near Miskolcz (pp. 117, 123).

So far only one discovery is known in Poland that is unquestionably of Palæolithic age. It consists of a fragment of skull top found by S. J. Czarnowski in the Aurignacian deposits of the cave of Oborzyskowielkie (Black Cave) near Ojców.

The following list gives in their chronologic order the most important human remains found in Europe and belonging beyond doubt to the Glacial Epoch.

EARLY PALÆOLITHIC

Pre-Chellean.

Mauer, near Heidelberg, lower jaw.

Chellean?

Piltdown, skull fragments and lower jaw.

Acheulean or *Pre-Mousterian.*

Taubach and Ehringsdorf, two lower jaws, three teeth, and frag-
ments of a child's skeleton.
Neu-Essing, Klause, one tooth.
Krapina, remains of about eleven individuals.
    (Possibly Early Mousterian?)

Early Mousterian.

Le Moustier, skeleton.
    (Possibly Late Mousterian?)

Middle Mousterian.

La Ferrassie, skeletons of two adults and of two children.
La Chapelle-aux-Saints, skeleton.
La Quina (base), skeleton.
Šipka, fragment of lower jaw.

Late Mousterian.

La Quina (upper level), skull of a child and ramus of a lower jaw.
Pech de l'Azé, skull of a child.
Petit-Puymoyen, fragments of upper and lower jaws.
Spy, two skeletons.
Jersey (La Cotte de St.-Brelade), thirteen teeth.

Early Palæolithic—cultural stage not determinable.

Malarnaud, lower jaw.
Arcy-sur-Cure, lower jaw.
Gourdan, fragment of lower jaw.
La Naulette, lower jaw.
Gibraltar, skull.
Bañolas, lower jaw.
Malta (Ghar Dalam), two molars.
Neanderthal, skull top and various fragments of a skeleton.
Ochos, fragment of lower jaw.

LATE PALÆOLITHIC

Aurignacian.

Crô-Magnon, four skeletons.
Combe-Capelle, skeleton.

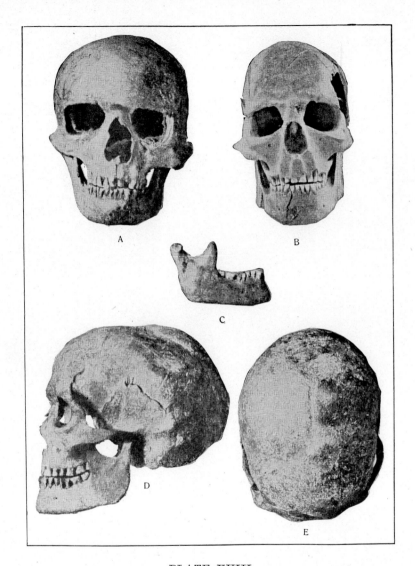

PLATE XVIII

Skulls of Aurignacian age from western Europe. A, C, D, E—Male
skulls and lower jaw of Crô-Magnon type, from the "Grotte des
Enfants" near Mentone. After R. Verneau. B—Male skull from
Combe Capelle, type of *Homo aurignaciensis* (?). After H. Klaatsch.

is even more simian in appearance than that of Neanderthal man, the great inflated brow-ridges being especially prominent and prolonged to a greater extent at the lateral angles. Although the new skull so much resembles that of Neanderthal man, the shape of the brain-case and the position of the foramen magnum are so different that we may hesitate to refer the two skulls to the same race." "The newly discovered Rhodesian man may be regarded as specifically distinct from *Homo neandertalensis* and may be appropriately named *Homo rhodesiensis*." "The Rhodesian man may therefore revive the idea that Neanderthal man is truly an ancestor of *Homo sapiens;* for *Homo rhodesiensis* retains an almost Neanderthal face in association with a more modern brain-case and an up-to-date skeleton. He may prove to be the next grade after Neanderthal in the ascending series."

Although, ever since 1844, Pleistocene age has been claimed for a number of human remains found in North America, yet, so far, it has not been possible to demonstrate beyond question any such degree of antiquity in the case of any of these remains. According to A. Hrdlička the stratigraphic position of these remains was not such as to afford any scientific verification of the age claimed, and he further notes that they present striking similarities to the characteristics of existing American Indians.

It therefore becomes necessary to exclude the following discoveries:

New Orleans, Louisiana, various bones,	1844
Quebec, Canada, skeleton (?)	
Natchez, Mississippi, pelvis	1846
Lake Monroe, Florida, various bones,	1853
Soda Creek, Colorado, skeleton,	1860
Charleston, South Carolina, various fragments (?)	
Calaveras, near Altaville, California, skull,	1866
Rock Bluff, Illinois, skull,	1866
Western Florida, fragments of skulls and skeletons,	1871-1878
Trenton, New Jersey, various skulls,	1879-1887
Trenton, New Jersey, a femur,	1899
Nebraska, ten skeletons,	1894-1906

Lansing, Kansas, skeleton,   1902
Rancho la Brea, Los Angeles, California, skeleton,   1914
Vero, Florida, two skeletons,   1916

Discoveries in Central and South America offer little more than those in North America. In the first place, the human skeleton found in 1884 at Peñon de los Baños, near Mexico City, must be positively excluded, as its age is entirely uncertain. The same is true of the human remains from Cuzco, Peru (excluded by Eaton and Gregory), and also of those from Lagoa Santa in the province of Minas Gerães, Brazil, which represent some thirty individuals.

A number of anthropological discoveries made in Argentina are also open to doubt. Here the question of the existence of Tertiary and Pleistocene man was raised, chiefly by F. Ameghino (1911), who opened the discussion by producing an atlas and a femur from Monte Hermoso in the southern part of the province of Buenos Aires, claiming that these remains were of Miocene age and belonged to individuals of the same species, which he named *Tetraprothomo argentinus*. But it proves that the femur belongs to a carnivore about the size of a fox, while the atlas is human. R. Lehmann-Nitsche and T. de Urquiza support the theory that the atlas represents a primitive fossil species peculiar to South America, which they name *Homo neogæus*. According to O. Aichel the atlas is a small human one which is deformed, and Ihering considers its origin altogether doubtful.

In his writings Ameghino also made mention of a skull fragment which he attributed to the early Pliocene, and which was discovered in the course of works carried out at the harbor of Buenos Aires. On the strength of this discovery Ameghino introduced his *Diprothomo platensis,* with a skull similar to that of the *Cebus* monkey. After critical examination G. Schwalbe has proved beyond controversy that the fragment is merely a part of a human skull of modern type, erroneously interpreted by Ameghino. If, however, it were otherwise, it would belong—according to G. Steinmann—to the Middle Pleistocene.

Also from "Pliocene" deposits, according to Ameghino, are some human teeth found in Buenos Aires (*Protopithecus bonaerensis* Amegh.), the fragments of three skulls from Necochea (*Homo pampæus* Amegh. = *Prothomo pampæus* Amegh.), two skeletons from Arroyo del Moro (*Homo sinemento* Amegh.), the skull from Miramar, also known as La Tigra (*Homo pampæus* Amegh. = *Prothomo pampæus* Amegh.), and the skeleton from Arroyo Siasgo (*Homo caputinclinatus* Amegh.), as well as various other skeletons to be mentioned later. All these remains belong to the Pampas formation, and—as shown by the excellent investigations made by R. Lehmann-Nitsche in collaboration with A. Döring, H. von Ihering, S. Roth, G. Steinmann, and others—could not possibly be of earlier date than the Pleistocene. J. Frenguelli also has recently expressed his opinion that the entire Pampas formation—from the Chapalmalal stage to that of La Plata—is synchronous with the European Pleistocene. None of the human remains mentioned shows any anatomical peculiarities such as might justify the creation of Ameghino's new species, according to A. Mochi.

Judging from the report of R. Lehmann-Nitsche (1907), the most ancient human remains discovered in the æolian loess of the Argentine Pampas are the poorly preserved skeletal remains found in 1887 by S. Roth near Baradero, Buenos Aires. These belong, at the earliest, to the middle Pleistocene, and show no characteristics that would differentiate them from the existing Indians of South America.

According to the same author the following discoveries belong to the upper loess of the Pampas, and must therefore be of late Pleistocene age.

Carcarañá, Santa Fé, incomplete skeletal remains of various individuals,	1864
Frías I, Buenos Aires, skull and other fragments of a skeleton (lost),	1870
Frías II, Buenos Aires, skeletal remains of at least two individuals,	1873
Saladero, near Pergamino, Buenos Aires, thigh bone and nine teeth,	1876
Fontezuelas, Buenos Aires (= Pontimelo), a fairly complete skeleton,	1881
Samborombón, Buenos Aires, an almost complete skeleton,[4]	1882
Arrecifes, Buenos Aires, skull,	1888

Chocorí, Buenos Aires, skull and other fragments of a skeleton,   1888(?)
La Tigra, Buenos Aires (Miramar), skull and other fragments of a skeleton,   1888(?)

In agreement with the above, H. von Ihering stated in 1914
that he had come to the conclusion that there is no ground
for suspecting the existence of Tertiary man in South
America; and he believes that man certainly entered South
America by way of the Isthmus of Panama some time during
the Pleistocene, together with other animals, such as the
horse and mastodon.

It should be noted that in the course of his detailed studies
Lehmann-Nitsche has never wavered in attributing the
above-mentioned skeletal remains to the Pleistocene, while
A. Hrdlička, the anthropologist, and Bailey Willis, the
geologist, both consider that such documents are of very
doubtful age, that the geologic and stratigraphic conditions
of discovery are in no case entirely free from objections,
and, moreover, that the skeletal remains differ in no respect
from the typical *Homo sapiens* of the present day.

Our own personal opinion is that the criticisms of these
two authorities err on the side of an exaggerated scepticism,
and we feel persuaded that later explorations made in
America will go to rehabilitate at least the greater part of
the list of discoveries accepted by R. Lehmann-Nitsche and
others.

In closing we may note that in 1921 M. A. Vignati discovered further human remains at Miramar, not far from
Buenos Aires, consisting of a fragment of lower jaw with
two molars still in it. According to Vignati it came from the
geologic formation of Chapalmalal. If this is demonstrated,
we have a discovery which probably belongs to the Early
Pleistocene.

From Australia quite recently comes the report of the
discovery of a skull at Talgai in the Darling Downs, Queensland. It was found in 1884 in the river drift deposits of a
small stream which also contained remains of Pleistocene
mammals and—it is claimed—stone implements of Palæolithic type.

Although the geologic position of the skull cannot, at this late date, be absolutely determined, it is none the less probable that it is of Pleistocene age, as it is much fossilized. It is badly crushed but shows the principal features that characterize native Australian skulls of present times. The upper jaw is exceedingly prognathous, and the unusual size of the teeth—especially of the canines—gives the skull a very primitive and apelike aspect, similar to that of the Piltdown specimen.[5]

It does not lie within the scope of this work to give a detailed anthropological description of the Pleistocene human remains of Europe. On the contrary, our aim is to assemble the certain conclusions of scientific research, and to present what is thus far known of Pleistocene human types, both as regards their peculiar characteristics and their chronologic order of succession.

Glancing at the list of discoveries given (pp. 298, 299), we find that these human remains fall naturally into two great divisions. The latest of these includes all belonging to the Late Palæolithic, and consequently the Aurignacian, Solutrean, and Magdalenian cultural stages, which we have found contemporaneous with the latest glacial stage and its postglacial phases. This entire division betrays a close similarity to modern European man (excepting certain discoveries in Moravia, which will be discussed presently); the skull is long and moderately broad or ''dolichocephalic'';[6] the forehead is well developed and the whole skull top high and well rounded; while the cranial capacity is very great, since it reaches 1600 ccm. The face is short, broad, and flat, the nostrils rather small; and the brow ridges extend above only the inner half of the orbit. The lower jaw is stout and the chin well marked. There is considerable variation in height. There are skeletons of tall individuals, such as the skeletons from Grimaldi with an average height of 187 cm.; and, on the other hand, there are others indicating a comparatively short stature, such as the male skeletons of Chancelade and Combe-Capelle, which are, respectively, 157.5 cm. and about 166 cm., and the female skeleton from Obercassel, which is about 147 cm. in height.

The skulls of these Late Palæolithic remains show great

similarity. The differences are of small importance and, so far, may well be considered as due to individual variation. Consequently, we classify them all under the title "Crô-Magnon Race" (Plates XVII and XVIII) in accordance with the great majority of anthropologists. Nevertheless, it must be noted that H. Klaatsch, V. Giuffrida-Ruggeri, and others consider the Aurignacian skeleton from Combe-Capelle, which they have named "*Homo aurignaciensis*," to be a separate variety differing from the Crô-Magnon type, especially in regard to the cephalic index and the very slender build of the skeleton. A number of French anthropologists also classify a few of the Magdalenian human remains—in particular the skeletons of Chancelade, Laugerie-Basse, and Sordes—as a separate "Chancelade Race" with affinities to the existing Eskimos of eastern Labrador and Greenland. In any case, however, they constitute races which are nearly related.

It is possible that new racial elements may come to light when the number of anthropological discoveries is increased. Some of those already known would seem to indicate this. R. Verneau has described the double sepulture found at the base of the Grotte des Enfants where a young man and an old woman were buried together (p. 290). The skulls are quite narrow and hyperdolichocephalic, with the cranial indices of the man and woman, respectively, 69.3 and 68.6, and the cranial capacity 1580 ccm. and 1375 ccm. The face is comparatively broad, and there was a fronto-nasal apophysis and well-developed brow ridges. The eye sockets were low and the nostrils apparently broad. The subnasal region and the upper and lower jaws are exceedingly prognathous. The woman's chin is quite pointed; the man's not so much. These peculiarities of skull and the relatively great length of the forearm inspired Verneau to assign the two individuals to a negroid race which he named the "Grimaldi Race" (Plate XIX).

Of prime importance are the numerous skeletons discovered by Maška at Předmost, Moravia (p. 297), a detailed description of which has not yet been published. The distinguished anatomist, C. Toldt, declares that the male skulls from this site have a flat retreating forehead and

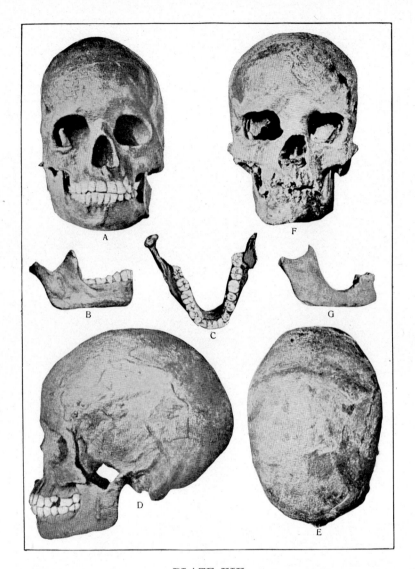

PLATE XIX

Skulls of the Grimaldi Race, found in the basal deposits of the "Grotte des Enfants" near Mentone. After R. Verneau. A, B, C, D, E—Skull and lower jaw of the young man. F, G—Skull and lower jaw of the old woman.

lians. The face is prognathous and in the outer part of the upper jaw the canine fossa or groove is entirely wanting. In the modern Mongol or Mongoloid races this fossa is sometimes scarcely indicated or very much flattened. The lower jaw is stout; but as to the chin prominence, there is only the merest rudimentary suggestion of it, showing its earliest beginning (Plates XVI, XX; Figures 123, 124, 126, 127, 129, 130).

The Neanderthaloid skulls of western Europe are narrow and dolichocephalic, with cephalic indices as follows:

La Quina	68.2	La Chapelle-aux-Saints,	75
Spy I,	70	Spy II,	75.8
Neanderthal,	73.9	Gibraltar,	77.9

The skulls of Krapina in eastern Europe look broader in proportion to their length (brachycephalic), but it is not possible to verify this by exact measurements. Seeing that both the length and breadth of the skull of La Chapelle-aux-Saints are much greater than in the ordinary human skulls of present times, it is not surprising that the cranial capacity amounts to 1626 ccm. Estimates for the other Neanderthaloids are much lower. They are as follows:

La Quina	1367 ccm. according to Boule
Neanderthal	1500 ccm. according to Manouvrier
Neanderthal	1230 ccm. according to Schwalbe
Neanderthal	1532 ccm. according to Ranke
Gibraltar	1260 ccm. according to Sollas
Gibraltar	1080 ccm. according to Sera
Gibraltar	1296 ccm. according to Boule

The Neanderthaloid brain, both in its general form and in its anatomical details—as shown by the impressions on the inside of the skull—was absolutely human, but lacking in the fine and delicate structure characteristic of the modern human brain.

The other bones of the skeleton are coarse and clumsy. In the forearm the shaft of the radius is decidedly curved, which is very characteristic of this ancient human type. The shin bone is very thick, and the thigh bone short and stout. As to the vertebræ, they are narrow and flattened.

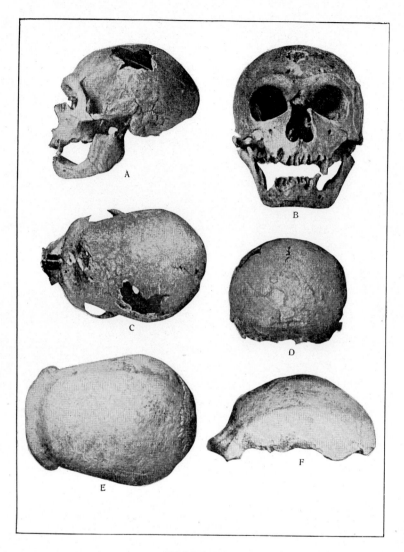

PLATE XX

Skulls of Neanderthal type. A, B, C, D—Skull from La Chapelle-aux-
Saints. After M. Boule. E, F—Skull-top of Neanderthal. After
H. Klaatsch.

The controversy in regard to the status of this interesting fossil is by no means settled as yet, and it would seem that its solution must be deferred, awaiting the light that further discoveries may throw upon the question.

The apelike characteristics found in the most ancient remains of fossil man—which we have just described—lead logically to the inference that there must be some relation between these ancient types of man and the anthropoid apes. It is, of course, only the fossil types of the latter that could be considered in this light.

As to fossil remains of the Simiidæ, recent discoveries during the last few decades—especially in Europe and India —have afforded quite a notable addition to the available material, and have been the subject of careful study by a number of palæontologists and anthropologists, foremost among whom are M. Schlosser, A. Gaudry, A. Keith, G. Schwalbe, A. Smith Woodward, H. F. Osborn, D. G. Elliot, G. E. Pilgrim, and W. K. Gregory.

The geologic succession of the most important anthropoid types is given in the following table, which is based chiefly on the reports of Schlosser, Pilgrim, and Gregory:

V. Holocene (present time).

Troglodytes (*Pan*), or chimpanzee,	Africa.
Gorilla,	Africa.
Hylobates, or gibbon,	Asia.
Simia satyrus, or orang utan,	Asia.

IV. Pleistocene or Glacial Epoch.

Pithecanthropus,	Java.

III. Pliocene.

Dryopithecus,	India, Europe.
Palæopithecus,	India.
Sivapithecus,	India.
Neopithecus (*Anthropodus*),	Europe.
Simia cfr. *satyrus,*	India.

II. Miocene.

Dryopithecus,	India, Europe.
Palæosimia,	India.
Sivapithecus,	India.
Pliopithecus,	Europe.

I. Oligocene.

Propliopithecus,	Egypt.

The earliest known traces of anthropoid apes were found in Oligocene deposits of the Fayûm, Egypt, and have been described by M. Schlosser under the name of *Propliopithecus*. The only species known as yet of this new genus, *Propliopithecus hæckeli*, was about the size of a small cat (about 40 cm. long), and appears to have been ancestral to all the anthropoid apes.

A branch of this ancestral type is probably represented by the Miocene *Palæosimia* (possibly identical with *Sivapithecus?*) and the late Pliocene *Simia*—forms probably ancestral to the orang utan.

The *Dryopithecus* branch is of greater importance. This group is represented by a number of small species from the Lower Siwalik deposits (Late Miocene) of India, while a larger species, *Dryopithecus giganteus*, is somewhat more recent. In Europe, *Dryopithecus* remains have been found in the Vienna Basin, in France, and in northern Spain—also in deposits of the Late Miocene. They are divided into a number of varieties, apparently all belonging to the same species, were about the size of a chimpanzee, and were probably arboreal in their habits. From the Early Pliocene of the Swabian Alb, Würtemberg, comes *Dryopithecus rhenanus*, otherwise known as *Paidopithex* or *Pliohylobates*. *Palæopithecus*, from the Early Pliocene of India, and *Neopithecus* (*Anthropodus*), from the Late Pliocene of Germany, may also stand in relation to this group. In any case, the *Dryopithecus* branch is of the greatest interest, not only because it seems to be ancestral to the modern gorilla and chimpanzee, but because *Pithecanthropus*—which we have classed as Pleistocene—also appears to be nearly related.

Pliopithecus, from the Late Miocene of Europe, is classed by Gregory among the Hylobatinæ. It was about the size of the existing gibbon, and seems to have been ancestral to the same.

None of these forms has been demonstrated to be directly ancestral to the human type, so that as yet we have no certain knowledge in regard to the Tertiary ancestors of man.[10]

Toward the very close of the last century, a fossil anthropomorph was discovered in Java, which appeared to bridge the gap in the genealogy of the anthropomorphs. It was at first supposed to be of Tertiary age, and was named *Pithe-canthropus erectus*. This discovery was made during the years 1891 and 1892 by E. Dubois, a Dutch army surgeon, on the banks of the Solo (or Bengawan) River near Trinil and at the foot of the Kendeng Hills in central Java.

As to the stratigraphic conditions of the discovery, E. Dubois, J. Martin, E. Carthaus, and H. Stremme advocate the theory that the principal bone-bearing deposit of these Kendeng strata (a sandstone-like tuff) does not represent a fossilized stream of mud, but rather a fluvial, lacustrine, or fluvio-lacustrine formation. It is not possible, however, to determine whether these fossil bones are in their original situation, or whether they have been redeposited.

As to the evidence of palæontology, a very adequate list of mammals belonging to the Kendeng formation is afforded by the researches of H. Stremme, W. Janensch, H. Pohlig, O. Jäkel, and E. Hennig.[11] From this it will be seen that all but five of the genera are recent, but that out of twenty-seven species which can be identified beyond question none is identical with the species existing to-day in the same locality. It will therefore be seen that the fauna of this deposit is purely Pleistocene in character—a view that is further confirmed by the fact that all the fresh-water molluscs from this formation were found by Martin to belong without exception to existing species in the same locality.

The flora of this deposit also indicates Pleistocene age, as it consists, without exception, of species and varieties still existing. According to J. Schuster the *Pithecanthropus* deposits indicate the culmination of a pluvial phase, while, on the other hand, J. Elbert considers that the plants of the bone-bearing deposit would indicate a temperate climate which, at that time, was from 3° to 6° Centigrade cooler than at present. According to the latter author, the plants which belong to the cool zone of vegetation in Java are found in strata quite a little higher than the bone-bearing deposits. Nevertheless, Elbert, Carthaus, and Schuster all agree that the Kendeng deposits represent a pluvial phase, and Schuster considers that the difference in climate consisted not only of a lowered temperature, but that a still more important feature was an augmentation of humidity. During this phase the limit of perpetual snow was about 800 meters lower than at the present time—that is to say, from 2200 to 2300 meters above sea level, whereas now it is from 3000 to 3100 meters. From this it may be concluded that the low-lying districts experienced a pluvial phase with temperate climate.

Summing up the results of various special investigations, M. Blanckenhorn comes to the conclusion that the *Pithecanthropus* deposits are contemporary with the principal pluvial phase in Java, and that they belong to the Early Pleistocene, corresponding for the most part with the First Glacial Stage in Europe, and in lesser measure with the Second Glacial Stage. A contrary opinion is held by W. Volz, who asserts that the tuffs in question are a product of the two volcanos, Lawoe and Kukusan; that these tuffs were deposited in part as volcanic sand and ash, but also very largely in the form of streams of mud spread over the slopes by the action of the rains; and that, in consequence, the bone-bearing deposits of Trinil were formed by a stream of volcanic mud and are not the result of flood deposits of the Solo River—from which it follows that the deposit was finally uncovered only by the erosive action of the river. According to various details of geologic evidence the eruptions of Kukusan took place for the most part during the Early Pleistocene, while the volcano Lawoe—still mildly active—must have reached its maximum of activity during the Late Pleistocene. From these important data it may be concluded that the Kendeng deposits are in no case more ancient than the Early Pleistocene, and, as they can hardly be of later date than the Late Pleistocene, it seems probable that they should be attributed to the Middle Pleistocene.

The *Pithecanthropus* remains consist of a skull top, two (three?) teeth, and a left thigh bone (femur). The skull top was found in October, 1891; the thigh bone in August, 1892, at a place fifteen meters farther upstream. Whether all these discoveries belong together—that is to say, belong either to the same individual, or to individuals of the same species— is very doubtful, especially in view of the fact that the skull top is decidedly anthropoid, while the thigh bone is decidedly human (Figure 134).

therefore on the same surface of rock, the one close to the other. The same is true of the designs on the painted pebbles of Mas d'Azil, with the result that the anthropomorphic figures (Figure 139) are intermixed with the simple and conventional reductions in such a way that the latter appear like "stenographic" reproductions of the human figure.

The proved existence of "human figures" among the designs on the Azilian pebbles gives rise to most interesting speculations in regard to their real significance, which was long supposed by many scientists to be that of religious symbols. In particular A. B. Cook and F. Sarasin have drawn attention to the apparent similarity of these stones to the "churingas" (or "tjurungas") found among the Australian tribes of the Arunta, Kaitish, Warramunga, and Achilpa, as well as in Tasmania. They are made either of wood or stone, and in the latter case are exceedingly similar to the Azilian pebbles, both in shape and design. As "ancestor stones" or "soul stones" they are supposed to embody deceased forefathers. P. Wernert recently (1916) extended this explanation, having come to the conclusion that both the modern churingas and the Epipalæolithic pebbles present two classes of design—the one with conventionalized human forms, and the other with symbolic, biomorphic signs; that is to say, with totem pictures. Both are derived from the belief that human creatures, as well as certain animals, plants, and so forth, are to be considered in the light of creating or protecting ancestors, and, as such, become the objects of a special cult. In the cave of Birseck near Arlesheim, Switzerland, F. Sarasin found a whole cache of painted Azilian pebbles, all of which had been deliberately crushed or broken. We think he is not mistaken in attributing this to the work of an enemy, seeking by the destruction of these "holy ancestor stones" to deprive some tribe of the protection and help of their ancestors.

If, however, these painted pebbles really were embodiments of a belief in manism, then the contemporary and closely related rock paintings must also stand for an ancestral cult, and can have nothing in common with the earlier notions of magic that belong to the Palæolithic time (pp. 260-264).

Group 1

Localities: *a, b, c, e,* Jimena (G.M.*); *d,* Covatillas (H.B.); painted pebble from Mas d'Azil (E.P.).

Standing figures, both male and female; *a* and *b* still quite realistic, with headdress, probably adorned with feathers, and arms akimbo. The Mas d'Azil design has retained the head, torso, and arms, but the legs are not indicated.

Group 2

Localities: *a, d,* Jimena (G.M.); *b,* Arabí (J.C.); *c,* Torre de la Peña (J.C.); *e,* Covatillas (H.B.); painted pebble from Mas d'Azil (E.P.).

Standing figures, both male and female; *a* and *c* with headdress, *b* with a "hat" and indications of the eyes. The discs shown halfway down the arm of the much simplified figure *e* seem to indicate elbow ornaments such as are unmistakably shown in figure *a* of Group 4, and in figure *b* of Group 8, and are still more directly reminiscent of the Palæolithic designs at Alpera and Cogul. The Mas d'Azil pebble shows the torso, arms, and elbow ornaments, but omits the head.

Group 3

Localities: *a, b,* Azogue (J.C.); *c,* Ciaque (J.C.); *d,* Cueva Ahumada (J.C.); painted pebble from Mas d'Azil (E.P.).

Female figures with kirtle (compare Alpera, Cogul, and also figure *a* of Group 4). The Mas d'Azil pebble shows torso, arms, and kirtle, but no head.

Group 4

Localities: *a,* Cueva Ahumada (J.C.); *b,* Cueva de los Piruétanos (J.C.); *c,* Tabla de Pochico (J.C.); *d,* Azogue (J.C.); *e,* Cueva Negra (Bosque) (J.C.); painted pebble from Mas d'Azil (E.P.).

Female figures; *a* with eyes, dress, and arm ornament; *b* much conventionalized but the eyes still indicated. The Mas d'Azil pebble shows torso, arms, and kirtle.

Group 5

Localities: *a,* Barranco de la Cueva (J.C.); *b, d,* Ciaque (J.C.); *c, e,* Cueva de los Piruétanos (J.C.); painted pebble from Mas d'Azil (E.P.).

Human figures: *a* shows the digits of hand and foot; *c,* a woman with four children. The Mas d'Azil pebble shows torso and arms exceedingly conventionalized, being reduced to the form of a cross.

Group 6

Localities: *a, e,* Prado de Reches (J.C.); *b, f,* Barranco de la Cueva (J.C.); *c, d,* Ranchiles (J.C.); two painted pebbles from Mas d'Azil (E.P.).

Female figures; *a* with head still discernable, *b* with sexual characters emphasized, *c* with eyes separately indicated. Of the Mas d'Azil pebbles, one shows torso and legs, the other only the legs.

* G.M.=after Gómez Moreno	J.C.=after Juan Cabré
H.B.=after Henri Breuil	H.O.=after Hugo Obermaier
E.P.=after Edouard Piette	M.G.=after M. Góngora

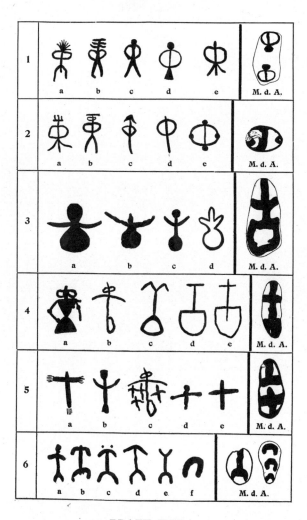

PLATE XXI A

Spanish petroglyphs—representing human figures
more or less conventionalized—compared with similar designs from the painted pebbles of Mas d'Azil.

It must be considered as beyond doubt that a large part of the rock paintings of Spain, on account of their close similarity to the Azilian painted pebbles, belong to the Epi-palæolithic. It is also equally certain that these geometrically conventionalized rock paintings persisted throughout the entire Neolithic and into the Age of Copper chiefly in their final Capsian forms, and only occasionally in more recent designs, among which the most numerous are "motifs" from dolmens and idols, pictures of wagons, and similar designs. This is established by numerous data, among which it is sufficient here to cite one typical example.

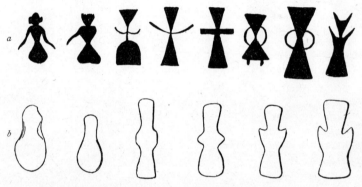

Fig. 140. *a* Petroglyphs, possibly representing female idols, from southern Spain. After H. Breuil. *b* Neolithic stone idols from Almería. After L. Siret.

It is long known that various designs of "female figures" in the rock paintings of Almería are repeated in the designs of certain flat stone idols which belong to the Late Neolithic (Figure 140). Certain animal designs from the rocks of Andalusia reappear on clay vessels of the Copper Age, as, for instance, on the inside of the bowl from Las Carolinas near Madrid, while the outside bears the characteristic decoration of "Ciempozuelos" type (Figure 141). No less enlightening is the ensemble of rock paintings at Peña Tú near Llanes, Asturias, discovered by Count de la Vega del Sella. Here, partly engraved and partly painted in red, is a great idol of the familiar type of the so-called "Menhir" figures; near it is the picture of a copper poignard, and also a number of very simply conventionalized human figures, quite similar to that shown as *d*, Group 11, in Plate XXI.

It is hard to say how much this late art of the Age of Copper retained of the psychologic attitude of the Epipalæolithic, or whether, perhaps, it stood for more advanced religious concepts. But in any case it served, in some measure at least, the purpose of a cult of ancestors and of the dead.

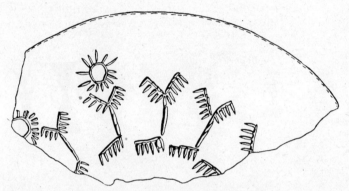

Fig. 141. Design of conventionalized stags and suns, engraved on the inside of a clay bowl belonging to the Age of Copper, from Las Carolinas, Madrid.

Three-fourths actual size.

We do not believe, however, that these symbols ever acquired the import and significance of a primitive system of writing. Even though they do actually show a certain similarity to the primitive hieratic characters of Egypt, Cyprus, and Crete, this may be merely an accidental superficial resemblance, and does not necessarily imply any organic relation between them. It is worth notice that similar geometrically conventionalized designs appear occasionally on clay vessels of central and eastern Europe belonging to the Age of Copper. In any case these conventionalizations have absolutely no connection with the rock paintings of Spain, but are of different and independent origin, the source of which —in all probability—should be sought in the Balkans in the region of the lower Danube. Finally, it may be noted that conventionalized designs of men and animals are also known on the pottery of Egypt and Persia belonging to the Age of Copper, and these also represent regions of independent artistic development which are of relatively recent age.

The Tardenoisian culture takes its name from the station of Fère-en-Tardenois, Aisne, France, and is characterized by extremely small and fine flint implements. These include many disc-shaped scrapers, quadrilateral scrapers, and, above all, numerous types of ''geometric microliths''— minute types, rhomboid, trapezoid, or triangular in form, or

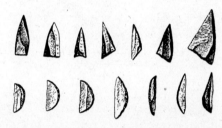

Fig. 142. Geometric microliths of Tardenoisian type from France.
After G. and A. de Mortillet.
Two-thirds actual size.

sometimes shaped like the segment of a circle (Figure 142). In France this industry is found only at sites in the open, and up to the present time neither animal remains nor bone implements have been found associated with it.

The inventory of geometric microliths of flint belonging to the French Tardenoisian agrees essentially with that of the final Capsian of Spain—previously described—and could not possibly be the result of a further local development from the Magdalenian of France, but, on the contrary, must be regarded as directly derived from the final Capsian of the Iberian Peninsula. The earliest phases of the French Tardenoisian are synchronous with this Epipalæolithic Capsian, and since the latter in northern Spain is known to have incorporated elements from the contemporary Azilian, it is therefore not surprising to find that in France also, and in the adjoining regions to the north and east, there frequently appears a hybrid industry which may best be designated as "Azilio-Tardenoisian" (Figure 147). From this earlier Tardenoisian are developed the more recent regional phases leading into the Neolithic, which itself shows survivals in the form of large geometric flint implements reminiscent of the Tardenoisian types (Figure 135, No. 7).

The pure Tardenoisian, or Azilio-Tardenoisian with the latter element predominant, in other parts of western Europe besides France is found quite abundantly in Belgium, as at Remouchamp, Zonhofen, etc., and in Great Britain, including Scotland and Ireland (Figure 135, Nos. 4, 5, 6).

These industries are also of frequent occurrence in central Europe. Besides the discovery site of Istein, Baden, especial importance attaches to the cave of Ofnet near Nördlingen, Bavaria. In 1907 and 1908 deposits were discovered here by R. R. Schmidt and strata belonging to the Aurignacian, Solutrean, and Magdalenian cultures. In the latter level and covered by Neolithic deposits, he excavated two great circular depressions which were filled with a thick layer of ocher. The larger was thirty inches in diameter and contained twenty-seven human skulls (Figure 143). The other was eighteen inches in diameter and contained six skulls.

All the skulls were placed facing westward, and with each was its lower jaw and one or more of the cervical (neck) vertebræ. Some of these vertebræ bore evident marks of cutting, showing that after death the head had been separated from the trunk. The sepulture of these heads did not take place all at the same time, but successively and by degrees, as is shown by the fact that the skulls at the center of the circle are all crushed or distorted while those near the edge of the circle are intact.

There were nine women's skulls, with ornaments for head and neck which consisted chiefly of shells and the canine teeth of stags, perforated. There were also twenty skulls of children and young persons less richly dowered with ornaments, and four men's skulls entirely without them. The stratigraphy and the nature of some of the geometric microliths indicate that these remarkable sepultures are of Azilio-Tardenoisian age. Among the skulls A. Schliz was able to distinguish both dolichocephalic and brachycephalic types, together with a number of forms intermediate between the two (Plate XXII).

An interesting supplement to the discoveries made at Ofnet was supplied by cultural deposits found in the small cave known as the "Hexenküche" (Witches' Kitchen),

Fig. 143. The great skull sepulture at the cave of Ofnet, Bavaria. After R. R. Schmidt.

which is also in the neighborhood of Nördlingen, on the southern side of the Kaufertsberg close to Lierheim. Here, in 1913, F. Birkner discovered both Magdalenian and Tardenoisian deposits—the latter characterized by typical microliths, small round scrapers, and small gravers and points. In unmistakable contact with this layer was a single skull sepulture. Unfortunately, there were no accompanying mortuary offerings; but close to the back of the skull, close to the foramen magnum, were the first and second neck vertebræ. The skull is mesocephalic, and in its other measurements is in close agreement with the two dolichocephalic male skulls from the Ofnet Cave. The face is narrow, the nose of medium width, and the orbits long and narrow.

zola near Dima; in Santander at a number of sites, almost all with flat harpoons—as, for instance, the caves of Valle, near Gibaja; Rascaño, near Mirones; Morín, near Villaescusa; Castillo, near Puente Viesgo; and Camargo and El Pendo, near Santander—and in Asturias at the caves of Balmori and Riera, near Posada, and the Cueva de la Paloma, near Soto de las Regueras. At the cave of Serinyá, Gerona, also, there have been found what would seem in all probability to be traces of the Azilian.

The Azilian deposits at Valle rested on a Magdalenian deposit, and were covered by a very thick stalagmitic layer. They had an average thickness of 50 cm. and contained remains of stag, roe deer, chamois, Pyrenean ibex, horse, wild ox, and wild boar. In the upper half these were accompanied by great numbers of snail shells.[3] Many flint implements were found—flakes and nuclei of Magdalenian form among them—but the chief forms are the small circular planing tools, graving tools with lateral point, small blades with blunted backs either straight or curved, and triangular or crescent-shaped microliths (Figure 135, No. 3). The implements of horn and bone include a whole series of flat harpoons, with either single or double rows of barbs (Figure 145, c, d), awls—some of them ornamented with simple parallel lines,—and a large polisher of stag horn.

In the course of investigations made in the caves of Riera and Balmori by Count de la Vega del Sella and the present writer, deposits belonging to the close of the Magdalenian were encountered in which microlithic implements predominated, while the thick and round planing tools betrayed an unmistakable tendency to evolve toward the small round or discoid forms, or those of rectangular shape with rounded corners. We therefore feel justified in assigning to this region the evolution of this very important characteristic type of the Epipalæolithic. These deposits show the gradual infiltration of the industry of the final Capsian, so that its minute geometric flints are associated with survivals of Magdalenian forms, thus resulting in that curious intermixture of types characterizing the inventory of Azilian stone implements (Figure 146).

As to the industry in horn and bone, the chief characteris-

tic form, the flat harpoon, must certainly be derived from the
"Cantabrian" harpoon as the only earlier type which also
has a perforated base (Figures 68, 75), the perforation
being made by the Azilian artisans in the center of the base.
It may be noted that two forms of this implement, which
was presumably used for fishing, are found—one with a

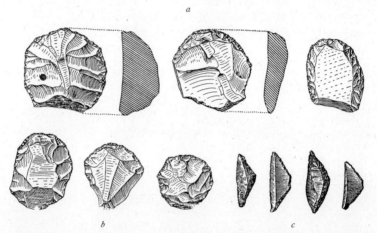

Fig. 146. Tiny stone implements (microliths) of Cantabrian Azilian
    type. a, b Rounded or polyhedral planing tools. c Geometric
    forms.

Actual size.

single row of large barbs and a coarse oval perforation, the
other with two rows of barbs and a round perforation—but
there is as yet no evidence to show which of these forms is
the older. Aside from these, there are only the ordinary awls,
piercers, and polishers.

Painted pebbles are of very rare occurrence in Spain, as
the damp rainy climate of the Cantabrian region is most
unfavorable to their preservation. However, in 1917, at the
entrance to the cave of Riera, at least one such pebble was
found bearing genuine Azilian symbols which were still quite
recognizable—thanks to a protecting film of stalagmitic
deposit. Nevertheless, there can be no question as to the
Spanish origin of these painted pebbles, in view of the geo-

metrically conventionalized human forms found on the pebbles and evidently derived from similar designs on the Spanish petroglyphs (p. 330, and Plate XXI).

In the light of our present knowledge the Azilian culture of the Cantabrian region may be subdivided into two phases, as follows:

Early Azilian.

Numerous small round planing tools, and occasionally some that are thick or bullet-shaped.

Many microliths, most with blunted back, and rarely of any regular geometric form.

A few bone implements of Magdalenian aspect.

Flat harpoons.

Late Azilian.

Numerous round planing tools and microliths.

Numerous small geometric forms.

Degenerate, coarsely worked bone implements.

Flat harpoons.

Painted pebbles.

The fauna of the Azilian stations of Spain is modern, consisting exclusively of existing species. The stag occurs most commonly, and the chamois, Pyrenean ibex, horse, and wild ox are of frequent occurrence. More rarely, remains of roe deer, wolf, lynx, and wildcat are found. Human remains of certain age are wanting.

The mollusc fauna found in Asturias includes shells of periwinkles and limpets, the commonest forms, both of which, however, are considerably smaller than their predecessors in the Magdalenian deposits (p. 350). The snail (*Helix nemoralis*) is not of frequent occurrence and seems not to have served for food.

Our conclusions in regard to the various industries of the Epipalæolithic may be summed up as follows:

As the earliest phase we recognize the final Capsian of Spain, which pervaded the Iberian Peninsula.

To the northwest in Cantabria this culture encountered the Azilian industry, which had been locally developed from the degenerating Magdalenian, and the result was the blending of these two elements—unsymmetrical microliths intermixed with the tiny geometric forms, and designs from the petroglyphs transferred to the Azilian painted pebbles.

From Spain France derived both the final Capsian (Capsio-Tardenoisian) and the Azilian, which resulted in the frequent occurrence of that intermixture of industries known as the "Azilio-Tardenoisian" (Figure 147).

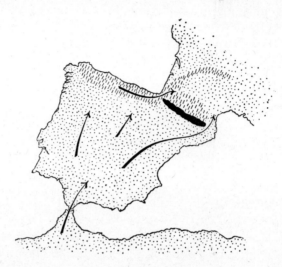

Fig. 147. Migration routes of the Capsio-Tardenoisian and Azilian industries—the former indicated by dots, the latter by dashes.

From France this Azilio-Tardenoisian culture spread eastward and northward. In central Europe and in the cultural phase of Maglemose, however, the Tardenoisian element with its geometric types is more pronounced than the Azilian, represented chiefly by the small round scrapers. In the British Isles, on the contrary, a fairly pure Azilian industry is found, characterized by the occurrence of flat harpoons.

The Late Tardenoisian of western Europe, which is found in contact with the Neolithic, lies outside the scope of this chapter; but it may be remarked in passing that "geometric types"—although of larger size—do occur sporadically, even down to the Age of Copper.

opposite side are left unworked—that is to say, they retain the original shape of the pebble of quartzite (Figure 148). Besides this characteristic form of implement, there is also found a limited number of coarse scrapers and cleavers developed from the same material (Figure 149).

Thus far no implements of worked bone have been found, but in Fonfría and Trescalabres there were discovered two

Fig. 150. An Asturian implement of stag horn, in the collection of the Count de la Vega del Sella.
Two-thirds actual size.

mounds was destroyed, leaving only from three to five feet in thickness of the basal deposits. At nearly all the caverns, however, there are layers of breccia adhering to the roofs of the caves and formed by the sinter deposit on the former surface of the mound; and this makes it possible to determine exactly the original dimensions of these Asturian shell mounds (Figures 152, 153), often extending high above the level of the existing deposit.

The erosive action of the present geologic phase naturally varies according to local conditions. At many sites—as, for instance, at Balmori—this action had already progressed so far by Neolithic times that the cave entrance was clear once more for the new inhabitants to dwell within. At other sites —as, for instance, at Riera—the cave entrance was completely blocked by the Asturian sinter deposit and the loose-lying strata of molluscs beneath it, so that only the outer unsheltered part of the shell mound had been washed away and scattered.

It is interesting to note that evidences of a post-glacial optimum climate, such as have long been known for the north, are now being accumulated for southwestern Europe. As previously remarked, this coincides with the warm moist phase of the Asturian, during which the edible periwinkle, so abundant during Palæolithic times, completely disappears, while the characteristic mollusc of this phase is the top-shell, *Trochus lineatus,* absolutely unknown in Palæolithic and Epipalæolithic times. More recently the coast climate of northern Spain has become somewhat less mild, so that the periwinkle has reappeared although the top-shell still persists.

To this same climatic phase should be assigned the peats and lignites of the western littoral of France—a view which is further confirmed by the occurrence of an Asturian station near Biarritz. This would also indicate the probability that the peats of the so-called "Infraneolithic" in the region of the Seine and the Somme belong to the same period.

Furthermore, the "black earth" ("tierras negras") of southern Spain and northern Morocco also belongs to this period. Beneath it—in the province of Cadiz—lie deposits of the Early Palæolithic, while Neolithic deposits are found

Fig. 153. The cave of Arnero near Posada, Asturias, showing the right wall of the cave. 1 Original height of the Asturian shell mound. 2 Present floor of the cave. 3 Aurignacian deposits with remains of Merck's rhinoceros (*R. merckii*).

in direct contact with its upper surface. As this apparently recent formation could not have been deposited under the present arid climatic conditions, it bears witness to a previous phase with a more humid climate.[5]

Somewhat more recent than the typical Asturian deposits is a group of shell mounds very similar in general features, but distinguished by a greater abundance of mussel shells, and by the occurrence of remains of the domestic sheep. In these mounds only quartzite pebbles are found,—generally of a rounded oval shape,—in which the only evidence of human handiwork consists of one or two shallow circular indentations worked into one or both sides. With these are found coarse-pointed, unpolished awls of bone. There is no trace of pottery.

In a third, yet more recent, group of sites, shells of mussels and snails are still more abundant. No stone implements have been found as yet, but the deposits contain shards of coarse pottery, scorched only on the inside, showing that the food was cooked by means of heated stones. It is of interest to know that in certain localities in the province of Guipuzcoa—even at the present day—milk is scalded in wooden vessels called "kaiku" by means of a heated stone called "esnekoarriya" or "milk stone" being immersed in it. (Basque Museum of San Sebastián.) As it would be very difficult to extract the living molluscs from the small shells of the periwinkle and top-shell, and as these shells do not seem to have been crushed or roasted, it may therefore be assumed that both in Palæolithic and Epipalæolithic times molluscs were stewed in wooden or leather vessels.

Discovery sites of the last two subdivisions are not sufficiently numerous and thoroughly investigated to afford a complete concept of the degree of cultural progress attained. Nevertheless, it seemed that a reference to them could not well be omitted, as they appear to constitute a phase transitional to the true Neolithic.

This much at least is certain, that the typical Asturian industry presents a Protoneolithic cultural phase, excessively specialized for the needs of tribes dwelling along the seacoast, and that this industry extended at least along the entire Cantabrian littoral, being practiced by peoples whose chief occupations were fishing and gathering molluscs. In point of time this phase is intermediate between the age of the shell mounds of Portugal, which are Capsio-Tardenoisian, and that of the kjökkenmöddings of northern Europe, with their Early Neolithic pottery; from which it may be concluded that chronologically it cannot be so very far removed from the Campignian culture, which we will now proceed to consider.

In France the Azilio-Tardenoisian is followed by an industry known as the Campignian, which is truly Protoneolithic in character, and introduces, as it were, a new and entirely different world in its cultural aspect. The name is derived from that of the hill of Campigny near Blagny-sur-Bresle, Seine-Inférieure, where in 1897 P. Salmon, G. d'Ault du Mesnil, and L. Capitan explored with great care certain artificial pits or depressions that had served as dwellings for prehistoric man. The faunal remains found here are limited to those of the stag, together with those of horse and ox—a fact which seems to indicate that the Campignian peoples practiced the art of stock raising, while the discovery of crude hand mills and of the impressions of barley seeds on shards of coarse pottery leads to the inference that they also cultivated plants. No implements of polished stone were found. A number of the flint implements bear a strong resemblance to the clumsy forms of the Early Palæolithic— as, for instance, the scrapers, hammer-stones, and planing tools. Others, such as the picks and choppers (tranchets), have finely finished edges and are more or less trapezoid in form (Figure 154). The last-named implements seem to have been hafted, and that in such curious fashion that the handle formed an angle with the head of the implement. The picks and "tranchets" are the characteristic implements of this culture, which is admirably represented in northern and central France, in Belgium, Scandinavia, and northern Germany. It is of rare occurrence in England. In the south it is found in Italy, Asia Minor, and Syria. Quite often in these regions the industry in stone is associated with slant-edged chisels of bone, and hammers made of stag horn.

In brief, it may be asserted that this Campignian constitutes a civilization entirely different from the Tardenoisian
—a civilization which must be classed as belonging to the
dawn of the Neolithic.

Fenoscandia in northern Europe is a field of study of
great importance for post-glacial geology and archæology.

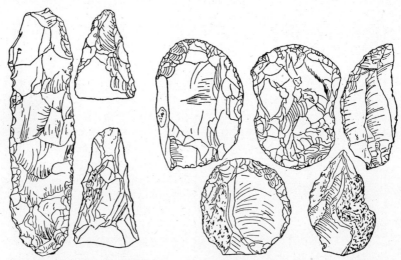

Fig. 154. Typical Campignian implements. After M. Hörnes. *Left:* A
"pic" and two "tranchets." *Right:* Scrapers, planing tools, and
points.

Two-fifths actual size.

In the north the recession of the ice-fields took place—as in
the Alps—in several distinct stages (p. 29).

During the fourth glaciation East and West Prussia,
Posen, Pomerania, Brandenburg, and Mecklenburg were
entirely covered by ice, which also extended over large por-
tions of Silesia, Prussian Saxony, Hanover, and Schleswig-
Holstein.

With the "Germaniglaciar" phase there began the
gradual dissolution of this great glacial mass, continuing
until halted by the Baltic Glacier Stage, which left its mark
in northern Germany and gave rise to the huge terminal
moraine along the southern coast of the Baltic Sea.

During the "Daniglaciar" phase the ice receded from the
Baltic moraine, continuing to retreat until arrested by the
stage of the South Swedish Glacier, with its moraines extending north of Scania. During both these phases a large
part of northern and central Scandinavia was covered by
glaciers, although the elevation of the land was much less
than at present. To the east Scandinavia was bounded by

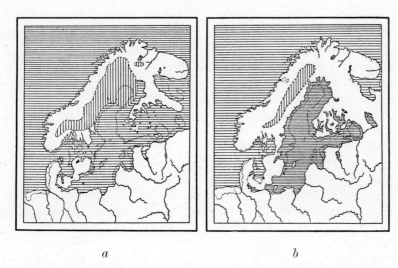

a   *b*

Fig. 155. Scandinavia during the maximum extension of the Yoldia
   Sea (*a*), and during the Ancylus Period (*b*). After G. de Geer.
   Mainland shown in white, sea indicated by horizontal lines, land-
   locked lake by close-ruled horizontal lines, glaciated areas by vertical lines.

the waters of an icy sea which was open to the White Sea
and beneath which northeastern Finland lay submerged.
To the southwest this sea was open to the North Sea and
the region around Stockholm, including lakes Wener and
Wetter, was also submerged (Figure 155, *a*). This glacial
sea which washed the shores of the Scandinavian island was
characterized by an Arctic fauna such as is now found at
Spitzbergen, its principal species being the mollusc known
as *Yoldia arctica,* on which account this period is known as
the Yoldia Period. Other typical species are *Idothea entho-*

ticated dog, at that time the only companion of man, of which remains of two or three individuals were found.[6]

The industrial remains include numerous implements of stone, among them typical geometric microliths of Tarde-noisian form, but there are absolutely no implements of polished stone. Pottery is also unknown. On the other hand, there is a magnificent variety of implements of horn and bone, including chisels, polishers, awls, needles, fish-hooks, and long narrow harpoons.

The Maglemose culture, therefore, is a northern phase of the Epipalæolithic or, more precisely speaking, of the Azilio-Tardenoisian (pp. 336, 337), and belongs to the latter half of the Ancylus Period. Further explorations in Denmark re-sulted in the discovery and excavation of an important site in the peat moor of Svaerdborg, near Vordingborg in the isle of Zealand, by K. Friis Johansen. Evidences of this culture are also found throughout northern Germany from Hanover to East Prussia, and in the Baltic Provinces, where it is well represented by a site in the marl strata of Kunda in Es-thonia. Finally, traces of this "Baltic" culture are also found in southern Sweden and in the peat moors of north-eastern England, where Boyd Dawkins has found a number of typical bone harpoons. The industry in stone is per-fectly characterized by the presence of the minute Tarde-noisian types, and furthermore it already includes some forms which in a measure anticipate those of the subsequent Kjökkenmödding phase. It would seem that implements of horn and bone played a far more important rôle than those of stone, since, in addition to the forms previously men-tioned, there were also hammers with a transverse edge, chisels, daggers, and polishers, as well as fish-hooks, orna-mental beads, needles, and harpoons, both with single and double rows of barbs. Most of these harpoons are long and narrow like the Magdalenian types, while broad forms re-sembling the Azilian occur more rarely. Noteworthy also are the slender points of bone with holes placed lengthwise for the insertion of microliths, by means of which the imple-ment could serve as a harpoon.

The artistic taste displayed by these men of Maglemose times is also surprising. Their artefacts bear numerous

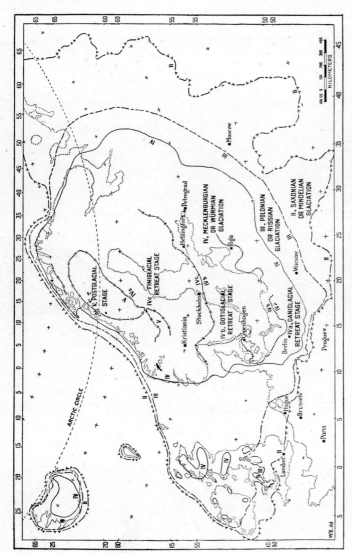

Fig. 157. Lines of the three major glaciations of northern Europe. After Osborn and Reeds (1922). II, III and IV, indicate successive terminal moraines. IV, b, shows the front line of the great Scandinavian glacier when Scania, the Goth country, first became inhabitable, between 12,000 and 10,000 B.C.

(Finiglacial) time took about 2000 years. The time elapsed since the disappearance of the ice at Ragunda, in northern Sweden, to the present time is estimated at about 7000 years.

It is thus possible to obtain the following approximate chronology for Scandinavia:

Gotiglacial Period	10,400–7400 B.C.
Phase of the Central Swedish moraines	7400–6700 B.C.
Scandiglacial Period	6700–4700 B.C.
(Disappearance of the Scandinavian ice-fields)	

This makes it possible to determine the Maglemose Period as about 7000-5000 B.C. and the age of the Kjökken-möddings as about 5000-4000 B.C.

The cultural phases which we have considered in this closing chapter belong in part to the last of the dying Palæolithic, and in part to the dawn of Neolithic civilization.

From a geologic standpoint this last belongs entirely to recent times, during which the European continent has undergone no appreciable modifications either in extent, in climate, or in fauna.

From the standpoint of cultural evolution, however, the Neolithic marks the beginning of a new world. The unstable conditions of the life of nomads and hunters are a thing of the past, and have been replaced by the continuous habitation of sedentary tribes whose dwellings are surrounded by cultivated fields and domestic animals. Chipped stone implements have been almost entirely superseded by those of polished stone, and there is an extensive manufacture of pottery which, on account of its fragility, is of little value in the nomadic life.

This Neolithic civilization in Europe lasted from about 6000 B.C. to 2500 B.C., being followed by the Age of Copper and the Age of Bronze (2500-1000 B.C.).

As the reader has doubtless noticed, our account of Fossil Man is confined almost exclusively to discoveries and investigations made within the limited area of Europe, for the reason that in other parts of the world the ancient past of Humanity is as yet unexplored and shrouded in impenetrable obscurity. This much at least has been made clear by

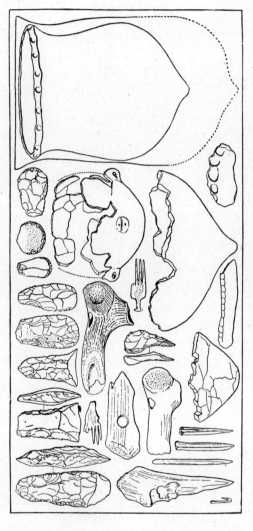

Fig. 158. "Kjökkenmödding" industry—implements found in the shell mounds of Denmark.
After P. Reinecke.
One-sixth actual size.

scientific study of prehistoric man—that the human race is like a mighty and ancient tree; that the peoples of the various cultural phases, both early and late, represent only very young and small branches of the same; and that its roots are lost in the depths of far-distant epochs.

It cannot be denied that our knowledge of the earliest beginnings of our race is only fragmentary, but already so much that is new and astonishing has been revealed that the liveliest interest is aroused and an ever increasing number await the most recent developments in our knowledge of Fossil Man.

APPENDIX

CHAPTER I

NOTES AND BIBLIOGRAPHY

Note 1, p. 3. Bourgeois, Abbé Louis—born 1819, died 1878. His collaborator was the Abbé Delaunay.

Note 2, p. 8. Notice that all lists and tables of races, cultural stages, faunas, etc., throughout this work are given not in chronological but in *stratigraphic* order, beginning with the *most recent* at the top and ending with the *oldest* at the bottom.

Note 3, p. 8. The Strepyan seems to us a purely hypothetic stage; the Mesvinian might actually be considered as Early Palæolithic. See also Note 4 to Chapter IV, p. 408.

ON THE EOLITHIC THEORY

Bourgeois, L.: Etude sur des silex travaillés de Thenay. *C. R. Congr. intern. d'Anthr. et d'Archéol. préhist.* Paris, 1867.

—— Sur les silex considérés comme portant les marques d'un travail humain et découverts dans le terrain miocène de Thenay. *C. R. Congr. intern. d'Anthr. et d'Archéol. préhist.* Brussels, 1872.

Mahoudeau, P., and Capitan, L.: La question de l'homme tertiaire à Thenay. *Rev. mens. de l'Ecole d'Anthr. de Paris,* t. xi, 1901.

Ribeiro, C.: L'Homme tertiaire en Portugal. *C. R. Congr. intern. d'Anthr. et d'Archéol. préhist.* Lisbon, 1880. (Otta.)

Oldham, R. D.: The alleged Miocene Man in Burma. *Nat. Sci.,* vol. vii, 1895.

Verworn, M.: Die archaeolithische Cultur in den Hipparionschichten von Aurillac. *Abhandl. d. k. Gesell. der Wissensch. zu Goettingen,* mathem.-phys. Klasse, n.F., Bd. iv, Nr. 4, 1905. (Puy-Courny.)

Rutot, A.: Le Préhistorique dans l'Europe Centrale. Namur, 1904.

—— Défense des éolithes. *Bull. Soc. d'Anthr. de Bruxelles,* t. xx, 1902.

—— Un grave problème. *Bull. Soc. belge de Géol.,* t. xxi (Mémoires), Brussels, 1907. (Boncelles.)

Abbott, W. J. L.: Worked flints from the Cromer Forest Bed. *Nat. Sci.,* vol. x, 1897.

MacCurdy, G. G.: The Eolithic Problem. *Amer. Anthropologist,* n.s., vol. vii, no. 3, 1905.

DE GEER, G.: Om Skandinaviens geografiska utveckling efter istiden. *Sveriges Geol. Undersökning,* ser. C, no. 161, Stockholm, 1896.

GEIKIE, JAMES: The Classification of European Glacial Deposits. *Journ. Geol.,* vol. iii, Chicago, 1895.

PENCK, A.: La période glaciaire dans les Pyrénées. *Bull. Soc. Hist. Natur. de Toulouse,* t. xix, 1885.

OBERMAIER, H.: Beiträge zur Kenntnis des Quartärs in den Pyrenäen. *Archiv für Anthr.,* n.F., Bd. iv, p. 299, and Bd. v, p. 244, Brunswick, 1906.

BOULE, M.: La topographie glaciaire en Auvergne. *Annales de Géographie,* t. v, Paris, 1896.

PARTSCH, I.: Die Eiszeit in den Gebirgen Europas zwischen dem nordischen und alpinen Eisgebiet. *Geographische Zeitschr.,* Bd. x, Leipsic, 1905.

SAWICKI, L.: Les études glaciaires dans les Karpates. *Annales de Géographie,* t. xxi, Paris, 1912.

SZÉKANY, B.: Die Eiszeit in Ungarn. *Zeitschr. f. Gletscherkunde,* Bd. x, Leipsic, 1917.

CVIJIC, J.: Beobachtungen über die Eiszeit auf der Balkanhalbinsel, in den Südkarpaten und auf dem mysischen Olymp. *Zeitschr. f. Gletscherkunde,* Bd. iii, 1908-1909.

—— L'époque glaciaire dans la Péninsule Balkanique. *Annales de Géographie,* t. xxvi, Paris, 1917.

LUCERNA, R.: Die Eiszeit auf Korsika. *Abhandl. d. k. k. Geographischen Gesell. in Wien,* Bd. ix, Vienna, 1910.

Asia.

ZIMMERMANN, M.: Etudes glaciaires dans le Caucase, le Tian-chan et l'Altai. *Annales de Géographie,* t. xxii, Paris, 1913.

BURRARD, S. G., and HAYDEN, H. H.: A Sketch of the Geography and Geology of the Himalaya Mountains and Tibet. Part iii. London, 1907.

SIMOTOMAI, HIDEZO: Die diluviale Eiszeit in Japan. *Zeitschr. d. Gesell. f. Erdkunde,* Berlin, 1914.

America.

WRIGHT, F.: The Ice Age in North America. New York, 1889.

CHAMBERLIN, T. C., and SALISBURY, R. D.: Geology. Vol. iii, ch. xix. London, 1908.

LEVERETT, F.: Comparison of North American and European Glacial Deposits. *Zeitschr. f. Gletscherkunde,* Bd. iv, 1910.

SIEVERS, W.: Die heutige und die frühere Vergletscherung Sud-amerikas. *Verh. des deutschen Naturforscher- und Ärztetages zu Karlsruhe, 1911,* Teil 1, Leipsic, 1912.

Africa.

GREGORY, J. W.: The Glacial Geology of Mount Kenia. *Quart. Journ. Geol. Soc.,* vol. l, 1894.

—— The Geology of Mount Ruwenzori. *Quart. Journ. Geol. Soc.,* vol. li, 1895.

KLUTE, F.: Ergebnisse der Forschungen am Kilimandscharo. 1912. Berlin, 1920.

Australia.

PENCK, A.: Die Eiszeit Australiens. *Zeitschr. d. Gesell. f. Erdkunde,* Bd. xxxv, Berlin, 1900.

HOWCKIN, W.: Australian Glaciations. *Journ. Geol.,* vol. xx, 1912.

GREGORY, J. W.: A Contribution to the Glacial Geology of Tasmania. *Quart. Journ. Geol. Soc.,* vol. lx, 1904.

Antarctica.

VON DRYGALSKI, E.: Die Antarktis und ihre Vereisung. *Sitzungs-ber. der Bayerischen Akademie der Wissenschaften,* mathem.-phys. Klasse, Munich, 1919.

VOLCANISM, LOESS, AND CLIMATOLOGY

BOULE, M.: L'âge des derniers volcans de France. *La Géographie,* t. xiii, Paris, 1906.

VON RICHTHOFEN, F.: China. Ergebnisse eigener Reisen und darauf gegründeter Studien. (Bd. i, Loess.) Berlin, 1877.

SCHUMACHER, E.: Die Bildung und der Aufbau des oberrheinischen Tieflandes. *Mitt. der Commission f. d. geol. Landesuntersuchung von Elsass-Lothringen,* Bd. ii, Strasbourg, 1890.

OBRUTCHEV, A.: La question de l'origine du loess. *Trudy Geol. Com.,* vol. xv, part 1, Petrograd, 1903.

MERZBACHER, G.: Die Frage der Entstehung des Loesses. *Peter-manns geog. Mitt.,* Gotha, 1913.

SOERGEL, W.: Lösse, Eiszeiten und paläolithische Kulturen. Eine Gliederung und Altersbestimmung der Lösse. Jena, 1919.

DAVID, T. W. EDGEWORTH: Conditions of climate at different geo-logical epochs, with special reference to glacial epochs. *Congr. géol. intern. C. R.,* Sess. x, Mexico, 1906.

Brückner, E.: Über die Klimaschwankungen der Quartärzeit und ihre Ursachen. *Congr. géol. intern. C. R.*, Sess. xi, Stockholm, 1910.

Arldt, T.: Die Ursachen der Klimaschwankungen der Vorzeit, besonders der Eiszeiten. *Zeitschr. f. Gletscherkunde*, Bd. xi, Leipsic, 1919.

CHAPTER III

ORIGINAL TEXT, NOTES, AND BIBLIOGRAPHY

Note 1, p. 37. In reviewing the manuscript of Obermaier's *Fossil Man in Spain* the text of the third chapter was found to be so exceedingly technical as to present grave difficulties to readers unfamiliar with scientific faunal nomenclature. It was therefore revised by Professor Henry Fairfield Osborn—the changes made consisting of a rearrangement and abbreviation of the text, with the addition of a few introductory and explanatory paragraphs. The complete translation of the author's text with no alteration or omission is given below.

Note 2, pp. 39 and 42. This is the view held by Professor H. F. Osborn. Professor Obermaier assigns Heidelberg man to the Second Interglacial Stage. See pp. 292, 396, 397.

FLORA AND FAUNA OF THE GLACIAL EPOCH

Flora of the Glacial Stages—Arctic-Alpine flora—Loess or steppe flora—Flora of the Interglacial Stages—Late Pleistocene floras—Early Pleistocene floras—Fauna—Division between Pliocene and Pleistocene—Fauna of the Glacial Stages—Tundra fauna—Arctic and Alpine fauna—Steppe fauna—Species indifferent to climate—Fauna of the Interglacial Stages—Molluscs—Mammals, their evolution and distribution—Classification of interglacial faunas in Europe—Early Pleistocene fauna—Middle Pleistocene fauna—Late Pleistocene fauna—Pleistocene fauna of Africa—Pleistocene fauna of Asia—Pleistocene fauna of North America—Pleistocene fauna of South America—Pleistocene fauna of Australia—Extinction of Pleistocene species.

In view of the geologic conditions in Europe during the different glacial stages (Plate II), it might be expected that the flora then existing in the territory between the great northern ice-sheet and the Alpine glaciation would be Arctic-Alpine in character. In fact, fossil remains of *Salix polaris, Betula nana, Dryas octopetala, Arctostaphylos uvaursi,* and *Polygonum viviparum* were discovered by A. Nathorst at Schwarzenbach in the Canton of Zürich, Switzerland, directly above the clays of the basal moraine. And he also discovered near Deuben, Saxony, evidence that in former times there was a true northern tundra flora along the border of the great northern ice-field. In the post-glacial tuffs of the Swabian plain near Schussenried there have been found species such as *Hypnum sarmentosum, H. aduncum* var. *grœnlandicum,* and *H. fluitans* var. *tenuissimum,* which at the present time are restricted to districts near seventy degrees north latitude and to the loftiest summits of the Alps. It would be easy to enumerate a list of typical deposits in Germany, the Baltic region, Denmark, and southern Scandinavia—some belonging to the glacial stages, and some to the first post-glacial retreat—their Arctic character being indicated by the presence of mosses, Arctic willows (*Salix retusa, S. herbacea, S. polaris*), *Betula nana,* and *Dryas octopetala.* But we will mention only that this same boreal flora also occurs repeatedly in England—as, for example, north of London, where Clement Reid has found a typical Arctic flora, including *Salix lapponum, Armeria arctica,* and others, in glacial deposits of the Lea Valley. Nevertheless, in those districts where glaciation was less severe, as in Bohemia and the region of the middle Rhine, there were probably some sparse stunted groves of birch, quaking poplar, and Scotch fir.

The tundra flora of those areas strongly affected by the ice indicates the rigorous climate of a glacial stage, with very long winters and very short, cold summers. The beginning and end of each glaciation appears to have been marked by a typical steppe phase, its geologic equivalent being the loess already described.

The fossil flora of the steppes shows a near relationship to that of the tundras, the transition from one to the other being hardly perceptible. As may be seen at the present time in Asia, the winter of the steppes is very severe, with many windstorms, conducing largely to the denudation of their surface. The summer is short, but comparatively warm, and in consequence there is an abundant growth of grass and shrubs. Similar conditions doubtless prevailed in Europe during the formation of the Pleistocene loess, and sparse growths of stunted trees bore witness to their inclemency. In the deposit of the "Mammoth Hunters" at Gobelsburg, Austria, were found pieces of carbonized wood, identified as *Pinus,* embedded in the loess. From a study of these pieces it was concluded that the annual growth of the Pleistocene *Pinus* was but a tenth of that of pines in the same region at the present time.

It must be borne in mind that what has been said of tundra and steppe conditions applies only to central Europe and the northern part of western Europe. Conditions in southern Europe, including the southern slope of the Alps were quite different. On the northern Alpine slopes there was a scanty growth of conifers which extended more than 500 meters above sea level. On the southern borders of the Alps the present limit of perpetual snow is 3000 meters, while during the Glacial Epoch it stood at 1800 meters. Such conditions would bring the tree line to a height of 900 meters above sea level, so that in these parts long glacial streams might have advanced through a veritable forest region. Still milder conditions prevailed in the Mediterranean zone, strictly speaking.

Far different is the climatic aspect of the interglacial stages. Under the influence of a warm and humid climate the steppe disappeared, retreating farther and farther eastward. The interglacial vegetation was characterized by a deciduous forest flora, as evidenced by a number of deposits. This flora indicates a climate more temperate than the present. At Celle-sous-Moret, Seine-et-Marne, lying above Pleistocene gravels containing remains of *Elephas antiquus*, there is a tuff deposit with fossilized remains of *Ficus carica* (fig), *Buxus sempervirens* (box), *Laurus canariensis* (Canary laurel), and *Cercis siliquastrum* (Judas tree). The presence of these indicates a climate both warm and humid, and a flora with Dalmatian features. The mean annual temperature of the Seine Basin was then from 15° to 16° C., while now it is not over 11° (Munier-Chalmas). The upper levels of this "warm" deposit at Celle-sous-Moret are composed of tuffs with flora indicating a cooler climate associated with an Acheulean industry.

Equally important are the discoveries in the breccia of Hötting, near Innsbrück in the Tyrol. This site is 1200 meters above sea level, on the left bank of the Inn. The breccia lies above basal moraines belonging to the second, or, more probably, to the third glaciation. Above it lies a moraine of the Fourth Glacial Stage.[1] R. von Wettstein has enumerated forty-one species of plants occurring in this deposit. Among them may be mentioned *Rhamnus hœttingensis* (a new species of buckthorn related most closely to *Rhamnus latifolia* of the Azores and Canary Islands), *Orobus* sp., *Rhododendrum ponticum* (the Pontic Alpine rose which now grows wild in southwestern Spain, Pontus, and the Caucasus, where the limit of perpetual snow is over 3000 meters above sea level), *Adenostyles schenckii, Arbutus unedo* (?), *Buxus sempervirens* (now found in southern and southeastern Europe as well as in the forest zone of Colcida, where their highest limit is 1800 meters below the snow line). None of these species is found at the present time in the neighborhood of Hötting. There are also other species in the breccia which still exist near Hötting, but not above an altitude of 1200

[1] Some authorities (Lepsius, Rothplatz) have held the Hötting breccia to be preglacial; but since the recent researches of O. Ampferer it is no longer possible to entertain any serious question as to the interglacial age of this deposit.

b Middle levels—Pleistocene deposits.

Elephas primigenius
Rhinoceros tichorhinus
Equus caballus
Bison priscus
Felis spelæa
Ursus spelæus
Hyæna spelæa
*Canis lagopus
*Rangifer tarandus
Cervus elaphus
Cervus megaceros
*Lepus variabilis
Antilope saiga
*Capella rupicapra
*Capra ibex
*Gulo borealis

Associated with Proto-Solutrean and Aurignacian industry. At the base a sterile layer with abundant remains of *Myodes torquatus* and *M. obensis*.

a Lower levels—Pleistocene deposits.

Ursus spelæus	frequent
*Rangifer tarandus	frequent
Equus caballus	frequent
Elephas primigenius	
Bison priscus	
*Capra ibex	
Canis lupus	
*Canis lagopus	
*Lepus variabilis	
*Myodes lemnus	very rare

Associated with Mousterian industry, both late and primitive.

3. The cave of Šipka near Stramberg in northern Moravia. Fauna according to K. Maška.

b Upper levels with Magdalenian industry.

Ursus arctos	
*Rangifer tarandus	frequent
Equus caballus	
Elephas primigenius	
Rhinoceros tichorhinus	
*Myodes torquatus	frequent
Lagomys pusillus	
Spermophilus rufescens	
Bos priscus	
Cervus alces	
*Canis lagopus	
*Lepus variabilis	

a Lower levels with Mousterian industry.

    Felis spelæa
    Felis pardus
    Hyæna spelæa
    Cuon europæus
    Ursus spelæus
    Ursus arctos
    *Gulo borealis
    *Arctomys marmotta
    *Myodes lemnus
    Bos primigenius
    Bos priscus
    *Capella rupicapra
    *Rangifer tarandus
    Equus caballus
    Elephas primigenius
    Rhinoceros tichorhinus

The tundra phase is followed by a cold steppe phase, with the loess as its typical deposit. In the steppes of Asia at the present time the terrible winter storms with heavy snow cause the death of hundreds of thousands of animals. Subsequently, as the abrupt seasonal changes of climate ensue, their bodies are covered by the loess transported by the windstorms of spring and autumn. It is thus easy to see why such abundant fossil remains are found in the loess of the Glacial Epoch.

A careful study of these remains shows that all the animals of the tundra lived also throughout the cold steppe phase. This mixture is not surprising when one considers that in nature two successive climatic and faunal phases are not sharply separated, but the transition is gradual and almost imperceptible. Nevertheless, it may be noted that the musk ox and lemming are of much rarer occurrence in the typical steppe, while at the same time new forms appear which are never found in the tundra and are also absent from the forest.

TYPICAL STEPPE FORMS[4]

Great jerboa	*Alactaga jaculus* Pallas
Spermophile	*Spermophilus citillus* Blasius
Rufous spermophile	*Spermophilus rufescens* Keys and Blasius
Steppe marmot	*Arctomys (Ochotona) bobac* Blasius
Tailless hare	*Lagomys pusillus* Pallas
Saiga antelope	*Saiga tartarica* Pallas

[4] The center of distribution for this fauna was in eastern Europe, embracing the south Russian, Aralo-Caspian region lying between the Dniester and Don rivers and the Black Sea.

During the steppe phase the woolly elephant or mammoth (*Elephas primigenius* Pallas, Figure 19, *c*) attained its maximum predominance, and also the woolly rhinoceros (*Rhinoceros tichorhinus* Cuvier, Figure 12).

The mammoth lived in almost all of Europe except the far north, its range extending southward as far as the Cantabrian coast and the province of Gerona in northern Spain, and also to the environs of Rome in central Italy, the northern Balkan regions, and the south shore of the Black Sea (Anatolia and the region south of the Caucasus).

The mammoth was a typical northern species, being marvelously protected from cold by its woolly coat. Its constant companion was the woolly rhinoceros, which was absent only in Italy. Remains of the Saiga antelope are found throughout central Europe and westward as far as Lot-et-Garonne, France, and the valley of the Thames, England. Very typical were the steppe horse and the kiang, or Asiatic wild ass (*Equus hemionus*); while less abundant were the wild cattle (*Bos primigenius*) and bison (*Bos priscus*), the stag or red deer (*Cervus elaphus*), the wapiti (*Cervus canadensis*), the maral deer (*Cervus maral*), the Siberian fallow deer (*Cervus pygargus*), and the steppe porcupine (*Hystrix hirsutirostris*).

Of the many Palæolithic loess stations in the open in Europe the following may be mentioned:

1. Loess deposit at Thiede near Brunswick, with Aurignacian industry. Fauna according to A. Nehring.

> *Equus caballus
> **Elephas primigenius*
> **Rhinoceros tichorhinus*
> *Alactaga jaculus
> *Lagomys pusillus
> **Spermophilus rufescens*
> *Felis spelæa*
> *Hyæna spelæa*
> *Cervus megaceros*
> [5]‡*Canis lagopus*
> ‡*Rangifer tarandus*
> ‡*Myodes lemnus*
> ‡*Lepus variabilis*
> ‡*Ovibos moschatus*

2. Loess station in the open at Předmost, Moravia, site of the Solutrean "Mammoth Hunters." Fauna according to K. Maška.

[5] Fauna marked with double dagger are found at the base of the deposit.

*Elephas primigenius	very frequent
Canis lagopus	very frequent
Canis lupus	very frequent
Lepus variabilis	very frequent
Rangifer tarandus	very frequent
*Equus caballus	very frequent
Gulo borealis	very frequent
Ursus arctos	frequent
Felis spelæa	frequent
Canis vulpes	frequent
Bos primigenius	rare
Bos priscus	rare
*Rhinoceros tichorhinus	rare
Ovibos moschatus	rare
Myodes torquatus	very rare
Cervus alces	very rare
Capra ibex	very rare
Castor fiber	very rare
Felis pardus	very rare

The character of the cold fauna of Předmost is unquestionably due to the inland situation of this celebrated deposit.

The faunal lists cited above belong to the fourth or final glaciation, and to its cold post-glacial phases, and therefore represent the most recent glacial fauna.[6]

Little is known of the Third Glacial Stage. Gutzwiller and Mühlberg have remarked the presence of *Elephas primigenius, Rangifer tarandus,* and *Cervus elaphus* in the Riss gravels of Switzerland. Of the same age is the "Mammoth Loam" of Cannstatt, near Stuttgart, Würtemberg. The geologic age of this loam has been determined in masterly fashion by E. Koken. It contains remains of *Elephas primigenius, Rhinoceros tichorhinus, Bos primigenius, Cervus elaphus, Cervus megaceros germaniæ, Rangifer tarandus, Equus caballus,* and *Ursus spelæus.*

It would seem that a part of the fauna of the Forest Bed of Cromer, England, belongs to the same period. According to E. T. Newton the following species are found there: *Hippopotamus major, Elephas trogontherii* (not *E. meridionalis), Machairodus* sp., *Equus stenonis,* and others, apparently with an intermixture of other faunal elements, such as *Gulo luscus, Ovibos moschatus,* and others.

[6] As explained later (Chapter VIII), it is impossible to assign the Mousterian to the Third Glacial Stage, in which case the lower levels of Sirgenstein, Šipka, and others would date back to the Riss. If this opinion were justified—which we do not admit—we would have for the third glaciation a very ample faunal list, differing in no particular from that of the fourth.

The warm fauna agrees well with that of the Second Interglacial Stage, and consequently the cold elements would correspond to the following Third Glacial Stage. Of the same age, or perhaps still older, is the *Rangifer tarandus* of Steinheim on the Murr, and the *Præovibos priscus* of Frankenhausen in Thuringia. In the lower gravels of Süssenborn, near Weimar, from eight to ten meters below the surface, W. Soergel came upon remains of *Rangifer* cfr. *tarandus*, which may probably be attributed to the Second Glacial Stage. These gravels were doubtless deposited previous to the maximum glaciation of Scandinavia, which covered that region with ice.

Glancing at the faunal lists already given and at those following, it will be noted that a number of species are common to both the warm and the cold climate. These species consist either of those that are easily adaptable, or those that flourish indifferently in a cold or warm environment. Among the most frequently occurring forms are the carnivores—the cave bear (*Ursus spelæus*, Figure 14), cave lion (*Felis spelæa*, Figure 15), cave hyena (*Hyæna spelæa*), leopard (*Felis pardus*), lynx (*Felis lynx*), wildcat (*Felis catus ferus*), wolf (*Canis lupus*), fox (*Canis vulpes*), and cyon (*Cuon europæus*). Of common occurrence also are a number of Cervidæ, including the giant deer (*Cervus megaceros*, also known as *C. euryceros* or *C. hibernicus*), stag (*C. elaphus*), and moose (*Alces palmatus* or *C. alces*). The Equidæ are represented by the horse (*Equus caballus*), both forest and Celtic types; and the Bovidæ by the wild ox (*Bos primigenius*) and bison (*Bos priscus*, Figure 17). In addition there are the otter (*Lutra vulgaris*), beaver (*Castor fiber*), and others. In the Lower Pleistocene many of these species are represented by their more primitive ancestral forms.

The frequent occurrence of roe deer, wild boar, bear, rabbit, wild cattle, and bison (*Cervus capreolus*, *Sus scrofa ferus*, *Ursus arctos*, *Lepus cuniculus*, *Bos primigenius*, and *Bos priscus*) indicates a mild climate, intermediate between the extremes of glacial and interglacial times.

It has been shown that the interglacial stages were characterized by warm forest phases, such as are typically represented by the flora of Celle-sous-Moret and Hötting (p. 380). At these times the climate was much warmer than at present, but, nevertheless, there is no very strong reason to assume that all of Europe was then covered by an impenetrable forest. The forests alternated with districts of bush and meadow, and it is probable that warm steppes extended over large areas.

Convincing evidence for the warm interglacial stages is afforded by the presence of certain molluscs, such as *Zonites acieformis*, *Palu-*

nyms, *H. major* Owen, *H. amphibius* Falconer) during the Glacial Epoch was distributed throughout the Mediterranean region with the exception of the Balkans. It extended from Africa by way of Tunis and Sicily into Italy, Spain, France, and southern England, and remains have also been found on the east bank of the Rhine at one site only, that of Mosbach-Biebrich near Wiesbaden.

Very similar is the area of distribution for the southern elephant (*Elephas meridionalis*). In western Europe it seems to have penetrated no further than the Rhine, and in the southeast of Europe its northern limit was the region of the Black Sea (Rumania, basin of the river Kuban, north of the Caucasus).

The straight-tusked or ancient elephant (*Elephas antiquus*) was another species common to the Mediterranean zone and also to western and central Europe, penetrating as far north as Antwerp, Berlin, and Warsaw. To the southeast the northern limit of its range was the northern shores of the Black Sea (Bessarabia) and the region of the lower Danube (Figure 19). The distribution of *Rhinoceros merckii* was almost identical.

Remains of *E. antiquus*—both large and dwarf forms—are also found in a number of the Mediterranean islands, such as Sardinia, Sicily, Malta,[7] Crete, and Cyprus.

E. trogontherii was, on the contrary, a species of more northern and continental habitat. The true "type" is limited to southern Russia, Germany, and England. Occasionally dwarf forms are found. It is of rare occurrence in France, and seems to have been completely lacking in Spain, Italy, and the Balkans.

The elasmothere (*Elasmotherium sibiricum* Fischer), a pachyderm adapted to exclusively herbivorous diet, occupies a unique position. It is related to the *Rhinoceros* type, and has been found in the Pleistocene of the Rhine and of southern Russia as far as the lower Volga and the Kirghiz steppes. According to A. Borissiak (1914) its occurrence in Siberia is doubtful.

Monkeys are represented in northern Italy by *Macacus florentinus* and *M. ausonius*, in southern France by *M. tolosanus*, in Würtemberg by *M. (Inuus) suevicus*, in Hungary (at Csàrnota, Baranya) by *Macacus*, nov. sp., in England by *M. pliocenus* of the Pleistocene "loam" of Grays, Essex, and in Sardinia by a *Macacus* of oriental type.

An authoritative classification of the numerous deposits with typically warm fauna has not yet been made. It has been hindered by the many divergences which have arisen in the attempt to define

[7] Three species are found in Malta—*Elephas antiquus, E. melitensis*, and *E. mnaidrensis*.

Lynchus issiodorensis
Castor fiber
Canis neschersensis
Hyæna arvernensis
Hippopotamus major(?)

Upper level.
Elephas trogontherii primigenius

Sands of Mauer, near Heidelberg, Baden, Germany.
(O. Schötensack and A. Wurm.)

*Elephas antiquus (frequent)
Rhinoceros etruscus (frequent)
Cervus elaphus (frequent)
Alces latifrons
Cervus capreolus
Bison priscus (frequent)
Equus stenonis (rare)
E. mosbachensis (rare)
Ursus arvernensis
**U. deningeri*
**Felis leo fossilis* (=*spelæa*)
F. pardus
F. catus
Canis neschersensis
Sus scrofa priscus
Castor fiber

Süssenborn, near Weimar, Germany.
(E. Wüst and W. Soergel.)

**Elephas trogontherii*[10]
Rhinoceros etruscus
Rhinoceros sp.
Equus süssenbornensis
E. cfr. *germanicus*
Bison priscus var. *süssenbornensis*
Bison sp.
Leptobos(?) sp.
Cervus elaphus trogontherii
*Cervus euryceros
Cervus capreolus
Cervus sp.
Alces latifrons
Castor fiber
Ursus sp.

[10] According to W. Soergel *Elephas meridionalis* and *Elephas primigenius* are not found in this deposit.

Steinheim on the Murr, Würtemberg.

(W. Soergel.)

Lower complex.

Elephas trogontherii
E. antiquus
Rhinoceros merckii
Cervus elaphus
C. megaceros germaniæ
Equus cfr. germanicus
Bison priscus

Upper complex.

Elephas primigenius
Rhinoceros tichorhinus
Ursus spelæus
Equus germanicus
Bos primigenius
Megaceros germaniæ

Abbeville, Somme, France.

(V. Commont.)

Elephas (meridionalis) trogontherii
E. antiquus
Hippopotamus major
Rhinoceros etruscus
R. merckii
R. leptorhinus (? H.O.)
Machairodus
Cervus solilhacus
C. somonensis
Equus stenonis

Solilhac, near Blanzac, Haute-Loire, France.

(M. Boule.)

Elephas cfr. meridionalis[11]
Rhinoceros merckii
Hippopotamus amphibius
Cervus elaphus
C. intermedius
C. solilhacus
Dama somonensis

[11] Probably *Elephas trogontherii* (H.O.).

Breccias with warm fauna at Montmaurin, Es-Taliens, and Montsaunés in southern France.

(E. Harlé and M. Boule.)

Rhinoceros merckii
Machairodus latidens
Hyæna striata
H. fusca
Macacus tolosanus
Hystrix major

To this group belongs the warm fauna of the "Forest Bed of Cromer," England (p. 388), and other forms.

The Late Pleistocene fauna of the Third Interglacial Stage—late phase of *Elephas antiquus*—is characterized as follows:

Last appearance of *Elephas antiquus, Rhinoceros merckii,* and *Hippopotamus major.*

Frequent occurrence of *Ursus spelæus, Felis spelæa, Hyæna spelæa,* and *Cervus megaceros.*

This phase corresponds to the "Chellean" of E. Haug—according to him the Third Interglacial Stage.

From their stratigraphy there can be no doubt that the following deposits in Switzerland belong to the Third Interglacial Stage: Flurlingen, near Schaffhausen, with remains of *Rhinoceros merckii;* and the coal pits of Dürnten in the canton of Zürich, with remains of *Elephas antiquus* and *Rhinoceros merckii,* which were covered by moraines of the Fourth Glacial Stage.

Grotte du Prince, northern Italy, near Mentone.

(M. Boule.)

Lower levels.

Lepus cuniculus
Ursus arctos
U. spelæus
Hyæna spelæa
Felis pardus
F. leo
Equus cfr. *stenonis*
E. caballus
Rhinoceros merckii
Hippopotamus major
Sus scrofa
Cervus elaphus
C. capreolus
C. (dama) somonensis
Capra ibex (rare)

Capella rupicapra
Bos primigenius or *priscus*
Elephas antiquus

Tuffs of Burgtonna and Graefentonna, near Gotha, Germany.

Elephas antiquus
Rhinoceros merckii
Felis spelæa
Hyæna spelæa
Cervus euryceros
Ursus cfr. *arctos*

"Chellean" gravels of the Seine, Paris.

Trogontherium cuvieri
Hyæna spelæa
Ursus spelæus
Equus caballus
Rhinoceros merckii
Elephas antiquus
Hippopotamus major

"Chellean" gravels of the Thames Valley, England.

Corbicula fluminalis
Unio litoralis
Elephas antiquus
Hippopotamus major

Lack of space prevents giving any detailed account of the Pleisto-cene fauna in other continents. Northern Africa is of especial interest as regards zoögeography on account of the relations of its fauna to that of Europe.

In the neighborhood of Constantine P. Thomas has distinguished three successive levels, as follows:

a Fluvio-lacustrine deposits with *Elephas meridionalis, Hipparion gracile, Equus stenonis, Hippopotamus hipponensis, Bubalus antiquus, Palæoreas gaudryi, Cynocephalus atlanticus,* etc.

b Alluvial deposits of the high levels with *Equus stenonis, Hippopotamus amphibius, Bos primigenius,* etc.

c Alluvial deposits of the low levels with *Elephas atlanticus, Equus africanus, Hippopotamus amphibius, Camelus* sp., etc.

Other deposits contained remains of *Felis antiqua, Hyæna vulgaris, Ursus libycus, Canis aureus, Camelus dromedarius, Mastodon borsoni, Elephas jolensis, Elephas africanus, Macacus proinuus,* etc.

A part of this fauna still survives in the South. Only the genus *Ursus* has completely disappeared from Africa.

In Asia the various caves of Lebanon, according to G. Zumoffen, afford the following fauna: *Ursus syriacus, Felis spelæa, Equus caballus, Rhinoceros tichorhinus, Bison priscus,* and others. The Pleistocene fauna of the island of Java is treated later (Chapter IX). From various deposits in China the following have been reported: *Felis* sp., *Hyæna sinensis, Equus* sp., *Rhinoceros sinensis, R. simplicidens* (approaching *R. merckii*), *Tapirus sinensis, Elephas namadicus* (=*E. antiquus*) from the caves of Zetchuan and Yunnan, and *Rhinoceros tichorhinus, Elephas primigenius, Bos primigenius, Bos priscus* from various loess deposits, according to M. Schlosser.

In America a different mammal fauna is found, which presents a combination of forms, at times in the highest degree extraordinary. The fauna of North America consists chiefly of species derived by migration from Asia, such as *Elephas primigenius* and very probably *Rangifer tarandus, Ovibos moschatus, Cervus alces, Bos bison, Ursus arctos, Castor fiber,* and a number of large felines.[12] In addition to these species there is also a completely autochthonous fauna which includes *Mastodon ohioticus* and a number of independent species of *Equus caballus, Platygonus, Erethizon dorsatum, Tapirus,* etc.

We will exclude a third group, consisting of forms which migrated from South America, and which are found only in the southern part of North America, being entirely lacking in Canada. These are Edentates of the genera *Megatherium, Mylodon,* and *Megalonyx.*

Thanks to the labors of H. F. Osborn, W. D. Matthew, B. Brown, E. D. Cope, and W. H. Dall it is possible to distinguish the three following groups:

a Early Pleistocene: *Mastodon mirificus, M. americanus; Elephas imperator, E. columbi; Hipparion; Equus excelsus, complicatus, fraternus, scotti, pacificus, occidentalis; Tapirus; Camelus americanus, Holomeniscus, Eschatius, Camelops; Antilocapra; Platygonus; Canis lupus; Bison occidentalis, B. alleni; Lutra; Castor; Microtus; Cynomys, Thomomys, Glyptotherium; Megalonyx leidyi; Mylodon harlani, M. sodalis,* etc.

b Middle Pleistocene: *Mastodon americanus; Elephas columbi; Tapirus americanus; Equus fraternus, pectinatus; Canis priscolatrans; Ursus americanus; Arctodus leidyi; Felis atrox; Smilodon mercieri, gracile; Mylohyus pennsylvanicus; Cervus canadensis; Alces americanus; Odocoileus virginianus; Bison antiquus, latifrons; Erethizon dorsatum; Sciurus calicinus; Lagomys; Lepus;*

---

[12] *Rhinoceros, Hippopotamus, Ursus spelæus,* and *Hyæna spelæa* are entirely lacking.

—— Note complémentaire sur les tufs quaternaires de La Celle, près Moret. *Bull. Soc. géol. de France,* 3ᵉ sér., t. v, 1877.

DE SAPORTA, G.: Sur l'existence constatée du figuier aux environs de Paris à l'époque quaternaire. *Bull. Soc. géol. de France,* 3ᵉ sér., t. ii, 1874.

VON WETTSTEIN, R.: Die fossile Flora der Höttinger Breccie. *Denkschriften d. mathem.-naturw. Klasse d. k. Akad. d. Wissenschaften in Wien,* Bd. lix, Vienna, 1892.

AMPFERER, O.: Über die Aufschliessung der liegenden Moräne unter der Höttinger Breccie. *Zeitschr. f. Gletscherkunde,* Bd. viii, 1914.

—— Verteidigung des interglazialen Alters der Höttinger Breccie. *Petermanns geog. Mitt.,* Bd. lxi, Gotha, 1915.

FAUNA
GENERAL WORKS OF REFERENCE

OSBORN, H. F.: The Age of Mammals in Europe, Asia, and North America. New York, 1910.

—— Review of the Pleistocene of Europe, Asia, and Northern Africa. *Annals New York Acad. Sci.,* vol. xxvi, 1915.

—— Men of the Old Stone Age. New York, 1915.

GAUDRY, A., and BOULE, M.: Matériaux pour l'histoire des temps quaternaires.
Fasc. 1. Fossiles de la Mayenne. Paris, 1876.
Fasc. 2. De l'existence des Saïgas en France. 1880.
Fasc. 3. L'Elasmotherium. 1888.
Fasc. 4. Les oubliettes de Gargas. 1892.

FRECH, F.: Die Säugetiere des Quartärs. *Lethaea geognostica,* Ser. iii, *Känozoikum,* Bd. ii, *Quartär,* Abt. i, Stuttgart, 1904.

HUE, E.: Musée ostéologique. Etude de la faune quaternaire. Paris, 1907.

DEL PAN, I.: Paleogeografía de los mamíferos cuaternarios de Europa y Norte de Africa. *Comisión de Investigaciones Paleontológicas y Prehistóricas,* Memoria 21, Madrid, 1918.

MONOGRAPHS
Europe.
Fauna of the glacial stages.

NEHRING, A.: Über Tundren und Steppen der Jetzt- und Vorzeit. Berlin, 1890.

SCHMIDT, R. R.: Die diluviale Vorzeit Deutschlands. Stuttgart, 1912. (Teil 2, by E. Koken, is devoted to palæontology.)

MAŠKA, K.: Der diluviale Mensch in Mähren. Neutitschein, 1886.

KOKEN, E.: Die faunistische Charakterisierung des älteren und jüngeren Lösses. *Ber. über die paläethnologische Konferenz in Tübingen, 1911*, Brunswick, 1912. (The Mammoth Loam and interglacial tuffs of Cannstatt.)

BAYGER, J. A., HOYER, H., KIERNIK, E., KULCZYŃSKI, W., ŁOMNICKI, M., ŁOMNICKI, J., MIERZIJEWSKI, W., NIEZABITOWSKI, E., RACIBORSKI, M., SZAFER, W., and SCHILLE, F.: Wykopaliska Starunskie:—Muzeum imienia Dzieduszyckich we Lwowie, vol. xv, Cracow, 1914. (Treats of the Pleistocene fauna from the petroleum deposits of Starunia, Poland.)

Evolution and phylogeny of the Pleistocene fauna.

POHLIG, H.: Dentition und Kraniologie des *Elephas antiquus* Falc. mit Beiträgen über *Elephas primigenius* Blum. und *Elephas meridionalis* Nesti. *Nova Acta d. K. Leop. Carol. Deutschen Akad. d. Naturf.*, Bd. liii, 1888; Bd. lvii, 1892.

SOERGEL, W.: *Elephas trogontherii* Pohl. und *Elephas antiquus* Falc., ihre Stammesgeschichte und ihre Bedeutung für die Gliederung des deutschen Diluviums. *Palæontographica*, Bd. lx, 1913.

—— Die Stammesgeschichte der Elephanten. *Centralbl. f. Mineralogie, Geologie und Paläontologie*, Stuttgart, 1915.

OSBORN, H. F.: Phylogeny of the Rhinoceroses of Europe. *Bull. Amer. Mus. Nat. Hist.*, vol. xiii, 1900.

WURM, A.: Über *Rhinoceros etruscus* Falc. von Mauer a. d. Elsenz bei Heidelberg. *Verh. d. naturhist.-medizin. Vereins zu Heidelberg*, n.F., Bd. xii, Heidelberg, 1912.

BOULE, M.: Révision des espèces européennes de *Machairodus*. *Bull. Soc. géol. de France*, 4e sér., t. i, 1902.

—— Les grands Chats des cavernes. *Annales de Paléontologie*, t. i, Paris, 1906.

SCHLOSSER, M., BIRKNER, F., and OBERMAIER, H.: Die Bären- oder Tischoferhöhle im Kaisertal bei Kufstein. *Abhandl. d. k. Bayer. Akad. d. Wissenschaft*, Klasse ii, Bd. xxiv, Abt. ii, Munich, 1909. (Ursidæ.)

POHLIG, H.: Die Cerviden des thüringischen Diluvialtravertins, mit Beiträgen über andere diluviale und über rezente Hirschformen. *Palaeontographica*, Bd. xxxix, 1892.

RÜTIMEYER, L.: Beitrag zur Kenntnis der fossilen Pferde, etc. *Verh. d. naturf. Gesell. Basel*, Bd. iii, Basle, 1863. (Equidæ.)

FORSYTH-MAJOR, C. J.: Beiträge zur Geschichte der fossilen Pferde, insbesondere Italiens. *Abhandl. d. schweizer. palaeont. Gesell.*, Bd. iv-vii, 1877-1880.

Boule, M.: Observations sur quelques Equidés fossiles. *Bull. Soc. géol. de France,* 3ᵉ sér., t. xxvii, 1899.

Fauna of the interglacial stages.

Rutot, A.: Note sur la position stratigraphique de la *Corbicula fluminalis* dans les couches quaternaires du bassin anglo-franco-belge. *Bull. Soc. belge de Géol.,* Mém. xiv, 1900.

Forsyth-Major, C. J.: On the Mammalian Fauna of the Val d'Arno. *Quart. Journ. Geol. Soc.,* vol. xli, London, 1885.

von Reichenau, W.: Beiträge zur Kenntnis der Carnivoren aus den Sanden von Mosbach und Mauer. *Abhandl. d. Grossherzogl. Hessichen Geol. Landesanstalt zu Darmstadt,* Bd. iv, 1906.

—— Revision der Mosbacher Säugetierfauna, etc. *Notizblatt des Vereins f. Erdkunde u. d. grossherzogl. geol. Landesanstalt zu Darmstadt,* Folge iv, Heft 31, 1910.

Depéret, C.: Note sur la succession stratigraphique des faunes de mammifères pliocènes d'Europe et du plateau central en particulier. *Bull. Soc. géol. de France,* 3ᵉ sér., t. xxi, 1894.

—— Sur le Pliocène du bassin du Puy. *Bull. Soc. géol. de France,* 4ᵉ sér., t. vii, 1907.

Boule, M.: Sur les gisements de mammifères fossiles de la montagne de Perrier. (Puy-de-Dôme.) *Bull. Soc. géol. de France,* 4ᵉ sér., t. v, 1905.

Dawkins, W. Boyd: Ossiferous cavern of Pliocene Age at Doveholes, Buxton. *Quart. Journ. Geol. Soc.,* vol. lix, no. 234, London, 1903.

Schötensack, O.: Der Unterkiefer des *Homo heidelbergensis* aus den Sanden von Mauer bei Heidelberg. Leipsic, 1908.

Wüst, E.: Untersuchungen über das Pliozän und das älteste Pleistozän Thüringens, etc. *Abhandl. d. naturf. Gesell. zu Halle,* Bd. xxiii, 1901.

Harlé, E.: Les brèches à ossements de Montoussé (Hautes-Pyrénées). *Bull. Soc. d'Hist. natur. de Toulouse,* 1892.

—— Découverte d'ossements d'Hyènes rayées dans la grotte de Montsaunés (Haute-Garonne). *Bull. Soc. géol. de France,* 3ᵉ sér., t. xxii, 1894.

—— Restes d'Hyènes rayées de la brèche d'Es-Taliens à Bagnères-de-Bigorre. *Bull. Soc. géol. de France,* 3ᵉ sér., t. xxiii, 1895.

—— Porc-épic quaternaire de Montsaunés. *Bull. Soc. géol. de France,* 3ᵉ sér., t. xxvi, 1898.

Boule, M.: Les grottes de Grimaldi (Baoussé-Roussé), t. i, fasc. iii and iv, Géologie et Paléontologie. Monaco, 1910 and 1919.

Fauna of the other continents.

THOMAS, P.: Recherches stratigraphiques et paléontologiques sur quelques formations d'eau douce de l'Algérie. *Bull. Soc. géol. de France,* 3ᵉ sér., t. iii, 1884.

POMEL, A.: Monographies de Paléontologie. Publiées par le Service de la carte géologique de l'Algérie. 13 fascicules. Algiers, 1893-1898.

MONNIER, L.: Paléontologie de Madagascar. Les Æpyornis. *Annales de Paléontologie,* t. viii, Paris, 1913.

SCHLOSSER, M.: Die fossilen Säugethiere Chinas, nebst einer Odontographie der rezenten Antilopen. *Abhandl. d. k. bayer. Akad. d. Wissenschaft,* Klasse ii, Bd. xxii, Munich, 1903.

OSBORN, H. F.: The Age of Mammals (see above), chapters v and vi. (With bibliography, chiefly on North America.)

GERVAIS, H., and AMEGHINO, F.: Les mammifères fossiles de l'Amérique du Sud. Paris, Buenos Aires, 1880.

AMEGHINO, F.: Contribución al conocimiento de los mamíferos fósiles de la República Argentina. *Actas de la Acad. Nac. de Ciencias de la República Argentina en Córdoba,* t. vi, Buenos Aires, 1889.

—— Paleontología Argentina. *Public. Univ.,* La Plata, 1904.

SCOTT, W. B.: La correlation des formations tertiaires et quaternaires dans l'Amérique du Sud. *Revista del Museo de La Plata,* t. xiv, Buenos Aires, 1907.

LEHMANN-NITSCHE, R.: Nouvelles recherches sur la formation pampéenne et l'homme fossile de la République Argentine. *Revista del Museo de La Plata,* t. xiv, Buenos Aires, 1907.

OWEN, R.: Researches on the Fossil Remains of the Extinct Mammals of Australia. London, 1877.

CHAPTER IV

NOTES AND BIBLIOGRAPHY

Note 1, p. 63. Science owes the first conclusive evidence of the existence of Pleistocene man to J. Boucher de Crèvecœur de Perthes (1788-1868), who pursued his researches from 1839 on, chiefly in the alluvial deposits of Abbeville, northern France.

The chronologic classification on page 63 was established by Gabriel de Mortillet (1821-1898), who based it chiefly upon the results obtained by the excavations of E. Lartet. The "Pre-Chellean" was established by V. Commont (1866-1918), and the "Aurignacian" by E. Cartailhac and H. Breuil.

Note 2, p. 69. The matter of the certainty and importance of types of Palæolithic implements as *forms characteristically typical of a special level* is no longer open to question. The many discoveries made and the typical forms found almost all over Europe in recent times have justified the admission of the theory and closed the discussion in scientific circles.

Note 3, p. 82. Loess with Acheulean industry was entirely absent at this site. The discovery might better have been called "Pre-Mousterian" at least, and not "warm Mousterian."

Note 4, p. 83. We cannot accept the "Strepyan" of A. Rutot (Chapter I, p. 8), but it seems probable that his "Mesvinian" corresponds to a very early Mousterian.

The large "poniards, swords, and maces" to which he refers are mostly forgeries; others belong to the early Neolithic. None of these specimens was ever found by a competent witness, or in a deposit of established stratigraphic age.

Note 5, p. 84. In southeastern France there are also a number of Mousterian deposits indicating the same warm climate during the same period, but not containing remains of hippopotamus, straight-tusked elephant, or Merck's rhinoceros.

At the shelter of Olha near Cambo, Basses-Pyrénées, in southwestern France, remains of *Rhinoceros merckii* have recently been discovered associated with a true Mousterian industry which must be considered as directly related to the "warm Mousterian" in the adjoining region of northern Spain.

GENERAL WORKS OF REFERENCE

DE PERTHES, M. BOUCHER: Antiquités celtiques et antédiluviennes. Paris, 3 t., 1847, 1857, 1864.

RIGOLLOT: Mémoire sur les instruments en silex trouvés à Saint-Acheul. Amiens, 1851.

PRESTWICH, J.: On the occurrence of flint implements associated with remains of animals of extinct species in beds of a late geological period in France, at Amiens and Abbeville, and in England at Hoxne. *Philos. Trans.*, 1860.

DE MORTILLET, G.: Musée préhistorique. Paris, 1881.

CARTAILHAC, E.: La France préhistorique. Paris, 1889.

EVANS, JOHN: The Ancient Stone Implements. London, 2d ed., 1897.

DE MORTILLET, G. and A.: Le Préhistorique. Origine et antiquité de l'Homme. Paris, 3d ed., 1900.

HÖRNES, M.: Der diluviale Mensch in Europa. Brunswick, 1903.

DÉCHELETTE, J.: Manuel d'Archéologie préhistorique, celtique, et gallo-romaine. T. I, Archéologie préhistorique. Paris, 1908.

OBERMAIER, H.: Der Mensch der Vorzeit. Berlin, 1912.

MUNRO, ROBERT: Palæolithic Man and Terramara Settlements in Europe. Edinburgh, 1912.

AVEBURY, LORD (Sir John Lubbock): Prehistoric Times, as Illustrated by Ancient Remains and the Manners and Customs of Modern Savages. London, 7th ed., 1913.

SOLLAS, W. J.: Ancient Hunters and their Modern Representatives. London, 2d ed., 1915.

OSBORN, H. F.: Men of the Old Stone Age, their Environment, Life, and Art. New York, 3d ed., 1918.

BURKITT, M. C.: Prehistory. Cambridge, 1921.

MONOGRAPHS

France.

COMMONT, V.: Les industries de l'ancien Saint-Acheul. *L'Anthr.,* xix, Paris, 1908.

—— Note sur le quaternaire du Nord de la France, de la vallée du Rhin et de la Belgique. *Annales de la Soc. géol. du Nord,* xli, 1912.

—— Chronologie et stratigraphie des industries protohistoriques, néolithiques et paléolithiques . . . du Nord de la France. *Congr. intern. d'Anthr. et d'Archéol. préhist.,* Geneva, 1912.

—— Les Hommes contemporains du Renne dans la vallée de la Somme. *Mémoires de la Soc. des Antiquaires de Picardie,* xxxvii, Amiens, 1914.

OBERMAIER, H.: Die Steingeräte des französischen Altpalaeolithikums. *Mitt. d. prähist. Kommission d. k. Akad. d. Wissenschaften,* Bd. ii, Vienna, 1908.

CHAUVET, G., and RIVIÈRE, E.: La station quaternaire de la Micoque (Dordogne). *Assoc. française pour l'avanc. des sciences,* t. ii, Saint-Etienne, 1897.

COMMONT, V.: L'Industrie des graviers supérieurs à Saint-Acheul. *Rev. de l'Ecole d'Anthr.,* t. xvii, Paris, 1907. (Levallois types.)

BOURLON, M.: Une fouille au Moustier. *L'Homme Préhist.,* Paris, 1905.

—— L'industrie moustérienne au Moustier. *Congr. intern. d'Anthr. et d'Archéol. préhist.* Sess. xiii, Monaco, 1906.

—— L'industrie des foyers supérieurs au Moustier.—L'industrie des niveaux moyen et inférieur de la terrasse du grand abri au Moustier. *Rev. préhist.,* Paris, 1910, 1911.

BOUYSSONIE, A. and J., and BARDON, J.: La station moustérienne de

—— The Prehistoric Period in South Africa (2d ed.). London, 1912.

PÉRINGUEY, L.: The Stone Ages of South Africa. *Annals of the South African Museum,* 1911.

BAZLEY, W.: Exploration of a Bushman's Cave in Alfred County, Natal. *Man,* vol. v, 1905.

OBERMAIER, H.: Ein "in situ" gefundener Faustkeil aus Natal. *Anthropos,* Bd. iv, Vienna, 1909.

DOUX, J. LEE: Stone Implements from South Africa. *Man,* vol. xiv, London, 1914.

WAYLAND, E. J.: Notes on the Occurrence of Stone Implements in the Province of Mozambique. *Man,* vol. xv, 1915.

Asia.

THOMPSON, R. CAMPBELL: On Some Prehistoric Stone Implements from Asia Minor. *Man,* vol. x, 1910.

ZUMOFFEN, G.: La Phénicie avant les Phéniciens. Beyrouth, 1900.

—— L'âge de la pierre en Phénicie. *Anthropos,* Bd. iii, Vienna, 1908.

BLANCKENHORN, M.: Über die Steinzeit und Feuersteinartefakte in Syrien und Palästina. *Zeitschr. f. Ethnologie,* Bd. xxxvii, Berlin, 1905.

KARGE, P.: Rephaim. Die vorgeschichtliche Kultur Palästinas und Phöniziens. Paderborn, 1918.

DE MORGAN, J.: Les stations préhistoriques de l'Alagheuz (Arménie Russe). *Rev. de l'Ecole d'Anthr. de Paris,* t. xix, 1909.

—— Les premières civilisations. Paris, 1909.

FOOTE, R.: The Foote Collection of Indian Prehistoric and Proto-historic Antiquities. Madras Museum, 1916.

MITRA, P.: Prehistoric Cultures and Races of India. *Calcutta University Journ. of the Dept. of Letters,* 1920.

DE BAYE, J., and VOLKOV, T.: Le gisement paléolithique de Aphontova-Gora. *L'Anthr.,* t. x, Paris, 1899.

SELIGMANN, C. G.: Quartz Implements from Ceylon. *Man,* vol. viii, 1908.

MUNRO, N. G.: Prehistoric Japan. Yokohama, 1908.

America.

BOULE, M.: L'Homme paléolithique dans l'Amérique du Nord. *L'Anthr.,* t. iv, Paris, 1893.

WILSON, T.: La haute ancienneté de l'homme dans l'Amérique du Nord. *L'Anthr.,* t. xii, Paris, 1901.

VOLK, E.: The Archæology of the Delaware Valley. *Papers of Pea-*

body Mus. of Amer. Archæology and Ethnology, Harvard University, vol. v, 1911.

WINCHELL, N. H.: L'Homme primitif dans le Kansas. *Congr. intern. d'Anthr. et d'Archéol. préhist.*, xivᵉ Session, Geneva, 1912.

WRIGHT, F.: Man and the Glacial Period. New York, 1912.

UHLE, M.: La arqueología de Arica y Tacna. *Bol. de la Soc. Ecuatoriana de Estudios históricos americanos*, t. iii, Ecuador, 1919.

OUTES, F.: La edad de la Piedra en Patagonia. *Anales del Museo Nac. de Buenos Aires*, t. xii, 1905.

CHAPTER V

NOTES AND BIBLIOGRAPHY

Note 1, p. 120. Belgium and England. The Solutrean in Belgium is sometimes referred to as ''Magritian'' (from the cave of Trou Magrite), the early Magdalenian as ''Goyetian'' (from the cave of Goyet), and the Late Magdalenian as ''Chaleuxian'' (from the cave of Trou de Chaleux).

In England a Proto-Solutrean level is found in the cave of Paviland, Glamorganshire, Wales, and Solutrean deposits have been found in Kent's Hole near Torquay, Devonshire, and in Robin Hood's Hole and Church Hole, both near Cresswell, northeastern Derbyshire.

Note 2, p. 120. It should be noted that, according to certain indications, it is not impossible that during the Pleistocene there was also in central Africa a center of Solutrean culture with large laurel-leaf points. This culture would be an evolution quite independent of Europe, but similar in development, and seems to have extended to the southern Sahara. The laurel-leaf points have a strong patina and are made of other material than the Neolithic implements of the same regions.

Note 3, p. 120. Kent's Hole, Devonshire, and Church Hole and Robin Hood's Hole near Cresswell, Derbyshire. From the last-named, Boyd Dawkins has described the figure of a horse incised on a piece of bone. Recently A. Smith Woodward has noted an incised drawing of the head of a horse on a fragment of rib. It was picked up in an old heap of quarry débris near the Bristol road, on the outskirts of Sherborne, Dorset. We too are of the opinion that this engraving is certainly of Magdalenian age.

Note 4, p. 130. The caves referred to are chiefly those of Gargas,

Portel, and Font-de-Gaume in southern France, and Castillo and Altamira in northern Spain. In the last-named region no "mutilated fingers" are found.

Note 5, p. 130. This is shown both by the superposition of paintings of later date upon such hand silhouettes, and also by the discoveries at the rock shelter of Blanchard, Dordogne. Here hand silhouettes were found upon slabs of rock which had fallen from the wall during the Middle Aurignacian. These pictures of hands, therefore, are perhaps even older than this Aurignacian industry, but in any case they fell during that period.

Note 6, p. 133. In central Europe Solutrean sepultures are more frequent. Among them are the sepulture at Brünn and the group sepulture at Předmost, Moravia (p. 297) ; and the Solutrean skeleton of Neu-Essing, Bavaria.

GENERAL WORKS OF REFERENCE

LARTET, E., and CHRISTY, H.: Reliquiæ Aquitanicæ, being contributions to the archæology and palæontology of Périgord and the adjoining provinces of southern France. (With 90 plates.) London, 1865-1875.
See also the list of general works of reference given for Chapter IV.

MONOGRAPHS

BREUIL, H.: Les subdivisions du paléolithique supérieur et leur signification. *Congr. intern. d'Anthr. et d'Archéol. préhist. C. R.* Sess. xiv, Geneva, 1912.

France.

BREUIL, H.: Les gisements présolutréens du type d'Aurignac. *Congr. intern. d'Anthr. et d'Archéol. préhist. C. R.* Sess. xiii, Monaco, 1906.
—— La question aurignacienne. (Etude critique de stratigraphie comparée.) *Rev. préhist.*, t. ii, Paris, 1907.
—— L'Aurignacien présolutréen. *Rev. préhist.*, t. iv, Paris, 1909.
—— Les Cottés, une grotte du vieil âge du Renne à St-Pierre de Maillé (Vienne). *Rev. de l'Ecole d'Anthr.*, t. xvi, Paris, 1906.
—— Etudes de morphologie paléolithique: L'industrie de la grotte de Châtelperron (Allier) et d'autres gisements similaires. *Rev. anthr.*, t. xxi, 1911.
—— Etudes de morphologie paléolithique: Les niveaux présolutréens du Trilobite. *Rev. anthr.*, t. xxviii, 1918.
BARDON, L., and BOUYSSONIE, A. and J.: Station préhistorique de la Coumbâ-del-Bouïtou, près Brive (Corrèze). *Bull. Soc. scient.*,

hist. et archéol. de la Corrèze, 1908. (See *Rev. de l'Ecole d'Anthr.*, t. xvii, Paris, 1907.)

—— La grotte Lacoste, près Brive (Corrèze). *Rev. de l'Ecole d'Anthr.*, t. xx, Paris, 1910. (New edition: Brive, 1910.)

—— Stations préhistoriques du Château de Bassaler, près Brive (Corrèze). i. La grotte de La Font-Robert. *Bull. Soc. scient., hist. et archéol. de la Corrèze*, 1910. (And *Congr. intern. de Monaco*, t. ii, 1906.)

DIDON, L.: L'abri Blanchard des Roches (Commune de Sergeac). *Bull. Soc. hist. et archéol. du Périgord*, 1911. (And *Congr. intern. de Genève*, 1912.)

BOURLON, M.: Essai de classification des burins. *Rev. anthr.*, t. xxi, Paris, 1911.

BOURLON, M., and BOUYSSONIE, J. and A.: Grattoirs carénés, rabots et grattoirs nucléiformes. *Rev. anthr.*, t. xxii, Paris, 1912.

RAYMOND, P.: La grotte du Figuier (Ardèche). Transition aurigno-solutréenne. *Rev. préhist.*, t. vi, 1911.

ARCELIN, A.: Les nouvelles fouilles de Solutré, près Mâcon, Saône-et-Loire. *L'Anthr.*, t. i, 1890.

PARAT, ABBÉ: La grotte du Trilobite. *Bull. Soc. scient. hist. et nat. de l'Yonne*, 1902.

BREUIL, H., and CLÉMENT, J.: Un abri solutréen sur les bords de l'Anglin à Monthaud (Indre). *Mem. Soc. des antiquaires du Centre*, t. xxix, Bourges, 1906.

MASCARAUX, F.: Les silex de Montaut (Landes). *Rev. anthr.*, t. xxii, 1912.

PEYRONY, D.: Nouvelles fouilles à Badegoule (Dordogne). Solutréen supérieur et transition du Solutréen au Magdalénien. *Rev. préhist.*, t. iii, 1908.

—— La station préhistorique du Ruth près Le Moustier (Dordogne). *Rev. de l'Ecole d'Anthr.*, t. xix, Paris, 1909.

PIETTE, E.: Etudes d'Ethnographie préhistorique. *L'Anthr.*, t. vi, 1895.

CAPITAN, L., BREUIL, H., BOURRINET, P., and PEYRONY, D.: La grotte de la Mairie à Teyjat (Dordogne). *Rev. de l'Ecole d'Anthr.*, t. xviii, Paris, 1908.

VIRÉ, A.: Abri sous Roche de la "Rivière de Tulle" près de Lacave, canton de Souillac. *L'Anthr.*, t. xx, 1909.

MASCARAUX, F.: La grotte de Saint-Michel d'Arudy (Basses-Pyrénées). *Rev. de l'Ecole d'Anthr.*, t. xx, Paris, 1910.

DE SAINT-PERIER, R.: La grotte des Harpons à Lespugne (Haute-Garonne). *L'Anthr.*, t. xxx, Paris, 1920.

AREAS OF DISTRIBUTION

Europe (except France), northern Africa, and western Asia.

Aurignacian and Capsian.

SOLLAS, W. J.: Paviland Cave, an Aurignacian Station in Wales. (The Huxley Memorial Lecture for 1913.) *Journ. R. Anthr. Inst. of Gr. Brit. & Ireland*, vol. xliii, London, 1913, pp. 325-373.

SCHMIDT, R. R.: Das Aurignacien in Deutschland. *Mannus*, Berlin, 1909.

SZOMBATHY, J.: Die Aurignacienschichten im Loess von Willendorf. *Correspondenzblatt d. deutschen Gesell. f. Anthr., Ethnol. u. Urgeschichte*, Bd. xl, 1909.

OBERMAIER, H.: Die am Wagramdurchbruch des Kamp gelegenen niederösterreichischen Quartärfundplätze. *Jahrb. f. Altertumskunde*, Bd. ii, Vienna, 1908.

STROBL, J., and OBERMAIER, H.: Die Aurignacienstation von Krems, Nieder-Österreich. *Jahrb. f. Altertumskunde*, Bd. iii, 1909.

SCHWEINFURTH, G.: Über das Höhlen-Paläolithikum von Sizilien und Südtunesien. *Zeitschr. f. Ethnol.*, Bd. xxxix, 1907.

PALLARY, P.: Instructions pour les recherches préhistoriques dans le Nord-Ouest de l'Afrique. Algiers, 1909.

DE MORGAN, J., CAPITAN, L., and BOUDY, P.: Etude sur les stations préhistoriques du Sud Tunisien. *Rev. de l'Ecole d'Anthr.*, t. xx, 1910, and t. xxi, 1911, Paris.

GOBERT, E.: L'abri de Redeyef. *L'Anthr.*, t. xxiii, 1912.

—— Introduction à la paléthnographie tunisienne. *Cahiers d'Archéol. tunisienne*, sér. 2, cahier 2. Tunis, 1914.

BLÁZQUEZ, A., and AGUILERA, DELGADO: Préhistoria de la región Norte de Marruecos. *Bol. de la Real Soc. Geog.*, Madrid, 1913.

ZITTEL, K.: Sur des silex taillés trouvés dans le désert Libyque. *Congr. intern. d'Anthr. et d'Archéol. préhist.* Sess. vii, Stockholm, 1874. (T. i.)

COWPER, H. S.: On a series of small worked flints from Hilwan, Egypt. *Man*, vol. xi, 1911.

BLANCKENHORN, M.: Über die Steinzeit und die Feuersteinartefakte in Syrien-Palästina. *Zeitschr. f. Ethnol.*, Bd. xxxvii, 1905.

ZUMOFFEN, G.: L'âge de la pierre en Phénicie. *Anthropos*, Bd. iii, Vienna, 1908.

DESRIBES, R.: Harpons trouvés dans la brèche paléolithique d'Antélias. *L'Anthr.*, t. xxv, 1914.

KARGE, P.: Rephaim. Die vorgeschichtliche Kultur Palästinas und Phöniziens. Paderborn, 1918.

RIVIÈRE, E.: Paleoéthnologie; de l'antiquité de l'homme dans les Alpes-Maritimes. 1878-1887.

CARTAILHAC, E.: Les grottes de Grimaldi (Baoussé-Roussé), t. ii, fasc. ii. (Archéologie.) Monaco, 1912.

MOCHI, A.: Industria paleolitica (aurignaziana) de la Grotta Romanelli in Terra d'Otranto. *Archivio per l'Antrop. e la Etnol.*, t. xli, Florence, 1911.

—— La succession des industries paléolithiques et les changements de la faune du Pléistocène en Italie. Florence, 1912.

MOCHI, A., and SCHIFF-GIORGINI: Esplorazione sistematica de la Grotta all'Onda. *Archivio per l'Antrop. e la Etnol.*, t. xlv, Florence, 1915.

Solutrean.

HILLEBRAND, E.: Das Paläolithikum Ungarns. *Wiener prähist. Zeitschr.*, Bd. vi, 1919.

MAŠKA, K., and OBERMAIER, H.: La station solutréenne de Ondratitz (Moravie) : *L'Anthr.*, t. xxii, 1911.

MAŠKA, K.: Der diluviale Mensch in Mähren. Neutitschein, 1886. (Předmost.)

KŘÍŽ, M.: Beiträge zur Kenntnis des Quartärs in Mähren. Steinitz, 1903. (Předmost.)

MAŠKA, K., OBERMAIER, H., and BREUIL, H.: La statuette de mammouth de Předmost. *L'Anthr.*, t. xxiii, 1912.

MAKOWSKY, A.: Der diluviale Mensch im Loess von Brünn. *Mitt. d. anthr. Gesell. in Wien*, Bd. xxii, 1892.

OBERMAIER, H.: Institut de Paléontologie Humaine. Travaux de l'année 1913. iii. Fouilles en Bavière. (Solutrean culture of Essing.) *L'Anthr.*, t. xxv, 1914.

Magdalenian.

WOODWARD, A. SMITH: Palæolithic engraving of horse on a bone. *Quart. Journ. Geol. Soc.*, vol. lxx, 1914.

SCHENCK, A.: La Suisse préhistorique. Le Paléolithique et le Néolithique. Lausanne, 1912.

SARASIN, F.: Die steinzeitlichen Stationen des Birstales zwischen Basel und Delsberg. (Unter Mitwirkung von H. G. Stehlin und Th. Studer.) *Neue Denkschriften d. Schweiz. naturf. Gesell.*, Bd. liv, Abhdlg. 2, Basle, 1918.

SCHMIDT, R. R.: Die diluviale Vorzeit Deutschlands. Stuttgart, 1912.

WIEGERS, F.: Die diluvialen Kulturstätten Norddeutschlands, etc. *Prähist. Zeitschr.*, Bd. i, 1909. (Andernach.)

OBERMAIER, H.: Fouilles en Bavière. *L'Anthr.*, t. xxv, 1914. (Magdalenian industry from the grotto of Essing.)

BIRKNER, F.: Der Eiszeitmensch in Bayern. *Beitr. z. Anthr. u. Urgeschichte Bayerns*, Bd. xix, Munich, 1914.

Note 3, pp. 147 and 179. In no respect do the elephant molars from Torralba resemble those of the type of *Elephas meridionalis,* as will be seen at a glance by comparing them with those from Valverde de Calatrava. Some specimens might be interpreted simply as very advanced mutations of this species, which, on the other hand, approach very closely to *Elephas antiquus.* The majority of the molars are clearly characteristic of *E. antiquus,* in agreement with which is the fact stated by Harlé that the tusks are almost all slender and that the curvature of most of them is limited to the same plane, both features being characteristic of *E. antiquus.*

Of the rhinoceros only a fragment of a molar was found at Torralba, which is not sufficient proof to justify any reference to *Rhinoceros etruscus.* The horse of the same site shows archaic features, but is not *Equus stenonis.*

Note 4, p. 148. The proper name of the Corsican pika is *Prolagus (Myolagus) corsicanus.* It appeared in Corsica during the Late Tertiary, and continued there throughout the entire Pleistocene down to historic times, that is to say, about to the Roman period.

Note 5, p. 150. No importance attaches to the presence of the ibex, which even yet is found in all parts of Spain. So far, the presence of the chamois is proved only by discoveries of bones found in the north, in the same region where it still lives. Duckworth's indications of the existence of the chamois in Gibraltar are very doubtful, since up to now only a single bone is known. Furthermore, during his excavations of 1910 to 1915, he encountered no faunal remains that were certainly of Pleistocene age.

Note 6, p. 152. It is possible that the fragmentary remains of antelopes recently found at Cape Figari in Sardinia may have also belonged to a *Myotragus.* If this supposition should be confirmed the genus would have had a considerable distribution in the Mediterraneon region, and would form a part of the "Tyrrhenian Pleistocene Fauna" of Forsyth-Major, one of the most interesting members of which is the genus *Prolagus (Myolagus).*

The Pleistocene fauna of Corsica, where there was a considerable glaciation, also contains, according to C. J. Forsyth-Major, species chiefly resulting from the evolution of precursors from the Late Tertiary, such as *Prolagus corsicanus, Rhagamys orthodon, Cervus gazioti, Ursus corsicanus, Ovis musimon,* and others.

In Sardinia an identical fauna is found (*Prolagus sardus, Macacus* sp., etc.). Nevertheless, the presence of a dwarf elephant indicates that the definite separation of this island took place in the Pleistocene.

Sicily was also connected with the continent during the first half of the Pleistocene, as is shown by the presence of the hippopotamus, the southern elephant (at Gravitelli), and the straight-tusked elephant in both large and dwarf forms.

Much more prolonged was the union of the island of Elba with Tuscany. Its fauna shows that a land bridge still existed between the two in the latter half of the Pleistocene, as is shown by the presence of the cave bear, cave lion, lynx, Merck's rhinoceros, hippopotamus, horse, wild boar, stag, and roe deer.

Similar conclusions are reached in regard to the islands of Malta (with elephant and hippopotamus), Crete (with straight-tusked elephant), and Cyprus (with elephant and hippopotamus).

In view of the extent and importance of the bibliography belonging to this chapter, the author has judged it best to give explicit page references, indicated by numbers in brackets. The reader will understand that space forbids citing a complete bibliography on the subject, and therefore only a selection is given.

The following abbreviations are used:

B.S.H.N.—Boletín de la Real Sociedad Española de Historia Natural (Madrid).

T.M.C.N., ser. geol.—*Trabajos del Museo Nacional de Ciencias Naturales* (Madrid), serie geológica.

C.I.P.P.—Comisión de Investigaciones Paleontológicas y Prehistóricas (Madrid).

(1) p. 138.

Mallada, L.: Explicación del Mapa Geológico de España. T. vii (and last). Sistemas plioceno, diluvial y aluvial. *Memorias del Inst. geol. de España,* Madrid, 1911.

(2) p. 138.

Penck, A.: Studien über das Klima Spaniens während der jüngeren Tertiärperiode und der Diluvialperiode. *Zeitschr d. Gesell. f. Erdkunde,* Bd. xxix, Berlin, 1894.

(3) p. 138. The most recent work on the subject is by

Obermaier, H.: Die eiszeitliche Vergletscherung Spaniens. *Petermanns geog. Mitt.,* Gotha, 1921.

(4) p. 139.

Penck, A.: Die Eiszeit in den Pyrenäen. *Mitt. d. Ver. f. Erdkunde,* Leipsic, 1883.

(5) p. 140.

Obermaier, H.: Estudio de los glaciares de los Picos de Europa. *T.M.C.N.*, ser. geol., núm. 9, Madrid, 1914.

(6) p. 141.

HALBFASS, W.: Der Castañedasee. *Petermanns geog. Mitt.*, Bd. lix, 1913.

ARAGÓN, F.: Lagos de la Región leonesa. *T.M.C.N.*, ser. geol., núm. 5, Madrid, 1913.

TABOADA TUNDIDOR, J.: El lago de San Martín de Castañeda. *B.S.H.N.*, t. xiii, Madrid, 1913.

(7) p. 142.

CARANDELL, J., and GÓMEZ DE LLARENA: El glaciarismo cuaternario en los Montes Ibéricos. *T.M.C.N.*, ser. geol., núm. 22, Madrid, 1918.

VICENTE, M.: Notas geológicas sobre el Moncayo. *Bol. d. l. Soc. Aragonesa de Ciencias Naturales,* t. ii, Saragossa, 1903.

(8) p. 142.

DE VASCONCELLOS PEREIRA CABRAL, F. A.: Traces d'actions glaciaires dans la Serra d'Estrella. *Communicações da Commissão dos trabalhos geologicos de Portugal,* t. i, Memoria xii, Lisbon, 1883-1887.

DELGADO, NERY: Note sur l'existence d'anciens glaciers dans la vallée du Mondego. *Communicações da Direcção dos trabalhos geologicos de Portugal,* t. iii, Memoria vi, Lisbon, 1895-1896.

FLEURY, E.: Sur les anciennes glaciations de la Serra da Estrella (Portugal). *C. R. de l'Acad. des Sciences,* t. clxii, nro. 16, Paris, 1916.

(9) p. 143.

SCHMIEDER, O.: Die Sierra de Gredos. *Mitt. d. geog. Gesell. in München,* Bd. x, Erlangen, 1915.

DEL VILLAR, H.: Los Glaciares de Gredos. *B.S.H.N.*, t. xv, Madrid, 1915.

—— Nueva contribución a la glaciología de Gredos. Las Hoyuelas del Hornillo. *B.S.H.N.*, t. xvii, Madrid, 1917.

OBERMAIER, H., and CARANDELL, J.: Contribución al estudio del Glaciarismo cuaternario de la Sierra de Gredos. *T.M.C.N.*, ser. geol., núm. 14, Madrid, 1916.

(10) p. 143.

FERNÁNDEZ-NAVARRO, LUCAS: Monografía geológica del Valle del Lozoya. *T.M.C.N.*, ser. geol., núm. 12, Madrid, 1915.

—— Sobre falsas huellas de glaciarismo en la Sierra de Guadarrama. *B.S.H.N.*, t. xv, Madrid, 1915.

OBERMAIER, H., and CARANDELL, J.: Los glaciares cuaternarios de la Sierra de Guadarrama. *T.M.C.N.*, ser. geol., núm. 19, Madrid, 1917.

(11) p. 144.

QUELLE, O.: Beiträge zur Kenntnis der spanischen Sierra Nevada. *Zeitschr. d. Gesell. f. Erdkunde,* Berlin, 1908.

Obermaier, H., and Carandell, J.: Los glaciares cuaternarios de Sierra Nevada. *T.M.C.N.*, ser. geol., núm. 17, Madrid, 1916.

(12) p. 146.

Puig y Larraz, G.: Cavernas y Simas de España. *Bol. d. l. Comis. del Mapa geológico*, ser. 2, t. i, Madrid, 1896.

Faura y Sans, M.: La Espeología de Cataluña. *Memorias de la Real Soc. esp. de Hist. Nat.*, t. vi, Madrid, 1911.

(13) p. 146.

Chapman, A., and Buck, W. J.: Wild Spain. London, 1893.

—— Unexplored Spain. London, 1910.

Miller, G. S.: Catalogue of the Mammals of Western Europe. London, 1912.

Cabrera, A.: Fauna ibérica. Mamíferos. *Museo Nacional de Ciencias Naturales*, Madrid, 1914.

(14) p. 147.

Harlé, E.: Les mammifères et oiseaux quaternaires connus jusqu'-ici en Portugal. *Communicações da Commissão do Serviço Geol. de Portugal*, t. viii, Lisbon, 1910.

—— Ensayo de una lista de mamíferos y aves del cuaternario conocidas hasta ahora en la Península Ibérica. *Bol. del Inst. geol. de España*, t. xxxii, 1911.

del Pan, I.: Paleogeografía de los mamíferos cuaternarios de Europa y Norte de Africa. *C.I.P.P.*, Memoria 21, Madrid, 1918.

In regard to the Pleistocene fauna of Catalonia, see the following:

Bataller, J. R.: Mamífers fòssils de Catalunya. *Inst. d'Estudis Catalans*, Barcelona, 1918.

Cazurro, M.: El Cuaternario y las estaciones de la época paleolítica en Cataluña. *Memorias de la Real Acad. de Ciencias y Artes de Barcelona*, época iii, t. xv, núm. 3, Barcelona, 1919.

Harlé, E.: Restes d'éléphant et de rhinocéros trouvés récemment dans le Quaternaire de la Catalogne. *Butlleti de la Institució Catalana d'Història Natural*, Barcelona, 1920.

(15) p. 147.

Sierra, L.: Restos del *Elephas primigenius* y otros animales en la mina "Inadvertida" (Santander). *Bol. de la Soc. Aragonesa de Cienc. Natur.*, t. xi, Saragossa, 1912.

Carballo, J.: Descubrimiento de restos de "mammuth" y de otros mamíferos en el cuaternario ferrífero de Pámanes (Santander). *B.S.H.N.*, t. xii, 1912.

(16) p. 150.

Harlé, E.: Les mammifères et oiseaux quaternaires connus jusqu'ici en Portugal. *Communicações da Commissão do Serviço Geol. de Portugal*, t. viii, Lisbon, 1910, p. 52.

(17) p. 151.

BATE, DOROTHEA M. A.: Preliminary Note on a New Artiodactyle from Majorca, *Myotragus Balearicus*, gen. et sp. nov. *Geol. Magazine*, September, 1909.

—— A Gigantic Land Tortoise from the Pleistocene of Menorca. *Geol. Magazine*, N.S., Decade vi, vol. i, London, 1914.

—— The Pleistocene Ossiferous Deposits of the Balearic Islands. *Geol. Magazine*, N.S., Decade vi, vol. i, London, 1914.

—— On a New Genus of Extinct Muscardine Rodent from the Balearic Islands. *Proc. Zoöl. Soc. of London*, 1918. (Published March, 1919.)

ANDREWS, C. W.: A Description of the Skull and Skeleton of a Peculiarly Modified Rupicaprine Antelope, *Myotragus Balearicus* Bate, with a Notice of a new variety, *M. Balearicus* var. *major*. *Philos. Trans. Roy. Soc. of London*, ser. B, vol. ccvi, London, 1915.

(18) p. 154.

FERNÁNDEZ-NAVARRO, L.: Los pozos artesianos en Madrid. Biblioteca de *La Revista Agrícola*, Madrid, 1908.

—— Notas geológicas. *B.S.H.N.*, t. ix, 1909.

—— Perforaciones artesianas en el cuaternario de Castilla la Nueva. *B.S.H.N.*, t. ix, 1909.

(19) p. 155.

HERNÁNDEZ-PACHECO, E.: Las tierras negras del extremo Sur de España y sus yacimientos paleolíticos. *T.M.C.N.*, ser. geol., núm. 13, Madrid, 1915.

Modified by

BREUIL, H.: Observations sur les terres noires de la Laguna de la Janda. *L'Anthr.*, t. xxviii, Paris, 1917.

(20) p. 155.

HERNÁNDEZ-PACHECO, E.: El yacimiento de mamíferos cuaternarios de Valverde de Calatrava y edad de los volcanes de Ciudad Real. *Tomo extraordinario del 50 Aniversario de la Real Soc. esp. de Hist. Nat.*, Madrid, 1921.

CALDERÓN, S., CAZURRO, M., and FERNÁNDEZ-NAVARRO, L.: Formaciones volcánicas de la provincia de Gerona. *Memorias de la Real Soc. esp. de Hist. Nat.*, t. iv (Memoria 5), Madrid, 1907.

Monographs and general works of reference.

(21) p. 156.

VILANOVA Y PIERA, J.: Origen, naturaleza y antigüedad del Hombre. Madrid, 1872.

Vilanova y Piera, J., and de la Rada y Delgado, J.: Geología y Protohistoria Ibéricas. Madrid, 1894.

Cartailhac, E.: Les âges préhistoriques de l'Espagne et du Portugal. Paris, 1886.

Siret, L.: L'Espagne préhistorique. *Rev. des questions scientifiques,* sér. 2, t. iv, Brussels, 1893.

Breuil, H.: Les subdivisions du paléolithique supérieur et leur signification. *Congr. intern. d'Anthr. et d'Archéol. préhist.* Sess. xiv, Geneva, 1912.

Obermaier, H.: Das Paläolithikum und Epipaläolithikum Spaniens. *Anthropos,* Bd. xiv-xv, Vienna, 1919-1920.

(22) p. 157.

Harlé, E.: Les grottes d'Aitzbitarte ou Landarbaso, à Rentería, près de Saint Sébastien. *Bol. Real Acad. Hist.,* t. lii, Madrid, 1908.

(23) p. 157.

de Gálvez-Cañero, A.: Nota acerca de las cavernas de Vizcaya. *Bol. Inst. geol. de España,* t. xxxiii, 1912.

(24) p. 157.

Sierra, L.: Notas para el mapa paletnográfico de la provincia de Santander. *Actas y Memorias del Ier Congr. de Naturalistas españoles,* Saragossa, 1908.

Obermaier, H.: Der diluviale Mensch in der Provinz Santander (Spanien). *Prähist. Zeitschr.,* Bd. i, Berlin, 1909.

(25) p. 157.

Breuil, H., and Obermaier, H.: Les premiers travaux de l'Institut de Paléontologie Humaine. *L'Anthr.* t. xxiii, 1912, and t. xxiv, 1913.

(26) p. 161.

Obermaier, H., and Breuil, H.: Fouilles de la grotte du Castillo (Espagne). *Congr. intern. d'Anthr. et d'Archéol. préhist.* Sess xiv, t. i, Geneva, 1912.

—— Travaux de l'Institut de Paléontologie Humaine. *L'Anthr.,* t. xxiii, 1912, t. xxiv, 1913, t. xxv, 1914.

(27) p. 168.

Breuil, H., and Obermaier, H.: Les premiers travaux de l'Institut de Paléontologie Humaine. *L'Anthr.,* t. xxiii, 1912.

(28) p. 169.

Cartailhac, E., and Breuil, H.: La caverne d'Altamira à Santillane près Santander (Espagne). Monaco, 1906.

(29) p. 171.

de la Vega del Sella, Conde: Paleolítico de Cueto de la Mina (Asturias). *C.I.P.P.,* Memoria 13, Madrid, 1916.

DA FONSECA CARDOSO, A. A.: Nota sobre una estação chelleana do valle d'Alcantara. *Rev. de Sciencias naturaes e sociaes*, t. iii, Oporto, 1895.

DE VASCONCELLOS, J. LEITE: Religiões da Lusitania. *Soc. de Geog. de Lisboa*, t. i, Lisbon, 1897.

—— Objetos paleolíticos do Casal do Monte. *Acad. das Sciências de Lisboa, Boletim da segunda classe*, t. viii, Coimbra, 1915.

CORREIA, V.: O paleolítico em Portugal. *O archeologo português*, t. xvii, Lisbon, 1912.

—— Facas e raspadores do estação paleolítica de Monsanto, 1. *O archeologo português*, t. xvii, 1912.

FONTES, JOAQUIM: Estação paleolítica do Casal do Monte. *O archeologo português*, t. xv, 1910.

—— Contribution à l'étude de la période paléolithique en Portugal. *Congr. préhist. de France*. Sess. vii, Nimes, 1911.

—— Subsidios para o estudo do Paleolítico português. *O archeologo português*, t. xvii, Lisbon, 1912.

—— Note sur le Moustérien au Portugal. *Congr. préhist. de France*, Sess. viii, Angoulême, 1912.

—— Sur quelques types inédits de coups de poing du Portugal. *Congr. intern. d'Anthr. et d'Archéol. préhist.* Sess. xiv, t. i, Geneva, 1912.

—— Station paléolithique de Mealhada. *Communicações da Commissão do Serviço Geol. de Portugal*, t. xi, Lisbon, 1915.

—— Note sur le Chelléen de Casal do Monte. *Bull. Soc. Portugaise des Sciences Naturelles*, t. vii, Lisbon, 1915.

—— Instruments paléolithiques des environes de Porto. Ibid. 1915.

—— Instruments paléolithiques dans la Collection de Préhistoire du Service Géologique. *Communicações da Commissão do Serviço Geol. de Portugal*, t. xii, Lisbon, 1917.

PEREIRA, F. ALVES: Industries lithiques sur les rives de la Lagune de Obidos. *Bull. Soc. Portugaise des Sciences Naturelles*, t. vii, Lisbon, 1915.

BREUIL, H.: Glânes paléolithiques anciennes dans le bassin du Guadiana. *L'Anthr.*, t. xxviii, 1917.

—— Impressions de voyage paléolithique à Lisbone. *Terra Portuguesa*, t. iii, Lisbon, 1918.

(50) p. 208.

DE LA VEGA DEL SELLA, CONDE: Avance al estudio del paleolítico superior en la región asturiana. *Assoc. esp. para el Progreso de las Ciencias*, Congr. de Valladolid, 1915. (T. vi: Ciencias Naturales.) Madrid, 1917.

OBERMAIER, H.: Das Paläolithikum und Epipaläolithikum Spaniens. *Anthropos*, Bd. xiv-xv, Vienna, 1920-1921.

CHAPTER VII

NOTES AND BIBLIOGRAPHY

Note 1, p. 255. The pictures published by J. Cabré in his *El Arte rupestre en España* (1916, Plate XXIV), which are contrary to this interpretation, are not exact reproductions, but have been influenced by his viewpoint. The present author had an opportunity in 1912 to see and study the originals, when they were still practically intact, and he feels convinced that there can be no doubt as to their identification as moose.

Owing to the wide scope of the subject, the bibliographic references for this chapter are indicated in the text by bracketed numerals corresponding to those given below. As in the bibliography for Chapter VI, it has been necessary to restrict the number of references given to the most important only, on account of the vast amount of literature on the subject.

Abbreviation: C.I.P.P.=*Comisión de Investigaciones Paleontológicas y Prehistóricas* (Madrid).

(1) p. 212.
The following works offer a scientific introduction to, and a broad general view of, the subject.

Breuil, H.: Les subdivisions du paléolithique supérieur et leur signification. *Congr. intern. d'Anthr. et d'Archéol. préhist.* Sess. xiv, Geneva, 1912, t. i.

Reinach, S.: Répertoire de l'art quaternaire. Paris, 1913.

Parkyn, A. E.: An Introduction to the Study of Prehistoric Art. London, 1915.

(2) p. 213.
Piette, E.: Notes pour servir à l'histoire de l'art primitif. *L'Anthr.*, t. v, 1894.

—— Classification des sédiments formés dans les cavernes pendant l'âge du Renne. *L'Anthr.*, t. xv, 1904.

—— L'art pendant l'âge du Renne. Paris, 1907. (111 pp. text and album of 100 plates.)

Breuil, H.: L'évolution de l'Art quaternaire et les travaux d'Edouard Piette. *Rev. archéol.*, sér. 4, t. xiii, 1909.

Cartailhac, E., and Breuil, H.: Les œuvres d'art de la collection de Vibraye au Muséum National. *L'Anthr.*, t. xviii, 1907.

(3) p. 213.

Piette, E.: La station de Brassempouy et les statuettes humaines de la période glyptique. *L'Anthr.*, t. vi, 1895.

—— Gravure de Mas d'Azil et statuettes de Menton. *Bull. Soc. d'Anthr. de Paris*, sér. 5, t. iii, 1902.

Reinach, S.: Statuette de femme nue découverte dans une des grottes de Menton. *L'Anthr.*, t. ix, 1898.

Lalanne, G.: Découverte d'un bas-relief à représentation humaine dans les fouilles de Laussel. *L'Anthr.*, t. xxii, 1911.

—— Bas-reliefs à figuration humaine de l'abri sous roche de Laussel (Dordogne). *L'Anthr.*, t. xxiii, 1912.

(4) p. 217.

de Bégouen, Comte: Les statues d'argile de la caverne du Tuc d'Audoubert (Ariège). *L'Anthr.*, t. xxiii, 1912.

(5) p. 219.

Breuil, H.: Exemples de figures dégénérées et stylisées à l'époque du Renne. *Congr. intern. d'Anthr. et d'Archéol. préhist.* Sess. xiii, Monaco, 1906, t. i.

(6) p. 222.

Volkow, T.: Nouvelles découvertes dans la station paléolithique de Mézine (Ukraine). *Congr. intern. d'Anthr. et d'Archéol. préhist.* Sess. xiv, Geneva, 1912, t. i.

(7) p. 225.

Rivière, E.: La grotte de La Mouthe. *Bull. Soc. d'Anthr. de Paris*, 1897, 1901, 1903.

(8) p. 225.

Capitan, L., and Breuil, H.: La grotte des Combarelles. *Rev. de l'Ecole d'Anthr. de Paris*, t. xii, 1902, pp. 33-46.

(9) p. 225.

Capitan, L., Breuil, H., and Peyrony, D.: La caverne de Font-de-Gaume aux Eyzies (Dordogne). Monaco, 1910. (A large volume with 65 plates.)

(10) p. 225.

Capitan, L., Breuil, H., and Peyrony, D.: Les figures gravées de la grotte de Bernifal (Dordogne). *Rev. de l'Ecole d'Anthr. de Paris*, t. xiii, 1903, pp. 202-209.

Capitan, L., Breuil, H., Peyrony, D., and Bourrinet: Les gravures sur cascade stalagmitique de la Grotte de la Mairie à Teyjat. *Congr. intern. d'Anthr. et d'Archéol. préhist.* Sess. xiv, Geneva, 1912, t. i, pp. 498-514.

(11) p. 225.

Capitan, L., Breuil, H., and Ampoulange, M.: Une nouvelle grotte préhistorique à parois gravées. *Rev. de l'Ecole d'Anthr. de Paris*, t. xiv, 1904, pp. 320-325.

(12) p. 225.

LALANNE, G., and BREUIL, H.: L'abri sculpté de Cap-Blanc à Laussel (Dordogne). *L'Anthr.*, t. xxii, 1911, pp. 385-402.

(13) p. 225.

CAPITAN, L., BREUIL, H., and PEYRONY, D.: Nouvelles grottes ornées de la Vallée de la Beune. *L'Anthr.*, t. xxvi, 1915, pp. 505-518.

(14) p. 225.

DALEAU, F.: Les gravures sur rocher de la caverne de Pair-non-Pair. *Actes d. l. Soc. archéol. de Bordeaux*, Bordeaux, 1897.

(15) p. 225.

CARTAILHAC, E., and BREUIL, H.: Marsoulas. *L'Anthr.*, t. xvi, 1905, pp. 431-444.

(16) p. 225.

CARTAILHAC, E., and BREUIL, H.: Gargas, Commune d'Aventignan (Hautes-Pyrénées). *L'Anthr.*, t. xxi, 1910, pp. 129-150.

BREUIL, H., and OBERMAIER, H.: Les premiers travaux de l'Institut de Paléontologie Humaine. *L'Anthr.*, t. xxiii, 1912.

(17) p. 226.

DE BÉGOUEN, COMTE, and BREUIL, H.: Peintures et gravures préhistoriques dans la grotte du Mas d'Azil. *Bull. Soc. archéol.* 1912-1913. Toulouse, 1913.

(18) p. 226.

CARTAILHAC, E., and BREUIL, H.: Niaux (Ariège). *L'Anthr.*, t. xix, 1908, pp. 15-46.

(19) p. 226.

BREUIL, H., JAMMES, L., and JEANNEL, R.: Les dernières peintures découvertes dans la grotte du Portel (Ariège). *Acad. d. Sci., C. R.*, Paris, June 1, 1908.

(20) p. 226.

DE BÉGOUEN, COMTE: Une nouvelle grotte à gravures dans l'Ariège, la caverne du Tuc d'Audoubert. *Congr. intern. d'Anthr. et d'Archéol. préhist.* Sess. xiv, Geneva, 1912, t. i, pp. 489-497.

—— Les statues d'argile de la caverne du Tuc d'Audoubert. *L'Anthr.*, t. xxiii, 1912, pp. 657-665.

(21) p. 226.

DE BÉGOUEN, COMTE, and BREUIL, H.: Un dessin relevé dans la caverne des Trois Frères à Montesquieu-Avantès (Ariège). *Acad. des Inscriptions et Belles-Lettres, C. R.*, Paris, 1920.

(22) p. 226.

In regard to the mural art of Spain, the following work giving a general view of the entire subject appeared in 1915.

CABRÉ, J.: El arte rupestre en España. Regiones septentrional y oriental. *C.I.P.P.*, Memoria 1, Madrid.

In this book the art of northern Spain is only briefly referred to, while that of eastern Spain is described much more fully. We feel it a duty to call the attention of scientific readers to the fact that this work needs a new scientific revision, which also holds good for a large part of the illustrations of the rock paintings, many of which are not altogether exact, being influenced by the author's viewpoint. In this connection we should like to draw attention to the following:

BREUIL, H.: Algunas observaciones acerca de la obra de D. Juan Cabré, titulada El Arte Rupestre en España. *Bol. de la Real Soc. esp. de Hist. Nat.*, t. xvi, Madrid, 1916, pp. 253-269.

(23) p. 226.
ALCALDE DEL RÍO, H., BREUIL, H., and SIERRA, L.: Les Cavernes de la Région Cantabrique (Espagne). Monaco, 1911, p. 14.

(24) p. 227.
Op. cit., p. 26.
(25) p. 227.
Op. cit., p. 112.
(26) p. 227.
BREUIL, H., OBERMAIER, H., and ALCALDE DEL RÍO, H.: La Pasiega à Puente Viesgo (Santander, Espagne). Monaco, 1913.

(27) p. 227.
ALCALDE DEL RÍO, H., BREUIL, H., and SIERRA, L.: Les Cavernes de la Région Cantabrique (Espagne). Monaco, 1911, p. 85.

(28) p. 227.
CARTAILHAC, E., and BREUIL, H.: La Caverne d'Altamira à Santillane près Santander (Espagne). Monaco, 1906.

(29) p. 227.
ALCALDE DEL RÍO, H., BREUIL, H., and SIERRA, L.: Les Cavernes de la Région Cantabrique (Espagne). Monaco, 1911, p. 59.

(30) p. 227.
OBERMAIER, H., and DE LA VEGA DEL SELLA, CONDE: La Cueva del Buxu (Asturias). *C.I.P.P.*, Memoria 20, Madrid, 1918.

(31) p. 228.
HERNÁNDEZ-PACHECO, E.: La Caverna de la Peña de Candamo (Asturias). *C.I.P.P.*, Memoria 24, Madrid, 1919. (The author mistakenly titles himself the discoverer of the cave.)

See also:
OBERMAIER, H.: La Caverna de la Peña de Candamo (Asturias). *Bol. Soc. Ibérica de Ciencias Naturales,* t. xix, Saragossa, 1920, pp. 45-51.

(32) p. 229.
BREUIL, H.: La vallée peinte des Batuecas (Salamanca). *L'Anthr.,* t. xxix, 1918-1919, pp. 1-27.

(33) p. 229.

Breuil, H., Obermaier, H., and Verner, W.: La Pileta à Benaoján (Málaga, Espagne). Monaco, 1915.

(34) p. 229.

Breuil, H.: Nouvelles cavernes ornées paléolithiques dans la province de Málaga. *L'Anthr.*, t. xxxi, 1921, pp. 239-253.

(35) p. 229.

Breuil, H., and Cabré, J.: Les peintures rupestres du Bassin inférieur de l'Ebre. *L'Anthr.*, t. xx, 1909, pp. 1-21.

See also:

de Bégouen, Comte: Notes d'Archéologie Préhistorique. Toulouse, 1913.

(36) p. 229.

Cabré, J., and Pérez Temprado, L.: Nuevos hallazgos de Arte rupestre en el Bajo Aragón. *Tomo extraordinario del 50 Aniversario de la Real Soc. esp. de Hist. Nat.*, Madrid, 1921, pp. 276-286.

(37) p. 229.

Cabré, J.: El arte rupestre en España. Madrid, 1915, pp. 152-170. The copies of the figures are, for the most part, correct.

(38) p. 230.

Breuil, H., and Cabré, J.: Los Toricos d'Albarracín (Teruel). *L'Anthr.*, t. xxii, 1911, pp. 641-648.

(39) p. 230.

Obermaier, H., and Wernert, P.: Las pinturas rupestres del Barranco de Valltorta (Castellón). *C.I.P.P.*, Memoria 23, Madrid, 1919.

(40) p. 230.

Hernández-Pacheco, Francisco: Escena pictórica con representaciones de insectos de época paleolítica. *Tomo extraordinario del 50 Aniversario de la Real Soc. esp. de Hist. Nat.*, Madrid, 1921, pp. 62-67.

(41) p. 230.

Breuil, H., Serrano, P., and Cabré, J.: Les abris del Bosque à Alpéra (Albacete). *L'Anthr.*, t. xxiii, 1912, pp. 529-562. (The reproductions of various pictures in the abris at Alpera, published by J. Cabré in El Arte Rupestre en España, 1915, etc., require extensive revision.)

(42) p. 231.

Breuil, H.: Les roches peintes de Minateda. *L'Anthr.*, t. xxx, 1920, pp. 1-50.

(43) p. 231.

Breuil, H., and Burkitt, M.: Les abris peints du Monte Arabí, près Yecla (Murcie). *L'Anthr.*, t. xxvi, 1915, pp. 313-328.

entreprises dans la grotte de Cotencher (Canton de Neuchâtel). *Eclogœ Helvetiœ* (Recueil périodique de la Soc. géol. Suisse), t. xiv, Lausanne, 1916.

SCHMIDT, R. R.: Die diluviale Vorzeit Deutschlands. Stuttgart, 1912. (Second part by E. Koken.)

KOKEN, E.: Die faunistische Charakterisierung des älteren und jüngeren Lösses, from the pamphlet *Ber. über die palaeethnologische Konferenz in Tübingen, 1911.* Brunswick, 1912.

COMMONT, V.: Chronologie et stratigraphie des industries proto-historiques, néolithiques et paléolithiques dans les dépôts holocènes et pléistocènes du Nord de la France et en particulier de la vallée de la Somme. Remarques et comparaisons relatives au loess et aux glaciations. *Congr. intern. d'Anthr. et d'Archéol. préhist.* Sess. xiv, t. i, Geneva, 1912.

WIEGERS, F.: Die geologischen Grundlagen für die Chronologie des Diluvialmenschen. *Zeitschr. d. deutschen geol. Gesell.* (Monatsberichte), Bd. lxiv, Berlin, 1912.

—— Über das Alter des diluvialen Menschen in Deutschland. *Ibid.*, Bd. lxv, 1913.

—— Über die prähistorische Untersuchung einiger deutscher Diluvialfundstätten. *Zeitschr. f. Ethnol.*, Bd. xlvi, Berlin, 1914.

—— Diluvialprähistorie als geologische Wissenschaft. *Abhandl. d. preussischen geol. Landesanstalt*, n.F., Heft 84, Berlin, 1920.

OBERMAIER, H.: Beiträge zur Kenntnis des Quartärs in den Pyrenäen. *Archiv. f. Anthr.*, n.F., Bd. iv, v, Brunswick, 1906.

DE LAPPARENT, A.: La chronologie des époques glaciaires et l'ancienneté de l'homme. *Rev. d. questions scient.*, Louvain, Oct., 1906. (Cfr. *La Géographie*, t. xiii, Paris, 1906.)

OBERMAIER, H., and BREUIL, H.: Fouilles de la grotte du Castillo (Espagne). *Congr. intern. d'Anthr. et d'Archéol. préhist.* Sess. xiv, t. i, Geneva, 1912.

PASSEMARD, M. E.: L'abri Olha (Basses Pyrénées). *Assoc. française pour l'avancement des Sciences, Congr. de Strasbourg, 1920.* Paris, 1921.

CHAPTER IX

NOTES AND BIBLIOGRAPHY

Note 1, p. 296. Human skeletal remains from Krapina: From the larger fragments it is possible to reconstruct two skull-tops of children, and the left front of an adult skull with the face and eye sockets, although the upper part of the forehead and the upper jaw are wanting. There are also a right parietal with the corresponding part of the frontal, another large fragment of frontal with the right *torus supraorbitalis,* two lower parts of frontals with their corresponding *tori,* several temporal bones, six maxillary fragments, nine fragments of mandibles (Figure 130), some 200 teeth, a number of vertebræ and ribs, fragments of shoulder blades, 21 clavicles, 19 fragments of humerus, 11 of radius, 11 of ulna, a number of phalanges, a few fragments of ischium, two femurs fairly well preserved, 15 patellæ, 3 fragments of tibia, 14 fibulæ, as well as calcanea, astragali, and other bones of the foot.

Note 2, p. 300. Elephas with affinities to *primigenius, Equus leptotylus, Sus scrofa, Cervus hortulorum, Elaphurus davidianus, Bos primigenius,* and *Bison exiguus.*

Note 3, p. 300. In the Pithecanthropus deposits of the Kendeng formation near Trinil there were found fragments of ivory, splinters of bone, and traces of fire consisting chiefly of wood ashes. With praiseworthy caution E. Carthaus has pointed out that these features may just as well be due to natural causes as to human agency, since traces of fire in a volcanic region may easily be due to forest fires.

Note 4, p. 305. The skeleton from the brook of Samborombón is at Valencia in the Palæontological Museum founded by D. José Rodrigo Botet. See the account by Eduardo Boscá Casanoves, titled "El esqueleto humano fósil del arroyo de Samborombón, América del Sur," published by the Asociación Española para el Progreso de las Ciencias, Congress of Saragossa, 1908.

Note 5, p. 307. At Victoria near Warrnambool, Hie-Hie, Australia, report has been made of peculiar indentations which are supposed to indicate the presence of primitive man. They occur in the sandstone of this region, formed by beach dunes of unknown age. Some of the impressions indicate the tracks of the dingo (!), kangaroo, and emu, and others have been interpreted by Archibald as the imprint of human buttocks. There must be some explanation of these impressions which, according to G. Gregory, have been hollowed out by the wind. The same holds good in regard to the supposed human footprints which present a contour resembling a man's foot, although it has been said that the foot in question certainly wore a shoe. F. Nötling, however, sees in these imprints only the traces of a fossil kangaroo.

Note 6, p. 307.

Cephalic indices.

Crô-Magnon, No. 1 . . . . . . 73.8
Grotte des Enfants (tall male) . . 76.26 (?)

Macacus nemestrinus L.
Pithecanthropus erectus

There are also numerous shells and remains of fishes and reptiles.

With the exception of *Stegodon* and *Leptobos,* now extinct, and of three new genera—which are, according to Stremme, *Mececyon, Feliopsis,* and *Duboisia*—all the genera are recent; but, among 27 species which can be identified beyond question, none is identical with those found to-day in the same locality.

Abbreviation: C.I.P.P. = Comisión de Investigaciones Paleontológicas y Prehistóricas (Madrid).

GENERAL WORKS OF REFERENCE

DE QUATREFAGES, A., and HAMY, E. T.: Crania Ethnica. Paris, 1882.

DE QUATREFAGES, A.: Introduction à l'étude des races humaines. Paris, 1889.

SCHWALBE, G.: Die Vorgeschichte des Menschen. Brunswick, 1904.

BOULE, M.: L'Homme fossile de La Chapelle-aux-Saints. Paris, 1913. (An excerpt from the *Annales de Paléontologie,* 1911-1913.)

DUCKWORTH, W. L. H.: Prehistoric Man. Cambridge, 1912.

BIRKNER, F.: Die Rassen und Völker der Menschheit. Berlin, 1913.

MARTIN, R.: Lehrbuch der Anthropologie in systematischer Darstellung. Jena, 1914.

KEITH, A.: The Antiquity of Man. London, 1915.

OSBORN, H. F.: Men of the Old Stone Age. Third (revised) edition. New York, 1918.

BOULE, M.: Les Hommes fossiles. (Eléments de Paléontologie humaine.) Paris, 1921.

CORREA, A. A. MENDES: Homo. (Os modernos estudos sôbre a origem do Homem.) Lisbon, 1921.

MONOGRAPHS

A. Skeletal Remains of Pleistocene Man.

France.

KLAATSCH, H., and HAUSER, O.: *Homo Mousteriensis Hauseri. Archiv f. Anthr.,* n.F., Bd. vii, 1909. (Le Moustier.)

CAPITAN, L., and PEYRONY, D.: Deux squelettes humains au milieu de foyers de l'époque moustérienne. *Rev. de l'Ecole d'Anthr.,* t. xix, Paris, 1909. (La Ferrassie.)

—— Station préhistorique de la Ferrassie (Commune de Savignac-du-Bugue, Dordogne). *Rev. anthr.,* t. xxii, Paris, 1912.

BOULE, M.: L'Homme fossile de La Chapelle-aux-Saints. Paris, 1913. (An excerpt from the *Annales de Paléontologie*, 1911-1913.)

MARTIN, H.: Présentation d'un crâne humain trouvé avec le squelette à la base du Moustérien de La Quina (Charente). *Bull. Soc. préhist. française*, 1911.

—— L'homme fossile moustérien de La Quina. Reconstitution du crâne. *Bull. Soc. préhist. française*, 1912.

KLAATSCH, H., and HAUSER, O.: *Homo Aurignaciensis Hauseri*. *Prähist. Zeitschr.*, Bd. i, Berlin, 1910. (Combe-Capelle.)

KLAATSCH, H., and LUSTIG, W.: Morphologie der palæolithischen Skelettreste des mittleren Aurignacien der Grotte von La Rochette. Dep. Dordogne. *Archiv f. Anthr.*, n.F., Bd. xiii, 1914.

HAMY, E. T.: Description d'un squelette humain fossile de Laugerie-Basse. *Bull. Soc. d'Anthr. de Paris*, sér. ii, t. ix, 1874.

—— Sur le squelette humain de l'abri sous roche de la Madeleine. *Ibid.*, 1874.

TESTUT, L.: Recherches anthropologiques sur le squelette quaternaire de Chancelade, Dordogne. *Bull. Soc. d'Anthr. de Lyon*, t. viii, 1889.

TOURNIER, G., and GUILLON, C.: Les hommes préhistoriques dans l'Ain. Bourg, 1895. (Les Hoteaux.)

SCHWALBE, G.: Der Schädel von Egisheim. *Beitr. z. Anthr. Elsass-Lothringens*, Heft 3, 1902.

Belgium.

FRAIPONT, J., and LOHEST, M.: La race humaine de Neanderthal ou de Canstadt en Belgique. *Bull. de l'Acad. Roy. de Belgique*, sér. 3, t. xii, 1886.

—— Recherches ethnographiques sur les ossements humains, découverts dans les dépôts quaternaires d'une grotte à Spy et détermination de leur âge géologique. *Archives de Biol.*, t. vi, Ghent, 1887.

FRAIPONT, J.: Les Hommes de Spy. *Congr. intern. d'Anthr. et d'Archéol. préhist.*, Paris, 1889.

England.

DAWSON, C., WOODWARD, A. SMITH, and SMITH, G. ELLIOT: On the Discovery of a Palæolithic Human Skull and Mandible in a Flint-bearing Gravel overlying the Wealden (Hastings Beds) at Piltdown, Fletching (Sussex). *Quart. Journ. Geol. Soc.*, vol. lxix, part 1, London, 1913.

—— Supplementary Note; On the Discovery of a Palæolithic Human Skull and Mandible . . . at Piltdown (Sussex). *Ibid.*, vol. lxx, 1914.

Boule, M.: La Paléontologie humaine en Angleterre. *L'Anthr.*, t. xxvi, 1915.

Woodward, A. Smith, and Smith, G. Elliot: Fourth Note on the Piltdown Gravel, with Evidence of a Second Skull of *Eoanthropus dawsoni*. *Proc. Geol. Soc. of London*, no. 1003, March 9, 1917.

Ramström, M.: Der Piltdown-Fund. *Bull. Geol. Inst. of Upsala*, vol. xvi, Upsala, 1919.

Marett, R. R.: Pleistocene Man in Jersey. *Archeologia*, vol. lxii, Oxford, 1911.

—— Further Observations on Prehistoric Man in Jersey. *Ibid.*, vol. lxiii, 1912.

Marett, R. R., and de Gruchy, G. F. B.: Excavation of a Further Portion of La Cotte de St. Brelade. *Bull. de la Soc. jersiaise*, nro. 38, 1913.

Sollas, W. J.: Paviland Cave: An Aurignacian Station in Wales. *Publ. Roy. Anthr. Inst., Occasional Papers*, vol. xliii, 1913.

Cook, W. H.: On the Discovery of a Human Skeleton in a Brick-earth Deposit in the Valley of the River Medway at Halling (Kent). *Journ. Roy. Anthr. Inst. of Gr. Britain & Ireland*, vol. xliv, 1914.

Spain.

Keith, A.: The Early History of the Gibraltar Cranium. *Nature*, London, 1911.

Falconer, H.: Paleontological Memoirs and Notes. London, 1868. (See *Quart. Journ. Geol. Soc.*, vol. xxi, London, 1865, p. 369.)

Broca, P.: Crâne et ossements humains des cavernes de Gibraltar. *Bull. Soc. d'Anthr. de Paris*, sér. 2, t. iv, 1869.

Sollas, W. J.: On the Cranial and Facial Characters of the Neanderthal Race. *Philos. Trans. Roy. Soc.*, vol. cxcix, ser. B, London, 1907.

Sera, G. L.: Nuove osservazioni ed induzioni sul cranio de Gibraltar. *Archivio per l'Antrop. e l'Etnol.*, t. xxxix, Florence, 1909.

Hernández-Pacheco, E., and Obermaier, H.: La mandíbula neandertaloide de Bañolas (España). *C.I.P.P.*, núm. 6, Madrid, 1915. (Geology by E. Hernández-Pacheco, Anthropology by H. Obermaier.)

Sergi, S.: La mandibola di Bañolas. *Rivista di Antrop.*, t. xxii, Rome, 1917-1918.

Antón y Ferrandiz, M.: Crânes quaternaires en Espagne. *Congr. intern. d'Anthr. et d'Archéol. préhist.* Sess. xiv, t. i, Geneva, 1912.

Correa, A. A. Mendes: Origins of the Portuguese. *Amer. Journ. Phys. Anthr.*, vol. ii, no. 2, 1919, pp. 117-145.

Italy.

RIVIÈRE, E.: De l'antiquité de l'homme dans les Alpes Maritimes. Paris, 1887.

CARTAILHAC, E.: Les grottes de Grimaldi (Baoussé-Roussé). Archéologie. T. ii, fasc. 2, Monaco, 1912, Chapter V.

Germany.

OBERMAIER, H.: Les restes humains quaternaires dans l'Europe Centrale. *L'Anthr.*, t. xvii, 1906.

SCHÖTENSACK, O.: Der Unterkiefer des *Homo Heidelbergensis* aus den Sanden von Mauer bei Heidelberg. Leipsic, 1908.

NEHRING, A.: Über einen menschlichen Molar aus dem Diluvium von Taubach bei Weimar. (Verh. d. Berliner anthr. Gesell., Sitzung Oct. 19, 1895.) *Zeitschr. f. Ethnol.*, Berlin, 1895.

VIRCHOW, H.: Der Taubacher Zahn des Prähistorischen Museums der Universität Jena. *Prähist. Zeitschr.*, Bd. ix, Berlin, 1917.

SCHWALBE, G.: Über einen bei Ehringsdorf in der Nähe von Weimar gefundenen Unterkiefer des *Homo primigenius*. *Anat. Anzeiger*, Bd. xlvii, 1914.

VIRCHOW, H.: Der Unterkiefer von Ehringsdorf. *Zeitschr. f. Ethnol.*, Berlin, 1914 (p. 869), and 1915 (p. 444).

—— Pyorrhoische Erscheinungen an einem zwischeneiszeitlichen Kiefer. *Berliner klinische Wochenschr.*, Nr. 35, 1917.

ADLOFF, P.: Der Molar von Taubach. *Prähist. Zeitschr.*, Bd. xi/xii, Berlin, 1919-1920, p. 203.

VIRCHOW, H.: Die menschlichen Skelettreste aus dem Kämpieschen Bruch im Travertin von Ehringsdorf bei Weimar. Jena, 1920.

VERWORN, M., BONNET, R., and STEINMANN, G.: Der diluviale Menschenfund von Obercassel bei Bonn. Wiesbaden, 1919.

Jugo-Slavia.

GORJANOVIČ-KRAMBERGER, K.: Der diluviale Mensch von Krapina. Wiesbaden, 1906.

OBERMAIER, H.: Les restes humains quaternaires dans l'Europe Centrale. *L'Anthr.*, t. xvi, 1905. (Treats also of discoveries in Czecho-Slovakia, Austria, Hungary, and Poland.)

Czecho-Slovakia.

MAKOWSKY, A.: Der diluviale Mensch im Löss von Brünn. *Mitt. d. anthr. Gesell. in Wien*, Bd. xxii, Vienna, 1892.

RZEHAK, A.: Der Unterkiefer von Ochos. Ein Beitrag zur Kenntnis des altdiluvialen Menschen. *Verh. d. naturf. Vereins, Brünn*, Bd. xliv, Brünn, 1905.

SCHWALBE, G.: Das Schädelfragment von Brüx und verwandte

Schädelformen. Das Schädelfragment von Cannstatt. *Zeitschr. f. Morphol. u. Anthr.*, Bd. i, Supplementheft, 1906.

Hungary.

HILLEBRAND, E.: Die diluvialen Knochenreste eines Kindes aus der Ballahöhle bei Repashuta in Ungarn. *Mitt. d. Höhlenforschungskommission d. Ungar. geol. Gesell.*, Budapest, 1911.

Asia.

MATSUMOTO, H.: On some Fossil Mammals from Ho-nan, China. *Sci. Repts. Tôhoku Imperial Univ.*, ser. 2, vol. iii, no. 1, Tokio, 1916.

SÁNCHEZ Y SÁNCHEZ, D.: Un cráneo humano prehistórico de Manila (Filipinas). *Memorias de la Real Soc. esp. de Hist. Nat.*, t. xi, núm. 5, Madrid, 1921.

Africa.

RECK, H.: Erste vorläufige Mitteilung über den Fund eines fossilen Menschenskeletts aus Zentralafrika. *Sitzungsber. d. Gesell. Naturf. Freunde zu Berlin*, 1914.

HAUGHTON, S. H.: Preliminary Note on the Ancient Human Skull-remains from the Transvaal. *Trans. Roy. Soc. of South Africa*, vol. vi, 1917.

North America.

HRDLIČKA, A.: Skeletal Remains Suggesting or Attributed to Early Man in North America. *Bur. Amer. Ethnol.*, no. 33, Washington, 1907.

South America.

AMEGHINO, F.: La antigüedad del hombre en el Plata. Paris, Buenos Aires, 1881.

—— Notas preliminares sobre el *Tetraprothomo argentinus*. *Anales Museo Nac. de Buenos Aires*, t. xvi, 1907.

—— Le *Diprothomo platensis*. *Ibid.*, t. xix, 1909.

—— Descubrimiento de un esqueleto humano fósil en el pampeano superior del arroyo Siasgo. *Congr. científico intern. amer.*, Buenos Aires, 1910.

—— Descubrimiento de dos esqueletos humanos fósiles en el pampeano inferior del Moro. *Ibid.*, 1910.

—— L'âge des formations sédimentaires tertiaires de l'Argentine en relation avec l'antiquité de l'homme. *Anales Museo Nac. de Buenos Aires*, t. xxii, 1911.

TROUESSART, E.: Les Primates tertiaires et l'Homme fossile sud-américain. *L'Anthr.*, t. iii, Paris, 1892.

Lehmann-Nitsche, R.: Die Gleichzeitigkeit der südpatagonischen Höhlenbewohner mit dem *Grypotherium*. *Archiv f. Anthr.*, Bd. xxvii, Brunswick, 1902.

—— Nouvelles recherches sur la formation pampéenne et l'homme fossile de la République Argentine. *Rev. del Museo de la Plata*, t. xiv, Buenos Aires, 1907.

—— L'Atlas du tertiaire de Monte Hermoso, République Argentine. *Ibid.*, 1907.

—— *Homo sapiens* und *Homo neogæus* aus der argentinischen Pampasformation. *Verh. des 16 intern. Amerikanisten-Congr.*, 1909.

—— El Hombre fósil Pampeano. *Soc. geog. de La Paz*, t. vi, 1910.

de Urquiza, T.: Nuevas investigaciones sobre el Atlas de Monte Hermoso. *Paleo-Antropología Argentina*, La Plata, 1912.

Mochi, A.: Appunti sulla Paleantropologia argentina. *Archivio per l'Antrop. e l'Etnol.*, t. xl, Florence, 1910.

Schwalbe, G.: Studien zur Morphologie der südamerikanischen Primatenformen. *Zeitschr. f. Morphol. u. Anthr.*, Bd. xiii, 1910.

Hrdlička, A.: Early Man in South America. *Smithson. Inst. Bur. Amer. Ethnol.*, Bull. 52, Washington, 1912.

von Ihering, H.: Das Alter des Menschen in Südamerika. *Zeitschr. f. Ethnol.*, Bd. xlvi, 1914.

Aichel, O.: Die Bedeutung des Atlas für die Anthropologie, unter Berücksichtigung des Fundes vom Monte Hermoso. *Zeitschr. f. Ethnol.*, Bd. xlvi, Berlin, 1914.

Romero, A. A.: El *Homo Pampœus*. *Anales Soc. científica Argentina*, t. lxxxvi, Buenos Aires, 1918.

Boman, E.: Encore l'homme tertiaire dans l'Amérique du Sud. *Journ. Soc. des Americanistes de Paris*, nouvelle sér., t. xi, 1914-1919. Paris, 1919.

—— Los vestigios de la industria humana encontrados en Miramar (República Argentina) y atribuidos a la época terciaria. *Revista Chilena de Hist. y Geog.*, t. xxxix, Santiago, 1921.

Frenguelli, J.: Los terrenos de la costa atlántica en los alrededores de Miramar (Prov. de Buenos Aires) y sus correlaciones. *Bol. Acad. Nac. de Ciencias de Córdoba*, t. xxiv, Buenos Aires, 1921.

Australia.

Branco, W.: Die fraglichen fossilen menschlichen Fusspuren im Sandsteine von Warnambool, Victoria, und andere angebliche Spuren des fossilen Menschen in Australien. *Zeitschr. f. Ethnol.*, Bd. xxxvii, Berlin, 1905.

Smith, S. A.: The Fossil Human Skull Found at Talgai, Queensland. *Philos. Trans. Roy. Soc.*, ser. B, vol. ccviii, London, 1918.

Revised by F. Broili and M. Schlosser. Third edition, Munich and Berlin, 1918.

FREUDENBERG, W.: Die Entdeckung von menschlichen Fussspuren und Artefakten in den tertiären Geröllschichten und Muschelhaufen bei St. Gilles-Waes, westlich Antwerpen. *Prähist. Zeitschr.*, Bd. xi-xii, Berlin, 1919-1920.

Pithecanthropus.

DUBOIS, E.: *Pithecanthropus erectus,* eine menschenähnliche Übergangsform aus Java. Batavia, 1894.

—— *Pithecanthropus,* eine Stammform des Menschen. *Anatomischer Anzeiger,* Bd. xii, 1896.

—— Das geologische Alter der Kendong- oder Trinil-Fauna. *Tijdschr. v. het k. Nederlandsch. nat. Aardrijksk. Genootsch.,* ser. 2, vol. xxv, 1908.

VIRCHOW, R.: *Pithecanthropus erectus* Dubois. *Zeitschr. f. Ethnol.,* Bd. xxvii, Berlin, 1895.

MANOUVRIER, L.: Discussion du *Pithecanthropus erectus,* comme précurseur de l'homme. *Bull. Soc. d'Anthr. de Paris,* sér. 4, t. vi, 1895.

—— Deuxième étude sur le *Pithecanthropus erectus. Ibid.,* 1895.

—— Réponse aux objetions contre le *Pithecanthropus. Ibid.,* t. vii, 1896.

MARTIN, R.: Kritische Bedenken gegen den *Pithecanthropus erectus* Dubois. *Globus,* Bd. lxvii, Brunswick, 1895.

—— Weitere Bemerkungen zur Pithecanthropus-Frage. Zürich, 1896.

SCHWALBE, G.: Studien über *Pithecanthropus erectus* Dubois. *Zeitschr. f. Morphol. u. Anthr.,* Bd. i, 1899.

—— Studien über das Femur von *Pithecanthropus erectus* Dubois. Herausgegeben von Eug. Fischer. *Zeitschr. f. Morphol. u. Anthr.,* Bd. xxi, Heft 3, Stuttgart, 1921.

VOLZ, W.: Das geologische Alter der *Pithecanthropus*-Schichten bei Trinil. *Neues Jahrbuch f. Miner., Geol. u. Paläont.,* Festband, 1907.

MARTIN, K.: Das Alter der Schichten von Sonde und Trinil auf Java. *K. Akad. v. Wetenschaften te Amsterdam,* 1908.

SELENKA, L., and BLANCKENHORN, M.: Die *Pithecanthropus*-Schichten auf Java; geologische und palaeontologische Ergebnisse der Trinilexpedition. Leipsic, 1911.

RAMSTRÖM, M.: Der Java-Trinil-Fund *Pithecanthropus. Upsala Läkareförenings förhandlingar,* ny följd, Bd. xxvi, Upsala, 1921.

GAUDRY, A.: Essai de Paléontologie philosophique. Paris, 1896.

CHAPTER X

NOTES AND BIBLIOGRAPHY

Note 1, p. 325. The shells of marine molluscs found in the "kjökken-möddings" or shell mounds at Mugem in the valley of the Tagus include those of *Lutraria compressa, Tapes, Cardium, Ostrea, Buccinum, Nucula, Pecten, Solen,* and others. The associated remains of mammals include *Bos, Cervus, Ovis* (or *Capra*), *Equus, Sus, Canis, Felis, Meles, Viverra,* and *Lepus.*

Note 2, p. 344. The fauna found in the "kjökkenmödding" at Oronsay excavated by A. H. Bishop in 1913 included *Halichœrus gryphus, Phoca vitulina, Lutra vulgaris, Cervus elaphus, Sus scrofa ferus,* and others. No remains of *Bos* or *Canis* were found.

Note 3, p. 345. The fauna found in the Azilian industrial deposits at Valle includes remains of *Cervus elaphus, C. capreolus, Capella rupicapra, Capra pyrenaica, Equus caballus, Bos* sp., and *Sus scrofa ferus.* The upper half of the deposit also contained huge masses of *Helix.*

Note 4, p. 350. The characteristic molluscs of the Asturian shell mounds are *Trochus lineatus, Patella vulgata* (the small variety), and *Cardium edule.* Others, less numerous, are *Nassa reticulata, Tuberculata atlantica, Mytilus edulis, Ostrea edulis, Triton nodiferus, Echinus,* and *Helix nemoralis.*

Embedded in these shell mounds are the remains of the following mammals: *Cervus elaphus, Cervus capreolus, Equus caballus, Bos, Sus scrofa, Capra pyrenaica, Capella rupicapra, Mustela putorius, Lutra vulgaris, Canis vulpes, Felis catus, Meles taxus,* and *Lepus timidus.*

Note 5, p. 358. On the "tierras negras" of southern Spain see:

HERNÁNDEZ-PACHECO, E.: Las tierras negras del extremo Sur de España y sus yacimientos paleolíticos. *Trabajos del Museo Nac. de Ciencias Naturales,* ser. geol., núm. 13, Madrid, 1915.

Modified by

BREUIL, H.: Observations sur les terres noires de la Laguna de la Janda. *L'Anthr.,* t. xxviii, Paris, 1917, p. 235.

Note 6, p. 364. The fauna found at Maglemose consists chiefly of *Bos taurus urus* (*Bos primigenius*), *Cervus alces, Cervus elaphus, Cervus capreolus,* and *Sus scrofa ferus.* Of less frequent occurrence are *Castor fiber, Ursus arctos,* etc. There are also remains of two or three individuals of *Canis familiaris.* Concerning the latter, it is interesting to note that the domestic dog is also found

OBERMAIER, H., and WERNERT, P.: Palaeolithbeiträge aus Nord-bayern. *Mitt. d. anthr. Gesell. in Wien,* Bd. xliv, Vienna, 1914.

OCTOBON: La question tardenoisienne. Ateliers des buttes de sable près de la ferme Montbani (Commune de Mont-Notre-Dame, Aisne). *Rev. anthr.,* t. xxx, Paris, 1920.

Azilian.

PIETTE, E.: Etudes d'ethnographie préhistorique. *L'Anthr.,* t. vi, 1895.

—— Etudes d'ethnographie préhistorique. ii. Les plantes cultivées de la période de transition au Mas-d'Azil. *L'Anthr.,* t. vii, 1896.

—— Etudes d'ethnographie préhistorique. iii. Les galets coloriés du Mas-d'Azil. *L'Anthr.,* t. vii, 1896. (With a portfolio of colored plates.)

—— Etudes d'ethnographie préhistorique. vi. Notions complementaires sur l'Asylien. *L'Anthr.,* t. xiv, 1903.

ANDERSON, J.: Notice of a Cave Recently Discovered at Oban, Containing Human Remains, and a Refuse-heap of Shells and Bones of Animals, and Stone and Bone Implements. *Proc. Soc. Antiquaries of Scotland,* vol. xxix, 1895.

TURNER, WILLIAM: Human and Animal Remains Found in Caves at Oban, Argyllshire. *Ibid.,* vol. xxix, 1895.

MUNRO, R.: Palæolithic Man and the Terramara Settlements in Europe. Edinburgh, 1912. (Azilian in England.)

SARASIN, F.: Die steinzeitlichen Stationen des Birstales zwischen Basel und Delsberg. *Neue Denkschriften d. schweiz. naturf. Gesell.,* Bd. liv, Abh. 2, Basle, 1918. (The painted pebbles of Birseck.)

BREUIL, H., and OBERMAIER, H.: Les premiers travaux de l'Institut de Paléontologie Humaine. *L'Anthr.,* t. xxiii, 1912. (The cave of Valle.)

Asturian.

DE LA VEGA DEL SELLA, CONDE: La Cueva del Penicial. *C.I.P.P.,* Memoria 4, Madrid, 1914.

—— Paleolítico de Cueto de la Mina (Asturias). *C.I.P.P.,* Memoria 13, Madrid, 1916, pp. 61-67.

WELSCH, J.: Les lignites du littoral et les forêts submergées de l'Ouest de la France. *L'Anthr.,* t. xxviii, Paris, 1917.

FEUILLADE: Traces de l'Homme préhistorique sur la plage d'Ilbarritz. *Bull. mens. de la Biarritz Assoc.,* t. xix, nro. 6, Bayonne, 1914.

Campignian.

SALMON, P., D'AULT DU MESNIL, G., and CAPITAN, L.: Le Campignien. *Rev. mens. de l'Ecole d'Anthr.,* t. viii, Paris, 1898.

KUPKA, P.: Das Campignien im nordeuropäischen Glazialgebiet. *Zeitschr. f. Ethnol.*, Bd. xxxix, Berlin, 1907.

Northern Europe.

Post-glacial Geology.

DE GEER, G.: Om Skandinaviens geografiska utveckling efter istiden. Stockholm, 1896.

—— A Geochronology of the Last 12,000 Years. *Congr. géol. intern.*, *C. R.*, Sess. xi, Stockholm, 1910.

BRÖGGER, W. C.: Om de senglaciale og postglaciale nivaforandringer i Kristianiafeltet. Christiania, 1900-1901.

XIᵐᵉ CONGRÈS GÉOLOGIQUE INTERNATIONAL: Die Veränderungen des Klimas seit dem Maximum der letzten Eiszeit. (A collection of articles prepared by the coöperation of specialists in various countries, and published by the executive committee of the XIᵐᵉ Congrès Géologique International. Edited by G. Andersson.) Stockholm, 1910.

ANDERSSON, G.: Die Veränderungen des Klimas seit dem Maximum der letzten Eiszeit. *Congr. géol. intern.*, *C. R.*, Sess. xi, Stockholm, 1910. (Results of discussions held at the Congress.)

DEUTSCHE GEOLOGISCHE GESELLSCHAFT: Die Klimaveränderungen in Deutschland seit der letzten Eiszeit. *Zeitschr. d. deutsch. geol. Gesell.*, Bd. lxii, Berlin, 1910.

OBERMAIER, H.: Der Mensch der Vorzeit. Berlin, 1912. (Teil 2, Chapter II.)

MENZEL, H.: Die geologische Entwicklungsgeschichte der älteren Postglazialzeit im nördlichen Europa und ihre Beziehung zur Prähistorie. *Zeitschr. f. Ethnol.*, Bd. xlvi, 1914.

BRÜCKNER, E.: Geochronologische Untersuchungen über die Dauer der Postglazialzeit in Schweden, in Finnland und in Nordamerika. *Zeitschr. f. Gletscherkunde*, Bd. xii, Leipsic, 1921.

Maglemose Culture.

SARAUW, G. F. L.: En Stenalders Boplads i Maglemose ved Mullerup. *Aarboger for nordisk Oldkyndighed og Historie*, ser. 2, vol. ii, Copenhagen, 1903.

—— Maglemose, ein steinzeitlicher Wohnplatz im Moor bei Mullerup auf Seeland, verglichen mit verwandten Funden. *Prähist. Zeitschr.*, Bd. iii, 1911, and Bd. vi, 1914. Berlin.

KOCK, LAUGE: Mullerupkulturens geologiske Alder. *Meddelelser fra Dansk geologisk Forening*, t. v, nr. 6, Copenhagen, 1916.

WERNERT, P.: Figuras humanas esquemáticas del Maglemosiense. *C.I.P.P.*, Nota 15, Madrid, 1917.

—— Figures biomorphes schématiques de l'ancien âge de la pierre du Danemark. *L'Anthr.*, t. xxx, Paris, 1920.

Friis Johansen, K.: Une station du plus ancien âge de la Pierre dans la tourbière de Sværdborg. *Mémoires d. l. Soc. Roy. des Antiquaires du Nord,* nouvelle sér., 1918-1919. Copenhagen, 1920.

Grewingk, C.: Geologie und Archaeologie des Mergellagers von Kunda in Estland. *Archiv f. Naturkunde Liv-, Est-, und Kurlands,* Ser. 1, Bd. ix, 1882.

—— Die neolithischen Bewohner von Kunda in Estland und deren Nachbarn. *Verh. d. gelehrten estnischen Gesell. zu Dorpat,* Bd. xii, Dorpat, 1884.

Shell Mound (Kjökkenmödding) Culture.

Madsen, A. P., Müller, S., Neergard, C., Petersen, J., Rostrup, E., Steenstrup, V., and Winge, H.: Affaldsdynger fra Stenalderen in Danmark, undersögte for Nationalmuseet. Copenhagen, 1900. (A work of general reference on the "kjökkenmöddings.")

Reinecke, P.: Zur Kenntnis der frühneolithischen Zeit in Deutschland. *Mainzer Zeitschr.,* Bd. iii, Mainz, 1908.

INDEX